Living Medicine

Dame Margaret Turner-Warwick,
President of the Royal College of Physicians (1989–92).
Portrait by David Poole PPRP ARCA, 1992.

Living Medicine
Recollections and reflections

Margaret Turner-Warwick DBE DM FRCP

Foreword by Stephen Holgate

ROYAL COLLEGE OF PHYSICIANS
2005

Acknowledgements

Many of the people who have supported and helped me over the years in so many different ways have been acknowledged in the course of this book. There are many others who should have been mentioned and are remembered with equal affection and gratitude.

I am especially grateful to all my friends and colleagues who have commented so helpfully on some or all of the chapters and to Richard who has read it from cover to cover and made many valuable comments. I, of course, remain entirely responsible for the controversial views and the textual errors – memory is a fickle thing.

It is a great privilege to have this work published by the Royal College of Physicians and I am especially grateful to Joanna Reid and Diana Beaven for their meticulous care in its production.

MTW

Hardback ISBN 1 86016 250 9
Softback ISBN 1 86016 248 7

ROYAL COLLEGE OF PHYSICIANS OF LONDON
11 St Andrews Place, London NW1 4LE

www.rcplondon.ac.uk

Registered Charity No. 210508

Cover: Portrait of Margaret Turner-Warwick by Jeff Stultiens
Typeset by Dan-set Graphics, Telford, Shropshire
Printed in Great Britain by The Lavenham Press, Suffolk

Contents

Reflections

Foreword

On 5 July 1948, the National Health Service was born. It came at a time after the Second World War when food was rationed, there was a massive housing crisis and building materials and fuel were in short supply. However, following a six-year period of despair during the war, everyone was keen to ensure that the new NHS worked and there was a tremendous sense of pulling together for the greater good of all. At the time no one knew what an enormous experiment Aneurin Bevan had initiated. To the credit of all concerned, for over 50 years the NHS has delivered to the UK population effective healthcare that was driven by high professional standards and, above all, was free at the point of access. A principal pillar of the NHS's success was the family doctor or general practitioner who served as a gate-keeper to the rest of the service, referring patients where appropriate to hospitals and prescribing medicines. A second pillar of its success was the quality of training and professionalism provided by doctors, allied health professionals and nurses that deservedly gave the NHS its enviable reputation worldwide as a service underpinned by high quality health care delivered economically with the cost being borne in relation to an individual's earnings.

So what is the NHS like today and is it continuing to provide the level of care that the public expects? In 2005 the NHS has a workforce of over one million people and a budget of around £42 billion per annum. The NHS website states that the service 'is a sophisticated and modern organisation with all of the advantages of state of the art technology'. However, the fundamental questions that Bevan had to face, of how to fund the NHS adequately, how to balance often conflicting demands and expectations of patients, staff and taxpayers and how to ensure finite resources are targeted where they are most needed, continue to challenge the system. Bevan stated that expectations will always exceed capacity – but after almost 60 years has the NHS got the balance right? Apart from issues relating to management a key question is whether the National Health Service has been more about managing illness with much less emphasis on maintaining good health and preventing disease. Patient surveys reveal that a considerable proportion is satisfied with some aspects of the service but not with others. They desire choice in their clinical management and the clinical staff involved, but is this achievable in the NHS as it currently exists?

Today the NHS is never out of the news. It has assumed centre stage in political debate and has been the target of continued change which has not always been for the better. Those who dictate health care policy, those that are expected to deliver care and those that manage this at local level do not sit comfortably together. Are medical, nursing and allied health professions becoming de-professionalised – is this impacting on patient care?

Living Medicine is a testimony of an individual who has dedicated her life to the care of patients. In the pages that follow, Margaret Turner-Warwick lays before us a rich history of her interactions with health care, clinical research and medical education. Her career is quite extraordinary, most people completing their working lives within 65 years – but not this pioneer – a further 20 years of exciting, innovative and impactive work followed with an enormous impact on patient care, clinical research and medical education. As I write this foreword I can say with all honesty that I have read every page of this autobiography and many of the conclusions drawn and the sentiments expressed resonate with me. Very rarely has an individual mapped their career course in medicine since the foundation of the NHS and distilled from this areas where there has been great progress, but at the same time accumulated wisdom that has crystallised into several basic principles. These have been part of Margaret Turner-Warwick's remarkable driving force for over six decades of service in medicine.

It is worth asking at this point how I fit into all of this apart from sharing with Margaret Turner-Warwick a specialism in lung disease. This remarkable woman was an enormous inspiration to young trainees, like myself, during the formative times of their career. I was fortunate enough to be one of many senior house officers at the Brompton Hospital in respiratory medicine in 1973, two years after she was appointed to the Chair of Medicine at the Cardiothoracic Institute and Brompton Hospital. Although early on in this autobiography MTW (as she was known affectionately to us all) states that she had no clear mentors herself, I for one, and I know of so many others, was stimulated by her dynamism, commitment and sense of excitement in the field of respiratory medicine that guided us all into this field.

So what is so special about MTW and this book? This is easy to answer. *Living medicine* provides a journey through a lifetime of experience in the delivery of healthcare, research and medical training that is scintillating to read. I may be biased, but each chapter of this book brought aspects of medicine to life as if one was still participating in one of Margaret's Brompton Hospital ward rounds. What emerges from reading this book is a woman always willing to take on a challenge, putting patients and the public first and exuding enthusiasm and interest in her subject, whether as a leader in lung disease, president of a Royal medical college or chairman of a hospital trust.

Our journey takes us through six stages ending with an epilogue. Each stage describes with extraordinary accuracy and poignancy moments that were pivotal in setting MTW's career. As one gets deeper into these, it becomes increasingly apparent that her professional life was far from planned. Indeed, some of her most important contributions have come through searching for alternative paths because of failure to progress through 'linear promotion'. From a disenfranchised specialty in medicine, MTW lifted lung disease to a level that has now placed it as one of the priorities for healthcare programmes and research.

Let me now describe the structure of this testimony. Before embarking in depth, we are provided with reasons why this book was written in the first place. While MTW states that she has written this book for her family, I would like to be one of many who are delighted that she has spent so much time and energy capturing her experience and translating it to the benefit of us all. Part one deals with her early life influences. It is clear that her parents were a great guiding light and that her childhood illnesses were certainly not going to hold her back. Even in this introductory section, a point is made that professional integrity is sacrosanct – a theme that permeates many of the other sections to follow. Part two provides fascinating reading because it maps out both the pleasures and difficulties faced by young doctors during their training which were especially difficult for a woman working in an almost totally male-dominated profession. How things have changed, with over 50% of places in our medical schools now occupied by women.

In Part three a vivid description is provided of what it was like to compete in, achieve and then change an emerging specialty both in the NHS and the University sector. On being appointed to the Chair of Medicine in 1972 at the Cardiothoracic Institute and Brompton Hospital there followed 12 years of leadership and dedication to lung disease. As one of Margaret's senior house officers, I vividly remember her multidisciplinary ward rounds that not only provided strong debate about clinical problems, but were notable in considering all aspects of diagnosis with due consideration being given to both the family and social environment in which the patient existed. These ward rounds were also memorable as outstanding opportunities for transfer of knowledge.

With almost 200 papers published in peer review journals and a large number of other reviews, books and atlases, MTW almost single handed has lifted the field of respiratory medicine to place it in a par with other medical specialties that have had a more glamorous history. It should be remembered that in 1972, when she was appointed to her Professorship, much of respiratory medicine had been focused on infectious disease and lung physiology and that knowledge about other aspects of the normal lung and how it is affected by disease processes was rudimentary. By conducting high quality research, particularly in interstitial lung disease, asthma, mesothelioma, occupational lung disease and uncommon inflammatory disorders, lung disease took on a new perspective that emerged out of an academic specialty that was poorly developed. It was this renaissance of mechanistic enquiry engaging many different investigational approaches that inspired so many of us as trainees to enter the specialty. The strong emphasis on integrating knowledge from all aspects of lung disease and connecting this with the patient's history and environment propelled this academic unit rapidly to national and international prominence. No better was this demonstrated than in Margaret's special interest in interstitial lung disease. Between 1972 and 1984 we witnessed an explosion of interest in the immunological and cellular basis of lung disease as well as the application of pharmacology and clinical trials to test new treatments. Throughout this period the research focus was always patient centred and this was made possible by an NHS enabling cross-regional referrals to specialist centres and the 'well worked up' patient as a source of new enquiry. The young apprentices, such as myself, had the opportunity of feeding off this unique substrate of clinical science that has a long-lasting influence over our subsequent careers. Her appointment to Dean of the Cardiothoracic Institute in 1984 provided her with a further opportunity to build upon the clinical and research success already achieved and to place the now renamed National Heart and Lung Institute as a truly international centre of excellence for both the delivery of clinical care, research and training.

Following a brief period to catch her breath, in 1978 MTW was to take on a whole new challenge – as the first woman President of the Royal College of Physicians at a time when the NHS and University sectors were undergoing great change. Thus in Section four a colourful description of her life as College President is described. Throughout her $3\frac{1}{2}$ years in this position of national leadership the NHS was experiencing the most significant cultural shift since its inception, with the introduction of the 'internal market' as outlined in the 1989 White Paper, *Working for patients*. The concept of purchasers and providers of healthcare was entirely new and it soon became clear that 'while the NHS needed to be run in business like way, it could not be run as a business'. As pointed out in Part four, in business 'unprofitable lines' can be discontinued but in health care patients cannot simply be discarded in this way. Margaret, in her role as President of the RCP, played a key role in framing these concerns and gradually changing the way the College operated so it could be effective in presenting these to government as well as being a champion for clinical standards. This section of the book is presented with such a sense of engagement and reality that the problems of the rapidly changing NHS management are brought into stark relief.

On relinquishing her Presidency and anticipating a period of quieter reflection, yet another challenge tempted her into translating her great experience into practice as Chairman of the Royal Devon and Exeter Healthcare Trust Hospital. There is a vivid description of what it is like to be at the sharp end of NHS management when decisions are to be translated at a local level in patient care. It is in this chapter that the concept of good patient care emerges out of respect, understanding and empathy as well as professional commitment, judgement, knowledge and skill. A further strong message also emerges – namely the need for government to make a clear distinction between its relationship with professionals who are responsible for delivering a service and its relationship to employees who are paid to work to whatever standards and conditions employers wish to set.

In drawing together a unique lifetime experience, Part five provides a thoughtful and constructive analysis of the NHS and the academic sector of medicine that lays before us a great example of how experience gained from such a wide variety of positions can be integrated into natural and well substantiated conclusions. Probably the most powerful of these develops the idea that the NHS, having passed through eras of expansion, cost containment and accountability and assessment now needs to enter a further era – one of partnership and trust.

At the outset, Margaret states that this book was written primarily for her family. She describes *Living medicine* as a woven cloth; chronology going one way and topics of interest going another. But it is equally clear from her writing and the touching and sensitive references to her husband Richard and to her children and other members of this family that there is an important third dimension of love and support that has enabled this remarkable woman to contribute so much to medicine and to public life. This aspect is brought together in a sensitively written epilogue that 'rounds the circle' and provides a living context for many things that Margaret Turner-Warwick has been able to achieve in life.

As Peter Watkins so eloquently stated in a recent editorial in *Clinical Medicine*,[1] commenting on medical care, 'It is humbling to believe that a doctor's effectiveness in alleviating symptoms may depend as much on the bedside manner as on the medication dispensed'. Margaret Turner-Warwick is a world-class exponent of both of these essential qualities which is the reason why she continues to inspire so many who have contact with her, as reflected so well in the pages of this book. This book is about professional values – what defines a professional person, why professional doctors are still required in modern medicine and what are the responsibilities of doctors, management and government in maintaining professionalism. The NHS continues to change. It is now said that the NHS is shifting the balance of power with the aim of designing a service centred around patients which puts them first. Whether primary care trusts, primary care commissioning, the Modernisation Agency, special heath authorities, strategic health authorities, Foundation Trusts and other new management structures can achieve this objective remains to be seen. However, what one learns from reading *Living medicine* is that management changes alone will not meet the expectations of patients without the full engagement of the professions whose responsibility it is to deliver this care. At the end of the day, what patients want is a competent healthcare practitioner who they can trust and who understands their individual problems and who can act to alleviate these. What still needs to be found is a balance between equity and diversity and the tensions between central control and devolution. As stated by Chris Ham in 2003, 'Faced with funding pressures on the one hand and service delivery failures on the other, policy makers have entertained radical solutions in the hope that they will lead to improvements in health care system performance. In practice, reform has in general fallen short of both the rhetoric and expectations, leading to re-appraisals of strategies pursued and a search for new policies.' In other words, there continued to be a gap between policy intent and delivery of care. The challenge for the future is to bridge this gap so that the healthcare practitioner can once again take ownership of his or her profession and use all of their skills to translate this into improved care respecting the individuality of each patient.

Experience gained during the enormous changes that have occurred in the NHS and University sector by Margaret Turner-Warwick provides a wonderful substrate for the aspiring clinician or academic. The book also provides a compelling read for anyone working in the health service or in medical research and education since it offers a real sense of optimism about the future but, at the same time, draws attention to pitfalls from which we can all learn.

Reference

1   Watkins P. The efficacy of treatment; therapy or therapist. *Clin Med* 2005;5:309-10.

October 2005

Stephen Holgate
MRC Clinical Professor of Immunopharmacology,
University of Southampton and Southampton University Hospital Trust

Illustrations

INTRODUCTION

1. Why write it down

Medicine is essentially about life. Medicine has also been my life for more than 50 years. *Living medicine* is a personal record of a professional career, caring for patients over a period when the NHS has been trying desperately to keep pace with increasing patient expectations, extraordinary medical advances and exponentially rising costs. Over this time, there have also been huge changes in opportunities in medicine for women, who now represent more than half of UK medical students. They will have to find their own balance between their home and professional commitments and this may have a major impact on how patients are cared for in the future. This story is not a grand one but it tries to describe what it has meant to work in medicine over a fascinating period and to juggle with all the conflicting pressures, each of which presents its own challenges – but also its own rewards. It raises some of the ethical principles of how doctors should respond to some extraordinary contemporary pressures and why these have occurred.

Memoirs are like a woven cloth; there is a warp and a weft – a chronology going one way and topics of interest going the other, cutting across the time zones. This presents problems. The easiest solution is a compromise – to mix them together rather like Strauss's *Ariadne auf Naxos* where the Commedia dell'arte and the Opera Seria are played simultaneously. It saves time and, like Ariadne, we shall be finished sooner.

This book is primarily for my family, who may regret urging me to write a personal record of life in medicine over the last half century. We have two grandchildren who are medical students and I felt it might also be of some interest for other aspiring young doctors. More than half of these are now women who will face many of the same dilemmas as we did. The acceptance of women in medicine has certainly come a very long way since 1878 when the Royal College of Physicians refused to allow them to sit their examinations on the grounds that 'if girls were encouraged to use their brains, the excitement caused thereby would produce insanity'. Perhaps that is my problem! Today there are more 'mature' medical students with non-medical or non-scientific backgrounds, who might also like a thumbnail sketch of how medicine has evolved and how managerial crises have been dealt with over the last fifty years, to help them

3

understand the present. Others are recruits to our new medical schools where different approaches to medical education are being explored. They may be interested to compare the new with some of the old. Indeed, they may be surprised to find that some things have not changed as much as many suppose. Still others may be struggling with some of the hurdles in medicine and this story might give encouragement to them about how much eventually comes right, with a huge amount of reward and fun along the way, even if life does not always work out exactly as planned.

Over the last fifty years there has been a huge expansion in medical knowledge as well as major changes in how medical care is delivered to those in need. Understanding some of the background of how the NHS and doctors have had to change is all part of the story. These wider aspects are very important. Indeed, the managerial aspects of this complex organisation have become so dominant that I have included some chapters on what I have learnt from patients about what they want from the service and the help doctors need in order to support their patients, to re-emphasise the 'bedside' perspective.

I have also tried to describe how apparent barriers in medicine for women are best overcome – mainly by ignoring them. This may give heart to the large number of women entering medicine who need to juggle professional, domestic and family responsibilities if they are to take advantage of what can surely be one of the best and most fulfilling lives anyone can imagine.

I have to admit with a certain political incorrectness that this book also stresses the things in medicine which do not, or in my view should not, change. These include an appreciation and understanding of the needs of *individual* patients, the massive incompleteness of our knowledge base requiring much greater professional humility, and the perennial need to build trust with all for whom we have responsibility. But trust is earned not given – an inescapable truth which often seems to be overlooked.

The story is not intended to be a comprehensive record of either events or people. It is more a *pot pourri*, using events to highlight principles and thoughts relevant to the time and particularly in the context of what has happened since.

I have had the privilege of working with a very large number of splendid people – my seniors, my contemporaries, and especially my juniors. I am constantly asked, 'Who are your role models?' It was not like that, I learned from all of them – admiring some things, respecting others and choosing not to do things that way in still others. To mention everyone would be impossible – those included are usually simply examples to illustrate a particular point; all those who are not mentioned are appreciated with equal affection and respect.

As with most controversial episodes in history, there are always a number of different points of view. While I have tried to describe some of the problems as I perceive them, this is not to say that my own viewpoint is necessarily always right or that I do not understand contrary opinions. In general, when policy decisions cause difficulties, it is often not so much the immediate effects of these strategies that cause the problem but the subtle knock-on effects which, although often predictable, may take time to emerge. One gets tired of the excuse that in retrospect lessons have been learnt, when the wiser policy is to try to avoid the problem in the first place – usually by undertaking more careful groundwork.

This story is essentially a family one because, let it be clear from the beginning, without my husband Richard's continual support most of the events recorded here would not have happened. He supported and indeed urged me to tackle every challenge, often when it was to his own disadvantage. Frequently he had imaginative (and sometimes outrageously original) ideas about how to solve apparently insoluble problems and he has always given me the 'space' to do my own thing. We never worked at the same hospital and rarely served on the same committees. This may be a good prescription for avoiding professional and personal conflict. In our view, it was much better to fight our own corner each in our own way, and indeed make our own mistakes independently.

Likewise we both recognise the immense support we received from our daughters, Gillian and Lynne, again usually at their own expense. They understood, and were able to accept from a very young age, their parents' conflicting demands between meeting the needs of the family and their responsibilities for patients – the latter so often having to come first. The greatest compromise in my life has been coming to terms with continuing guilt: while I was caring for patients I felt I should have been at home and vice versa. Unless, with family support, one can find a *modus vivendi* to manage this dilemma I suspect that clinical medicine is simply not the right job. The other day I came across a letter written by Lynne aged about four. She was obviously getting bored and Nanny suggested that she write me a letter; it read as follows: 'Dear mummy, I hoape you don't git to tired at hospidol looking at the pashnts – If you do in the midol of a pashnt finish the pashnt then come home. Love from Lynne'. With amazing maturity she had understood the priorities. On another occasion, at roughly the same age, she was approached by an American colleague of Richard's at a small party we were giving at home. He asked her, 'What do you really think about having your mummy at work all day at the hospital?' Her reply was, 'What do you mean? Do you think I want mummy at home all day when I have just got things organised the way I want?' Was this simply independence, loyalty or, probably, a bit of both?

Gillian too had extraordinary insight into how adults, including her parents, were feeling. When she was about seven, her class was being addressed by the headmistress because there had been an episode of bullying in the school playground. She came home exceedingly distressed and we asked her what the teacher had said to upset her so much. 'Oh, it wasn't what she said that was so upsetting,' she said, 'it was what she was thinking!'

The fact that, some fifty years on, we remain marvellously close demonstrates that life-long family values can survive and indeed can flourish, in spite of both parents leading very busy lives and, by conventional standards, neglecting their children disgracefully. We were all very aware of the compromises which had to be made, and although we worked hard to try to identify the priority of the moment, be it hospital or home, the magnitude of the compromises should never be underestimated.

Some of this story is therefore highly relevant to the current debates on life–work balance and the flexible working patterns required to enable both parents to hold down rewarding jobs. Much of this debate seems to focus on how individuals can adapt their energies to get more out of life. This may be a fundamental mistake. Obvious as it is, the fact remains that the greatest rewards usually result from what one has been able to contribute rather than to get. In any case, this orientation seems to me to be very much safer, because one has less to lose.

Thus the story is a blend of biographical facts and how they interweave with the medical and political scene of the time; a blend of professional and family life, which runs as a continuous thread throughout and cannot be compartmentalised. It covers a range of medical commitments, first and foremost the care of patients and trying to understand their needs and what they can teach us. This is mixed with clinical research, teaching, international communication, and management involving both the medical profession and that of the National Health Service. I appreciate that parts of this story will be mundane, but this is what *Living medicine* is about: enjoyment of the ordinary can be just as much fun as the extraordinary.

I believe that today younger doctors, both men and women, have the opportunity to strike a fine balance between personal and professional life, which in some ways may be better than fifty years ago. If they can ensure that their professional integrity in the selfless care of patients is sacrosanct then all will be well for the future of medicine. However, if doctors allow their commitment to patients to be pushed into second place by political and managerial diktats, or more personal factors, then medicine will be at risk of losing its soul. In the end, the future of medicine will depend on those who really care for patients.

Recollections

Part 1

EARLY LIFE AND INFLUENCES

2. The beginnings:
Early days, parents and principles

This childhood story is one of a professional family with little money to spare but which put the fun of intellectual values before materialistic things – in my view, a very happy prescription.

My father believed in the doctrine of spares and regarded, in his inimitable but analytical way, his four daughters as 'two replacements' and 'two spares'. I was the first spare, in other words the third daughter. I was born on 19 November 1924 at Smith Square, Westminster, in London. We lived there because father wanted to become a Member of Parliament, but he never achieved this.

Dad, William Harvey Moore, was a West Country man. He was the eldest of four children of William Robert Moore and Ethel Tapp. He was sent to school at Clifton College, went up to New College, Oxford, and was called to the Bar from the Inner Temple. My grandfather also went to Oxford – Worcester College – but was sent down for some misdemeanour and subsequently went up to Cambridge. He too was called to the Bar but inherited Highbullen at Chittlehamholt, built by my great-grandfather, and an estate in North Devon which he ran as a gentleman farmer. Highbullen has now been converted into a friendly family hotel with magnificent outdoor facilities and wonderful views. My father inherited the property, but he wanted an active practice at the bar and to become involved in politics, so he sold up in 1922 and the family moved to London. Over the next 15 years he stood variously for Labour (more than once) and as an independent Member of Parliament. In those days, I believe that domination by the Party was rather less than it is today; representing the people in the constituency was what mattered, and he cared for ordinary people greatly.

My mother was Maud Baden Powell, daughter of Sir George Baden Powell, Member of Parliament for Kirkdale in Liverpool, and Frances Wilson. They lived in considerable comfort in Cheltenham but her life was sad. Her father died when she was just three and her mother died when she was 16. She then became a ward of Stephen Robert Baden Powell (Uncle Stevie), the Chief Scout (later Lord Baden Powell), and

George Wilson who lived in St Andrews. She, like so many of the Baden Powells, was a highly independent child; her grandmother commented when she was just 10 years old that 'dear little Maud is worryingly wayward', and would have to be sent to a boarding school to acquire some self-discipline. But her grandmother also recognised her intelligence and fascination with scientific matters, and her ease with formal adult company whenever they were discussing such things. Letters show that careful calculations were done which demonstrated that the cost of a governess, together with her board and keep, as well as the upkeep and equipment of the schoolroom, was as great as that of a boarding school and, thus, she went to Cheltenham Ladies College. When she left school she declared her intention to study medicine, believing that Uncle Stevie would fully support the idea of equal opportunities for girls. However, this was absolutely vetoed as an unsuitable career for a lady. She therefore went to live with the Wilsons and entered St Andrews University to read chemistry (because she liked science and scientific thought) and Hebrew (because she wished to read the Old Testament in the original). I suspect she may have been the only graduate of that university to have read that combination of subjects; she was almost certainly the first woman to do so, wayward or not! On reaching her majority, she kept to her plan and entered the Royal Free Medical School but, having completed her first two years successfully, had to leave to look after her younger brother, Donald, to whom she was devoted and whose life was in danger following a serious wound during the First World War. Her priorities in life were always quite clear. During this interlude she met my father and never returned to medical school. Uncle Donald recovered and became a well-respected archaeologist at Oxford.

Everyone knows that to understand an adult one must understand the environment of the child, so our background is relevant. Our parents' own childhood was thus late Victorian, and it was natural for them to adopt a certain distancing from my sisters and me although, as I shall describe, they both had a powerful influence on our perspectives on life. Our immediate needs were met by a magical nanny (later termed 'Noodle' by all and referred to thus in this book) who joined our family when I was just three weeks old. She was a contemporary of my mother at Cheltenham Ladies College but had to leave suddenly when her father's shipping business failed, to train quickly as a nursery nanny in order to earn her own living. Noodle never showed any resentment at her changed circumstances. She simply adopted her new role and gave the four of us great love and caring. She was always meticulously fair and had remarkable insight about our differences. Whether this closeness with Noodle augmented our parents' emotional withdrawal or whether their withdrawal instinctively promoted Noodle's emotional closeness is uncertain – but it probably suited them both.

When it came to practical matters of sharing her interests, mother came to the fore. She had a great breadth of knowledge acquired from the many interesting adults invited in a constant stream to her childhood home and a good deal more from the coachman whom she always sought out when the answers to her questions from other adults were, in her view, unsatisfactory. She was extremely knowledgeable about wild flowers; she painted watercolours and was a member of the Royal Watercolour Society and pupil of Holding. She had a passion for all types of crafts including leatherwork, tatting, lace making, linocuts, pewter work and carving in plaster or even soap. She expected us to be interested and we were. At the same time, she was a philosopher, psychologist and mystic and greatly admired the works of Jung. Her thoughts were often far away as she performed more routine domestic tasks. There is a famous passport photo of her, in the family referred to as the 'picture of mummy not listening'. Her philosophic intellect, her Presbyterian upbringing and the practicalities of being suddenly short of money following the slump of 1932 contrived together to enable her, and to encourage us, to 'travel very lightly'. Practical essentials were fine but excess worldly goods simply held a very low priority. Shopping bored her and things were expected to last indefinitely – and why not? When materialist discussions became too complicated her oft-quoted response was simply 'fuss, fuss, fuss', always expressed in a very quiet, slightly reproving, but never dismissive way.

In spite of the somewhat remote attitude to the emotional development of her children, many of her principles in life rubbed off on us in a powerful way. She had huge tolerance. Later she became a highly respected Quaker and contributed much to their philosophic studies as a Seeker.

Father was different. He had a strong Baptist background but later joined the Church of England as an active participant. He loved books and built up a very large library. He had a classical education at Clifton College and read Law at New College, Oxford.

Under a somewhat gruff exterior, he had a very soft heart kept under stern control. He did his best to engage us in intellectual dinnertime conversations and debate at which my older sister, Cynthia, excelled. I remained largely out of my depth but was too proud to admit it. Many of his principles also rubbed off powerfully. Tact was important and hurting people's feelings either within or outside the family circle was quite unacceptable. When we complained of some perceived injustice, he always insisted we looked at it from the other person's point of view, as all good lawyers do.

His love of music was instilled in us because it was compelling for him. He could not go to bed without playing a hymn tune or Bach Chorale on his harmonium (which is still in the family) or playing one of his large collection of gramophone records. Haydn's *Insanae et vanae curae* was especially loved by us all as we strained our ears from our beds to catch the delicate ornamentation. A hand-wound gramophone always accompanied us on our family camping trips. As Mother and Noodle cooked supper, he would restore our weariness with some wonderful music. Tchaikovsky's VIth was a great favourite, which was also much appreciated by the cows in the field who gathered around to listen.

Our parents set very clear standards, albeit somewhat puritanical, but always for very good reasons. We were never deprived, but the atmosphere encouraged us to use our time and opportunities constructively and never ever to waste money. It was a serious childhood but I think this suited my own temperament. As my father said in exasperation when I suspect I was being tiresomely un-childlike over something, 'The trouble with you is you were just born old'.

These thumbnail sketches illustrate the combination of our parents' remoteness but closeness, which is in fact no paradox. It is a subtle relationship where much adult strength can be applied happily to quite young children, leavened in our case, I have no doubt, by the indispensable Noodle.

Noodle's capacity to fill the gaps left by our parents in an unselfish and non-possessive way was remarkable. She got away with many things of which they allegedly disapproved. Card games were regarded as a waste of time by our parents but somehow a game of rummy supervised by Noodle was acceptable. Betting, on the other hand, was 'out'. Noodle never breached this taboo for us, but declared quite openly when she herself had put a bet on the Grand National or such like – and she clearly enjoyed saying so.

The principles of discipline and responsibility were instilled at a young age. We had to play a major part in tidying our toys regularly, but as we tired there was a magical phrase, 'You have done enough dear, I will do the rest'. Ever since, I have never found the last bits of clearing up easy. On the other hand discipline was strong. My younger sister Anne and I were taken by Noodle every day to St James Park where there was a kiosk which sold penny currant buns. I soon learnt that to ask or indeed turn my eyes ever so slightly in that direction would receive a kindly, 'Not today dear'. Just very occasionally, when I had kept my eyes glued firmly straight ahead, there might be 'Would you like a bun today?' As if she thought there could be any doubt about the answer.

Principles were instilled simply, directly and in practical terms – not in a prescriptive way, but as a matter of form and always allowing room for explanations. Above all, we knew there was no room for manoeuvre if we tried to play off our parents against Noodle or *vice versa*. The solidarity and loyalty of the well-trained Norland Nanny was total.

As we grew older, Noodle became companion to my mother and later she lived with my aunt who was headmistress at a County Grammar School in Faringdon, Oxfordshire where she was in charge of the catering. Later still, at the age of about 55, she returned to our home and cared for Gillian and Lynne for 10 formative years. They loved her dearly and she did for them what she had done for us. In her retirement she lived in her own flat in Richard's mother's home, each giving the other much companionship and vying with each other over the daily crossword. Thus, Noodle joined the family in 1924 when I was just three weeks old and remained within our family, taking on different roles, until her death at the age of 80. Perhaps this is a record in family loyalty by a Norland Nanny.

3. Kid's stuff: Schooling

Before I went to school, I had two medical experiences which have stayed with me and taught me to respect the views of even very young children. When I was four, I needed a tonsillectomy. This required a week in hospital and although visitors were allowed the time was strictly limited. I was taken in by Noodle and was absolutely clear in my own mind that I would be able to handle things provided that she did *not* visit again until she could collect and take me home – I much preferred to stick it out on my own, than face another parting if she visited. Although I cannot remember being able to tell her this, I think she understood and I managed on my own for the week. Paediatricians and parents may need to consider that there may be other four-year-olds out there today who have similar, albeit unorthodox, views. I wonder how we find out. The other experience was when I was slightly older and having a myringotomy at home with the general practitioner giving me a 'gas' anaesthetic. However, I was not asleep when the surgeon got going in spite of my making every effort, rather noisily I fear, to make my point. The moral of these two episodes is that, as all good paediatricians know, doctors need to listen carefully to even quite young children. They can often tell us what is right for them.

My two older sisters, Joan and Cynthia, went to the City of London School for Girls. At the age of $4\frac{1}{2}$, I was taken to their sports day and met Miss Helby, the first form mistress. In a kindly way she asked me when I would join them and, taking her at face value, I asked her for a 'trial day' which was customary at the time. Together we arranged one. She did not ask my age and I did not volunteer the information. I was duly offered a place before she realised that I was under age. However, she kept her promise. It was a splendid school and did many imaginative things besides the three 'R's, including clay modelling (an all-time favourite), cross-stitch with wonderful coloured Silko thread, and watercolour painting and perspective drawing taught by a specialist art teacher, Miss Hooper, for the seven- and eight-year-olds. This was serious work – not just splashing about – and it was submitted for external grading by the Royal Drawing Society. We loved to see our work carefully mounted and labelled for exhibition. So much for debates on the undue stresses caused by too-early external assessments. Each week we were bussed down to

Grove Park in south London for sporting activities but I was very bus sick and did not enjoy it. We were taken swimming at St Brides Baths, close to the school in the City. Drama too was sophisticated – this was not limited to children's plays but included serious works like *A Midsummer Night's Dream* in which many children throughout the school were involved. At the age of about seven I was to be a fairy. Unfortunately, I was laid low with another infection and was bitterly disappointed at the prospect of missing it. So much so that as compensation, my father gave me my first watch – an Ingersol costing about £2. At the very last minute, however, I made a miraculous recovery and was able to perform (provided I promised not to cough on stage) and was allowed to keep the watch, which I still have. My conscience has never been quite clear since.

Academically I did poorly. A major contributing factor was recurrent otitis media and recurrent bronchopneumonia which, before the days of antibiotics, caused prolonged absences from school.

At the age of eight a critical decision had to be made. Our father had said that there would be no dowries in the family but he expected all his daughters to undertake a professional training and he would cover the cost. My oldest sister, Joan, was heading for botany to become a plant pathologist and Cynthia had decided to become a teacher of modern languages. Thus the arts and science slots had been taken and he turned to me and asked what I would do. It appeared to me that most of the options had run out, so I quickly decided on medicine as the only thing left – apparently recognising even then that it was neither wholly an art nor a science. Being a very obstinate child and having declared my hand in this way there was no way of going back. However, the more the idea took root the more convinced I became that this was a very good thing. I regarded it as my prerogative to acquire medical information whenever there was an opportunity and cross-examined the GP whenever he visited the family about his diagnosis and treatments. I have never regretted the decision, although I remember feeling acutely embarrassed when I realised that the medical training was far longer than others and that I might have asked for more than my fair share of father's education budget.

From the age of about nine, all seven of us including Noodle lived in a top flat at 12 King's Bench Walk in the Inner Temple. It had two large front rooms overlooking the Inner Temple gardens and the Thames and one small back bedroom. My father slept in a fold away bed in his study surrounded by his books and music. My mother and two older sisters also slept in foldaway beds in the large front 'workroom' which was the centre of activity for the whole family. Noodle, with my younger sister and myself sleeping in a bunk bed, were allocated the back bedroom. Although somewhat squashed we learned to live and travel very lightly; it was certainly extremely convenient for the School, then located in Carmellite Street just around the corner. It was a huge privilege living in the seclusion of the Temple, in the heart of the legal world. We were given a special key to the gardens where we were allowed to play provided we did not shout or scream. The rules were strict but the environment was very special. We were also extremely fortunate that we were able to get away at weekends to a small country cottage at Otford, Kent.

Unfortunately, all of us children were sickly and both my older sisters had to have mastoid operations which without antibiotics were potentially life-threatening. It was therefore decided that we should move to Kent and go to a local school, Walthamstow Hall, in Sevenoaks. In spite of its good reputation and through no fault of the school, it was a disaster for me and I hated it. I was placed in a form in advance of my age; I did not understand what was going on and only later was it discovered that I was also considerably deaf due to Eustachian tube blockage. The only redeeming feature was being forced to take part in the school play as Patience in *Pilgrim's Progress*. This involved sitting on a stool on the stage and not batting an eye throughout the entire two-hour performance. Since I neither knew, heard nor cared one jot about the proceedings, my performance of total detachment was a very real statement of my feelings. However, this was misinterpreted by the local newspaper as extreme self-discipline and I was commended for my 'performance' as the ultimate Patience – little did they know the truth.

Fortunately, within the year it was decided that the whole family should move to Exeter since my father, who was on the Western Circuit, thought that a better plan was to set up practice as a barrister in Exeter so that the circuit judges could come to him.

Thus we moved to 5 Pennsylvania Park in a splendid terrace of six large Regency houses on a hill overlooking the city – now largely owned by the University and turned into flats. When I was about eleven we transferred to the Maynard School, which also had an outstanding reputation and which, after an initial disappointment, did us all proud. This time I was placed in a form below my age because I had lost so much time through sickness and the debacle of Walthamstow Hall. However, it was promised that if I achieved an average 8½ out of 10 marks in all subjects every week until half term I would be moved up. I worked extremely hard and achieved this. However, the school renegued and decided, with the consent of my parents but not me, that it was better to stay in a lower form where I was at the top, rather than struggle in a higher form. I saw the sense of this but my *amour propre* was dented – and I felt that a promise had been broken. The decision was of course absolutely right and as a point of honour I had to remain near the top throughout my time at the

Maynard. I enjoyed greatly both the academic work and the sport. I got into the quarter finals of the school tennis championships at the age of about 14 by lobbing so excruciatingly that it put off my opponent, who was in the sixth form and in the first team. She was rightly very indignant.

We enjoyed all sorts of ordinary things; we rode some lovely horses at Mrs Jackson's stables on the Duryard Estate – now part of the University; we walked miles on Dartmoor; and we got all sorts of badges as Girl Guides because mum thought we really should join. There was of course no television and teenagers had not been invented, so life was very uncomplicated. We learned the piano with Miss Jacko and, following a Philharmonic concert given in the Rougement Hotel, I took up the violin to which, in spite of playing with enthusiasm but little talent, I have been addicted ever since.

In 1941 Exeter was bombed by the Germans in a reprisal raid for damage done to Lubeck and the school was hit, fortunately without casualties. Remarkably, within 24 hours lessons were reorganised by three outstanding science teachers, Miss Evans, Miss Clissold and Miss Ryan, and we shared premises with Bishop Blackall School, where we continued calmly to dissect our dogfish as if nothing had happened. Due to massive evacuation programmes and bombings, school teachers developed a most remarkable talent for flexible organisation during the war years, for which they have been given very scant recognition. On the morning after the first air raid on Exeter the thought in everyone's mind was, 'Has the Cathedral been damaged?' At first light the entire population, or so it seemed, converged on the Cathedral and was aghast to see that the South Transept had received a direct hit. However, standing in the ruins was the Dean. With considerable presence of mind and understanding of people he told everyone to go home, collect a bucket, return and pick up every scrap of stained glass so that it could all be stored carefully and used in the restoration.

At this time (1942) father had returned to London, undertaking cases in the Law Courts while most of the younger barristers were away in the war. The London bombing and the Battle of Britain were over and he felt that if we were going to be bombed in Exeter we might as well all move back together to London. We lived in a spacious Victorian House in Chiswick with a garden running down to the Thames and its own dinghy with a lug sail, hanging on davits. In those carefree days, I would launch myself alone, without any knowledge of sailing, tides or water traffic regulations and no life jacket, on to the Thames and, as often as not, had to be rescued by the River Police or Port of London Authority, from whom I would hitch a lift home. Safety awareness has certainly changed mightily over the years, but at that time, risk management was simply not on the agenda. It is not surprising that childhood accidents were very common and only quite recently, with objective data, have serious attempts been made to reduce them.

My sister Anne and I transferred to St Paul's School. I joined the sixth form and this was not easy but I was in good company because so many people were being shuttled around due to the war. The school was remarkably welcoming and life was very full in spite of the international situation, the VJ rockets and Doodlebugs. All the scientists in the sixth form had compulsory English and current affairs lessons, both of which were excellently taught. In particular, the music was wonderful. Miss Stocken taught me the violin and pushed hard to expand my repertoire if not my technique (which in retrospect was rather a pity). She introduced me to chamber music and orchestral playing.

The crunch came when father insisted, because of the length of the medical training, that I sat the entrance examination for Oxford and Cambridge *before* sitting the Higher Certificate (now 'A' levels), instead of the usual practice at St Paul's of spending an extra six months and taking it after the Higher Certificate exam. This convention ensured that many Paulinas got scholarships, enhancing the glory and reputation of the school. Miss Strudwick, the Headmistress at the time, was adamant (and right) that I was not up to standard and that I would let down both myself and the school by sitting Oxford entrance prematurely. Father was equally adamant, believing that I had nothing to lose. So it was that I sat the exam as he wished. However, I was presented with an unexpected dilemma. It was known that Part A of the paper was for those wanting a Commoners place (I would be lucky indeed to get one) and Part B was to be taken only by those intending to compete for a scholarship (which was certainly out of the question). On reading the paper through, I found to my horror that I could not answer any of the questions in Part A. However, I found I could write at least something about the necessary number of questions in Part B. I knew that I could not possibly reach the scholarship standard and would blow my chances whichever part I tackled. Like father, I decided I had nothing to lose and did Part B. To everyone else's and my astonishment, I was offered an open scholarship to Lady Margaret Hall at Oxford. To the eternal credit of the school, Miss Strudwick and the staff were most gracious in their congratulations – perhaps just a little because the honour of the school had indeed been maintained – but we all knew it was not deserved.

By today's standards I certainly would not have achieved high enough grades in the Higher Certificate to get into a medical school at all, but fortunately having achieved a scholarship, I got onto the very restricted women's medical quota (seven women in the whole Oxford intake of

100 medical students each year). In consequence, I was able to opt for the local Oxford exam of Responsions which was relatively easy and I never had to face the ignominy of failing Higher Certificate.

I was also offered an exhibition at Girton and a place at Newnham in Cambridge, but the choice was clear. And so it was that I went up to Oxford in October 1943.

4. Relatively carefree days: Oxford

In truth, Oxford was perhaps the most challenging and intellectually exciting time of all. This was because learning took on an entirely new dimension and it suggested processes for the analysis and dissection of problems which have helped enormously ever since – both inside and outside medicine. I am so glad that most medical schools in the UK, including the newest, are now realising that helping students to understand the ways in which problems are tackled is a safer approach to medical education than trying to learn facts by rote. Gone were the school days of didactic teaching – at Oxford it was a matter of exploration and discussion of ideas with extremely knowledgeable people in one-to-one tutorials. Unlike many other medical schools at the time, there were very few set lectures and only minor reference to basic textbooks – but more of this later. It is mind boggling to me that the importance of this most fundamental system of further education (one-to-one, or at least few-to-one tutorials), which has proved itself over centuries, by providing tens of thousands of great contributors to world knowledge and development in so many fields of life, is so decried by those set on destroying it.

Achieving a place at Lady Margaret Hall (LMH) was a great good fortune; getting onto the women's quota was quite difficult because of the very small number allocated for women. However, adversity can often be turned to good because it enabled us to gain experience, right from the beginning, of working in an environment where women were in an extreme minority. By far the best way to cope with this was to ignore gender attitudes altogether, even when snide remarks or evident prejudice was expressed. However well justified the anger and frustration at such attitudes may be, rising to the bait only exacerbates the situation. By contrast, not responding to such aggravation allowed us to learn how to adapt in ways which could foster real equality. Not that we should take all the credit. There were a great many people around, both staff and students, who were hugely supportive even when they too had had little experience of coeducation. I remember a physiology experiment when several in the class had to run round the grounds (the Parks) to the point of exhaustion, so that increased blood lactic acid levels on exercise could be studied. A few of us volunteered and the boys running with us were very solicitous to make sure we got back safely without collapsing and others offered to do all the laboratory measurements for us, while we went to lunch early. If we were game, they were too. It is rather sad to watch some women today rebuffing common male courtesy in order to demonstrate their equality. Why not appreciate a little male graciousness and enjoy it? On the other hand, the deliberate policy of systematically ignoring gender prejudice because it is irrelevant to medicine and other management situations has served well throughout the rest of my career which, for most of the time, has continued to be substantially male-dominated. This attitude has, I suspect, caused many 'glass ceilings' to simply disappear without the need to crack them. It is surprising how many things disappear if they are ignored. An alternative explanation is that I have simply been very lucky working with wonderful people who share the same philosophy. However, as I will describe later, there were some things which in the early days were insurmountable, and compromises had to be made. I recognise from reading other women's autobiographies that in those early days many were not so lucky and had a much tougher time in spite of their best efforts. Many showed huge tolerance and courage.

Because of the constraints of war, men were only allowed to train in reserved occupations (such as doctors and some scientists) at Oxford in the early 1940s. The women were more fortunate because a full range of subjects was available, but in 1942 the length of the honours course was reduced from three years to two. Thus, in 1943 there was a bumper intake of 80 students to LMH. This gave us a splendid opportunity to meet a wide range of new and interesting people reading all sorts of exciting subjects. Indeed, it was very tempting for many of us to consider switching subjects and I even toyed with the idea of changing to PPE (Politics, Philosophy and Economics) and many people did. Collegiate life was fun although under constant pressure because of a draconian ruling necessitated by war that to fail in any examination, even once, resulted in being 'sent down' and 'called up'. Indeed, many good people tripped and fell. Some came back and completed their degrees after the war; others accepted their lot bravely. At a very recent Gaudy (reunion) in 2003, especially for the wartime cohort, a large number returned to LMH, demonstrating their continued loyalty.

During this time there was six hours of compulsory war work a week. I worked at the Radcliffe Infirmary to get a feel for hospital life, but in fact it mostly involved doing the washing up. I also helped to dig up LMH's rather splendid lawns and garden to grow vegetables. Because I have always enjoyed gardening this was no great hardship and digging is a great way to think. Indeed, much later, my secretary always knew when I had been dictating letters which I had thought out while digging (I kept the dictaphone at the end of the row) because she could hear the birds in the background. We also 'fire watched' at the Radcliffe Medical Library. This had the advantage of enabling us to work the whole night through in the library instead of being turned out at 10 pm. However, it soon taught us that excessive hours of study alone can be fairly useless and does not replace quality thinking time.

There were very few systematic lectures but a few were given by enthusiasts, who openly declared that they offered them to clear their own minds – not always successfully. Other key lectures were given to provide a general orientation. Professor Le Gros Clarke (WLGC), Professor of Anatomy with a background in surgery, gave a unique series on the basic structure of the tissues of the body, based on his equally unique book. Dr Alice Carlton, whose 'day job' was a consultant dermatologist, had a very original way of teaching anatomy by constructing, through free-hand drawing on the blackboard, cross sections of the body to show anatomical relationships. This was how she taught in 1940, some 40 years before doctors had to relearn their anatomy in exactly this way in order to understand computer assisted tomography (CAT scanning). I understand that at least one of our newest medical schools (Peninsula Medical School) is now engaging the radiologists to teach basic anatomy in this way from the beginning.

Because of staff shortages, our weekly tutorials, either solo or in pairs, were undertaken by many tutors outside the College. This Faculty-based arrangement greatly broadened the range of our teachers. They included a number of young physicians from the Radcliffe Infirmary, including Frances Gardner (later Dame Frances, a distinguished Dean and Consultant Cardiologist at the Royal Free Hospital). She took her task very seriously and I am afraid we gave her rather a bad time; students can be very tiresome when they insist on asking impossible questions. Although the individual tutorial system is very labour intensive it was an invaluable way to learn because ideas could be explored in depth and problems explained individually. Textbooks such as Starling's *Physiology* were used only for the barest framework; the majority of physiology was learnt from study of original papers or the invaluable *Physiological Reviews*. Anatomy was taught in meticulous detail almost completely through practical dissection, augmented with weekly individually marked *viva voce* examinations conducted by quite a large number of demonstrators, many of whom were trainee surgeons. For those with visual memories, anatomy was fascinating and fun. Even as a physician, I found it highly relevant to clinical problems later – but interestingly it was often the minute detail that was needed to localise exactly specific lesions, not just an understanding of the general overall main structures. The dumbing down of anatomy in the current curriculum of so many medical schools may prove to be misplaced. I worry particularly for aspiring surgeons and radiologists. It will be interesting to see which of the seductive newer sciences that have understandably squeezed out anatomy in the current curriculum for the time being, will prove to warrant their place in the fullness of time, when it comes to clinical relevance for many practising doctors. I appreciate that this is currently an heretical thought.

In the practical physiology classes, we undertook all sorts of investigations on ourselves which would not be permitted in today's insurance-ridden era, but they often taught us what we would later expect our patients to endure. These included a range of blood tests – which on very rare occasions picked up serious but asymptomatic disorders such as anaemias, leukaemias and metabolic and enzyme deficiencies – respiratory physiological measurements, analysis of gastric juices which involved swallowing a gastric tube, and many more. The idea that medical students should not test their own body fluids in case they discover an asymptomatic abnormality about which they have not been adequately counselled seems quite bizarre. Personal testing should be part of the commitment to medicine and identification of asymptomatic disease can quite often turn out to be a blessing.

The Oxford course was very different from many other medical schools at the time, where systematic didactic lectures backed up by lecture notes and textbook memorization was the norm. At Oxford (and indeed Cambridge) the emphasis was on exploration from original sources and individual learning. The basic reason for this different approach to learning was that Oxford did not regard itself as a medical school in the conventional sense. It was running an attenuated (because of the war) honours degree course focussing on the basic sciences relevant to medicine. Insofar as these subjects related to humans, the emphasis was on the healthy 'normal' structure and function as a basis for understanding more easily and in context the deviations from health of people with disease. Today, medical courses go to great lengths to obfuscate terminology to give it a contemporary flavour. At Cambridge I believe 'anatomy' is now 'functional architecture of the body', 'physiology' is 'homeostasis' and 'biochemistry', is 'molecules in medical science'. This delightful obfuscation of terminology is not of course limited to medical teaching. In primary schools, the posh way of being modern is to call sums 'numeracy' and reading and writing 'literacy'. A rose by any other name perhaps?

In addition, and in order to whet the appetite of the medical students, Dr Alec Cooke, a wonderful broadly based physician at the Radcliffe Infirmary, used to give a weekly clinical demonstration to illustrate how some of the things we were learning were relevant to disease. Even in the 1940s, Dr Cooke was already exploring the notion of integrated learning in medicine, now common practice worldwide. Unfortunately, he clearly found some difficulty in demonstrating the clinical relevance of many things we were learning. Some of this has gradually been corrected over the years.

In the 1960s, the exploratory and non-didactic approach to medical learning was further developed by McMaster University in Canada and Newcastle in Australia. They used problem solving as well as integrated learning through the introduction of clinical experience much earlier in the course. Neither of these schools, I believe, recognised how much of the non-didactic approach was based on a fundamental principle used at Oxford decades before.

Understandably, the General Medical Council (GMC) now insists on more fully integrated learning, where health and disease are studied concurrently. Certainly this is a particularly attractive approach for those strongly motivated by vocation and it has now become the norm in most medical schools. Some interesting new variations on integrated learning are also being explored in both the new and the older medical schools and professional educationalists are adding a new dimension. However, unless very carefully crafted, there is a danger that the complexities of the abnormal will confuse students with little or no prior understanding of the normal and its variations – potentially making the actual learning process more difficult. It is all too easy for *avant garde* teachers, course designers and even experienced physicians who are talented teachers, to forget that students inevitably have very little basic background knowledge. A strong argument can be made that early understanding of inherently complex structure and function in healthy people can actually make it easier to understand and remember the highly complex world of abnormality later on. Interestingly, the importance of this has been raised by a number of highly organised analytical youngsters I have met. It is just possible that in following the enlightened directive from the GMC to make medical teaching more relevant from the beginning, and the enthusiasm of educationalists for fully integrated courses, the pendulum has swung too far in some medical schools so that learning is actually made more difficult for the students. Naturally not all educationalists will agree with this sentiment and I appreciate there are other agendas such as trying to cut corners to shorten the course. However, the old adage of 'not trying to run before you can walk' is worth a thought, even if it is not always quite so excitingly innovative.

This does not mean that the 'serial' approach cannot be improved or that the 'parallel' system is less good. The question is what system facilitates the easiest way to acquire the appropriate knowledge and retain it in the long term. There are obvious advantages and disadvantages of both approaches, but I suspect more work needs to be done on defining the best balance between the two, especially as good teachers are becoming increasingly hard to find and teaching costs are rising. The problems have been accentuated by the recent rapid increase in numbers of students, the intake of mature students, some of whom have less scientific backgrounds, and the move towards reducing the length of courses for economic reasons. It is axiomatic that there are many different ways of acquiring knowledge and many different orders in which it may be presented. At the end of the day, the students may or may not be measurably different in their competence. The question remains, however, which way is the easiest, the most stimulating, the most efficient and the most fun? There is still plenty of room for research here before educationalists can convince us that they have found the holy grail. It is likely that different methods will appeal to different students. Let us therefore hope that the versatility in medical educational programmes can be retained. The large number of medical schools around the UK now provides ample opportunity to explore different educational methods, and perhaps more could be done to help recruits understand these different approaches so that they can choose which may be best for them, rather than having to accept with some relief just anywhere that offers them a place, on the assumption that their methods are all much the same.

With the pressure of the Second World War, the academic departments within the Oxford medical school were forced to apply their minds in more practical ways. This made Oxford a very exciting environment where we as students saw fine academics applying their minds to contribute to the war effort. Thus Professor Sinclair turned his biochemical skills to those of nutrition and he worked closely with the Government, including Lord Woolton, to maintain healthy nutrition in the country. Of course many people, such as McCance and Widdowson at Cambridge and those at other universities, also contributed enormously to this programme. This admirable and very effective scientific/political partnership helped to ensure a basic healthy nutrition for everyone in spite of the very strict rationing needed to minimise imported goods, which were so costly in terms of human lives and ships due to the blockading efforts of German U boats. The Oxford Department of Anatomy, under the direction of Graham Waddell, turned its attention to the better design of seats for armoured tanks and anti-aircraft guns. Other biochemists focussed on the protection of soldiers from chemical warfare and developed British Anti Lewisite (BAL) – an antidote to mustard gas. A number of other seminal discoveries were, however, more fortuitous thanks to the recognition that even in the darkest days of the war, basic scientific research was still essential. The serendipitous discovery of penicillin was perhaps the most famous.

The long hours of hands-on laboratory work and the very lengthy times spent in the library at Oxford did not allow students much opportunity for leisure interests, but we seemed to make time. The Oxford orchestra flourished under Christopher Longuet Higgins, as did the Bach Choir under the direction of Dr Reginald Jacques. A group of us got permission from the Master of St John's to play chamber music in its magnificent Long Gallery, although our rendering of Mozart's clarinet quintet was not up to the standards of musical medical students of today. Patience Proby and I played the fiddle together and started a before-breakfast Scottish dancing club at LMH. This was soon stopped because of the anti-social noise it made.

It was at Oxford that I met Richard, who was a year ahead of me. I knew him by sight because he had, most politely and in his inimitable way, challenged Professor Le Gros Clarke during one of his lectures on his description of the circulation of the aqueous humor (circulation of fluid in the chambers of the eye). To challenge a professor openly on a factual point was rather an uncommon thing for students to do in those days and I admired his courage. He stuck to his guns, not to be difficult but because he believed that it would mislead other students to let the matter rest. In the end, WLGC agreed that they would both go away and look it up and report back the following week. The Professor kept his word and reported that Richard had been right.

I gave the episode no more thought. However, two terms later, after my year had received the results of our histology exam in which I had done well, Richard on his bike stopped me in the car park to congratulate me. This was a surprise, as I had no idea how he should know my name. He then asked whether I was going in for the Welch anatomy prize which that year was to be on histological illustrations of the skin, a prize he had won the year before on illustrations of the aqueous humor (that was why he knew he was right when he argued with the Professor). He added that if I wanted to know more I had better come to tea! So I went. In due course, I also won the prize and one of the paintings (a histological picture of an arterio-venous anastomois) has been included in subsequent editions of Le Gros Clarke's *Tissues of the body* which I find a rather sentimental reminder.

The friendship with Richard was also fuelled by an unlikely source. The self-same Professor, who was widely recognised for his fairly dour temperament, had asked Richard, who intended to become a surgeon, to undertake some prosecting of special specimens for demonstration purposes during the vacation. Some days later, the Professor sidled up to me and suggested that I too might like to stay up and help. He then contrived to ensure that we were prosecting together on the same specimen. Such was our romantic beginning.

The Oxford first BM examination was taken at the end of the second year and was equivalent to the 2nd MB. This essentially included anatomy, physiology, biochemistry and normal histology. Most students then moved on to teaching hospitals in London to do their three clinical years. In the 1940s, Oxford was debating whether it should continue to focus on postgraduate medicine or whether it should expand into clinical undergraduate education. Thus only a few remained at Oxford for the relatively new clinical course, which was not particularly popular at the time, but has now expanded into a magnificent one. Most students preferred to leave the rarefied atmosphere of Oxford and join the rough and tumble of London teaching hospitals which, it was considered, could offer wider clinical experience.

In spite of the wartime constraints, Oxford pursued another most enlightened policy. While most undertook the two-year course in order to qualify as quickly as possible, Oxford took a long-term view and realised that if the country survived the war then some people would be needed to lead medical research and teaching into the post-war era. Thus it was that ten out of 100 students were selected and offered a third-year honours degree course in physiology. In the centrally regulated world of today such imaginative flexibility at a time of great uncertainty would be very improbable, especially under the dire circumstances of the war. Indeed, it raises the wider fundamental and unresolved problem of balancing diversity in the length of medical training on the one hand and the ever-tightening central prescriptive regulated uniformity on the other. This topic is in urgent need of further debate. Today, of course, all students at Oxford (and Cambridge) undertake a three-year honours degree course and the range of subjects has been greatly extended.

Richard not surprisingly was duly selected for this honours degree course in 1946. This gave him, as a surgeon, that essential academic base which has influenced his entire career. In 1947 the war was over and he stayed up at Oxford for a fourth year to read for a research BSc (recently upgraded to an MSc when the relative quality of university degrees was reviewed). He studied the olfactory system under WLGC. As President of the Oxford University Boat Club and rowing in the crew, he and his opposite number at Cambridge agreed that the Boat Race should be taken back to the Tideway. Oxford won by four lengths. Those two academic years in Oxford also set his sights on a large number of student prizes at the Middlesex Hospital, including the Broderip Scholarship for the student of the year. Perhaps of even great importance it instilled his lifelong attitude to original investigation of structure and function. He later obtained his Oxford Doctorate of Medicine by a research thesis on breast lymphatics as well as a thesis for his MCh in surgery. He passed the

MRCP examination of the Royal College of Physicians as well as, of course, all his postgraduate surgical examinations. His academic background led him to publish over 150 original papers in international and specialised journals. At the end of his career, he published a magnificent book covering his original thinking and ideas over his whole career with over 1,400 illustrations, most developed from his own original sketches. We both believe that learning the fundamental methodology of how to approach new problems, which began at Oxford, set in train his lifetime of academic contribution.

The critical value of these extended times for free thinking and learning for some people should be remembered in these days of centralised prescriptive training. There seems to be an obsession with shortening medical education and limiting its scope on the false premise that as medicine and surgery becomes more specialised so training can be shorter and more restricted. This cannot be right because as the population ages, multiple pathology increases and training needs to be broader. Most of the best young doctors I have known have been keen to broaden their horizons to aid their experience and their capacity for lateral thinking and innovation, even if it took longer. This broader approach so often pays off for patients, especially those who present with all manner of problems not tidily compartmentalised in the textbooks. Breadth of knowledge and interdisciplinary exchanges are essential too for inspired teaching and add hugely to the sense of real fulfilment in medicine. Who then is the loser? And why is the breadth of medical education and training being assiduously crowded out? I hope that young doctors themselves, helped by their senior mentors, will insist on allowing scope for breadth, at least for those who want it.

The beginning of my second year (1944) at Oxford offered another opportunity which also came in very useful much later. Although the workload of the medical course was very time consuming and I was not an instinctively gregarious person, in College I enjoyed a very wide range of friends. To my great surprise I was elected President of the Junior Common Room and this gave me my first experience of people management, representing the students and liasing with the College Fellows (Senior Common Room). It was not a particularly arduous job but as well as the standard tasks it gave me the opportunity to lead the student body in the celebrations to honour the retirement of Linda Grier who had been the College Principal for 26 years. I remember the highlight was an open air Masque written and performed by the students from the Department of English in the sunken gardens outside the Wordsworth Building. The job also involved welcoming and helping to introduce the new Principal, Dr (later Dame) Lucy Sutherland.

In 1946, a year after Richard, I was fortunate enough also to be selected as one of some ten students for the honours course in physiology and this gave me too a taste, which lasted a lifetime, for the identification of research opportunities to investigate medical problems.

Things, however, are not always straightforward and in my last term at Oxford, life took a potentially shattering turn which, in the event, allowed me the privilege to experience a life-threatening situation with which many unfortunate patients have to come to terms.

I noticed a fairly hard lump about the size of a pigeon's egg in my neck just above my left clavicle. The GP in Oxford said it had the textbook qualities of a Virchow gland, commonly linked with carcinoma of the stomach, although he added, I was rather young for this to be likely. Richard and I decided to consult his father who was senior surgeon at the Middlesex Hospital. After consultation with his colleagues, he thought Hodgkin's disease was more probable. I looked up both diagnoses in the textbooks and the prognosis seemed at that time to be equally bad – although dramatic advances have of course been made, particularly for Hodgkin's disease, in recent years.

Thus within eight weeks of finals I was admitted to Mount Vernon Hospital for investigations. Arising from one of these, the pathologist found that the Paul Burnell test was positive, suggesting glandular fever (but this as so often in medicine proved to be a red herring). This diagnosis of course was much more hopeful, but the clinical presentation of a single large hard lymph gland was very uncharacteristic, so it was decided to obtain a biopsy. Conventional wisdom suggested that needle aspiration of potentially cancerous nodes is contraindicated because malignant cells can spread along the needle track; however, how and when to break conventional rules is one of the great arts in medicine and an aspiration was performed and thick caseous material indicative of tuberculosis was obtained. Further, closer examination of the chest X-ray taken previously showed that there was indeed a small lesion in the apex of the left lung. While a great reprieve from a diagnosis of cancer or Hodgkin's disease, it cast a very long shadow over our future. There were no anti-tuberculous drugs at the time and treatment depended on a prolonged period confined to bed in a sanatorium and an unpredictable long-term outlook. Although at that time many patients recovered, a substantial number did not.

The immediate question was what to do about finals. There were three choices. First, to remain in hospital, hoping to come back and sit finals the following year or later. This was not a practical proposition and the idea of having to repeat all the work or, worse, sitting the exam having been out of touch for months, made no sense. Second, it was possible on a doctor's recommendation to omit taking the examination and be awarded an *igrotat* unclassed degree on the basis of satisfactory reports from one's academic supervisors. This was not a satisfactory solution either because the reason for obtaining an unclassed degree would have to be explained for the rest of one's career – if one survived. The third choice was to return to Oxford forthwith, delay hospital admission, work as much as one was able, take finals as best one could and go back to hospital and sanatorium for treatment immediately afterwards. This seemed the best option for me. In retrospect, I find it remarkable that the doctors had the insight and understanding to agree to put their best medical treatments on hold and to regard other considerations, from the patient's point of view, as overruling. This for me illustrates both their wisdom and compassion, which in today's parlance would be classified as magnificent holistic medicine; putting the patient first. It certainly proves that 'patient choice' has been practised (when allowed) by good physicians and surgeons for a long time and is not a novel innovation of 2003. My College Tutor, Dr Celia Westropp, was also wonderfully supportive. In the event, I took finals and obtained a 2nd Class degree which at the time was a disappointment but is probably what I deserved anyway.

Further orthodox medical training was then on hold as I went away to learn a lot about tuberculosis and medicine from a patient's viewpoint – an experience which was absolutely invaluable.

In spite of this vicissitude, Oxford holds the happiest of memories and it is a privilege to return there regularly as Honorary Fellow of LMH, and later of Green College, and to serve on their Advisory Councils. To receive an Honorary DSc in 1995 and the Osler Medical Medal in 1996 added the final touches to my affection for a wonderful university which has given such spectacular opportunities to so many people. In today's climate of political accusations of elitism I am delighted to record that this was certainly not in evidence at LMH. Out of a mere handful of women on the medical quota in 1943-44, one had quite recently taken refuge in this country from Germany and another was the daughter of a railway worker. Both had been selected entirely on merit and both did outstandingly well. Social or conventional elitism was simply not a just charge against student selection at LMH even 60 years ago. The justification, or rather the unjustification, for the rigorous medical quota for women set by the University is of course an entirely different matter.

5. Being patient: Tuberculosis

The guiding principles of treatment of tuberculosis before the introduction of antituberculous medication were to rest the lung (which could be done in a variety of ways) and to endeavour to build up the body's defences through good nutrition. During two months in the Middlesex Hospital, various attempts were made to achieve these. The induction of an artificial pneumothorax by introducing air into the pleural cavity intended to collapse the lung failed because of adhesions between the lung and the chest wall caused by the disease. As an alternative, the left dome of the diaphragm was paralysed by crushing the phrenic nerve in the neck.

Plans were then made in November 1947 to go to a sanatorium in Montana in Switzerland, run on English lines by an Australian named Dr Roche. I knew the family could barely afford this, which was a worry, but it was strongly recommended because of the food shortages in England at the time. In Switzerland, I was confined to bed for about six months; the phrenic nerve was re-crushed and luckily another attempt made by a Swiss surgeon to cut the adhesions and establish an artificial pneumothorax (AP) was successful. The AP was maintained with refills of air every one or two weeks for the next five years. Control of the disease was carefully monitored each month to establish that tubercle bacilli could not be identified in the sputum, that blood tests to monitor indirectly evidence of inflammation (the erythrocyte sedimentation rate (ESR)) returned to normal, and that any cavities in the lung had closed.

The methodology of formally designed control trials in humans to validate the effectiveness of such treatments had not been perfected at that time and since then there has been much scepticism about the value of such attempts to rest the lung. However, while death from the disease was not inevitable, and long periods of remission were common, mortality was quite high without treatment and these interventions certainly had a rational if unproven basis. Serial observations also showed that treatments to collapse the lung could close cavities and that when this was achieved tubercle bacilli usually disappeared from the sputum. Thus indirect evidence suggested the usefulness of this approach to treatment. Probably the nearest attempt at a comparative trial was published by Dr Foster Carter, Superintendent of Frimley Sanatorium. In his fourth statistical report, published in 1952, 75% of 644 patients treated with an AP survived for five years compared to 58% without this treatment. Case selection may of course have had a major influence on these results.

The theory of controlled studies in the laboratory were of course well established and to wile away the time in bed in Switzerland I undertook an entertaining spoof of my own to assess the effect of various pharmacological drugs namely phenobarbitone, aspirin and benzedrine (all kindly supplied by the most cooperative nurses) on the viability of *Carchesium regis* (King Cups), easily available from a local mountain stream, The endpoint for the health of these plants was meticulously classified as 'turgid,' 'droopy' or 'dead'. The results were clear. Aspirin caused most rapid death, phenobarbiturate caused delayed death, and benzedrine maintained life as efficiently as the controls without any added medication. For some reason which now escapes me, I concluded that the 'present concept of time, death and logic could not be applied to certain scientific experiments and that the results were significant but inconclusive'. I still have the manuscript but no attempt was made to get it published – just as well, but it was fun! However, it did demonstrate my commitment to the methodology of controlled trails in 1947, before they had been routinely established to test medication in humans and even before I had started clinical training.

During the nine months in Switzerland I think I learnt a great deal about myself and how to cope with prolonged isolation in a single room and away from England, the tedium of very slow and variable progress with its ups and downs, the uncertainty of outlook, and the varied responses of other patients. I tried to learn German and improve my French, neither at all successfully because everyone spoke very good English. I had a systematic reading list including Boyd's *Textbook of pathology* which I read cover to cover, and a good deal of philosophy. I also designed and knitted a rather complicated Fair Isle patterned jersey to give to Richard when he came out to visit me during his summer vacation and which he still wears with special memories. All the patients talked together at length about their hopes and fears and I was especially struck by the non-lethal but psychological impact of some forms of tuberculosis on normally active men who often found their incarceration particularly hard to bear. Many patients in the sanatorium had much more severe disease than I and a number did not survive. There was great excitement when a small amount of streptomycin was flown in from America for a youngster of 14 years with terminal illness. Although she showed an early response with a dramatic remission of her fever, the supply ran out and she relapsed and died.

I probably did not appreciate at the time the full significance of the precariousness of life and its potential effect on my hopes of marrying

Richard or on the arduous career training ahead. At the age of 22, one simply got on with the business of the day. Neither do I think I appreciated adequately the inevitable pressures on the bystanders. The brunt was carried by Richard and his and my family but their philosophy – loyalty and no-nonsense acceptance – was hugely supportive. On the positive side, it was an extremely formative experience especially when trying to understand and communicate later with seriously ill patients of all ages.

It is an interesting reflection of the times that Dr Hall, one of the Consultant Chest Physicians, insisted on personally undertaking my pneumothorax refills – every few weeks for five years – to save me hours of queuing in the routine outpatient clinic. Dr Nicholson personally supervised my progress over the years and gave much wise advice on the way. I owe him a huge debt of gratitude. As a medical student one was already regarded as a member of the profession and such was the special care taken by consultants of their medical students. My chest X-ray is now a museum piece, showing the evidence of successful treatment of yesteryear.

In the end (or at least until my 80th year!), after five years of refills to the pneumothorax as well as certain adjustments during clinical training and early hospital posts to lighten the load, all has been well. Today there is much talk of accessibility to medicine by those with disabilities of various types and how far modifications can be made to the training programme while at the same time ensuring that professional standards are maintained. In our attempts to achieve a more inclusive society, one must always remember that those with various longish-term disabilities must play their part in accepting, where appropriate, the limitations to their career paths and that compromises have to be made. It is often implied that in the old days consultant doctors refused to make any allowances for individual students, perhaps especially if they were women. It is good to report that this was not my experience at all. Even fifty years ago I received great personal support and flexibility during my training by many people at University College Hospital.

After a year out of action I returned home and in October 1947 was declared fit to resume my clinical studies at University College Hospital.

Top: Father and Mother. *Bottom:* An egalitarian picnic on Dartmoor in 1931. My grandparents, William and Ethel Moore (with their cook and housemaid), our family (sister Anne on mother's knee in centre), with Nanny ('Noodle', extreme left), aunt Phil (second from right) and her daughter, Valerie, on her knee.

Top: M aged three years with serious reading.
Bottom: M on pony with older sisters, Joan and Cynthia.

Our wedding at St Dunstan's in Fleet Street, London, 1950.

Family snaps: *Top:* Richard and M at Oxford.
Bottom left: Gillian aged three on Magpie.
Bottom right: Lynne aged three on Magpie.

Top: 5, Pennsylvania Park, the family home in Exeter, 1937–42.
Bottom: The home we built in Highgate and extended on demand between 1953 and 1992.

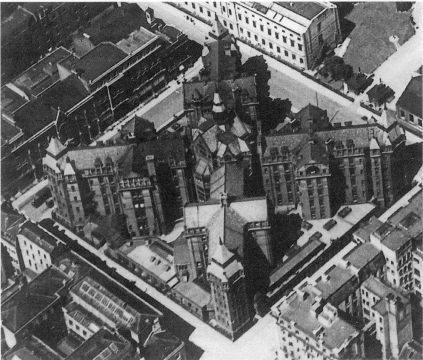

Top: Wordsworth Building, Lady Margaret Hall, Oxford. (My room was on the first floor at the right-hand end, overlooking the garden but extremely cold without heating in 1946.)
Bottom: Aerial view of the Cruciform Building, University College Hospital.

Part 2

FROM TRAINEE TO CONSULTANT: LEARNING FROM PATIENTS

6. Walking the wards:
The medical scene in 1947–50 and clinical training at University College Hospital

To understand the clinical training of students in the late 1940s, it is important to set the scene on the dramatically changing face of medicine during the immediate post-war years. In the light of the huge advances in medicine over the last few decades, it is easy to forget that dramatic changes were also occurring some fifty years ago.

Academic medicine had burgeoned after the Second World War in all major teaching hospitals throughout the UK, and clinical professorial departments were becoming widely established. They were largely funded from university sources but the number of academic posts was inevitably strictly limited. Vacancies mainly occurred when those at the top retired, allowing either the appointment of an 'outsider' or promotion up the ranks. Today's more sensible career structure for clinical academics, with flexible opportunities for personal Chairs to be appointed on individual merit, is a great advance. Research on clinical problems was high on the agenda in clinical professorial departments; basic research was mainly done in the traditional departments of physiology, pathology, biochemistry, pharmacology and bacteriology (later renamed microbiology).

The principle of assessing pharmaceutical advances through randomised control trials (RCTs) was promoted, particularly by the statistician, Professor Bradford Hill, and was extended by others such as the epidemiologist, Dr Archie Cochrane. This set the stage for the scientific validation of clinical treatments, thus preceding the concept and use of 'evidence-based medicine' by some fifty years. It opened up major controversies over the ethical principles of allocating patients at random to different forms of treatment, the use of standardised protocols, and the status and protection of volunteer patients. Above all, such trials posed a challenge to individual physicians convinced of the value (often with inadequate proof) of long-standing practices. All of these controversies, rehearsed in the early 1950s, are still taking place today, especially in fields such as complementary medicine where the same debates are regularly aired by patients and believers alike.

45

The application of controlled trials was taken up by the Medical Research Council (MRC), most notably in their systematic testing of anti-tuberculous drugs. This was perhaps the first example in medicine where, following a pharmaceutical breakthrough, the development of drug regimes in the treatment of a disease in humans was tested in a controlled scientific way *from the outset*. Their studies demonstrated many of the different ways of using these drugs. These included how to handle multiple medications to achieve cure without the development of drug resistance, safe but shorter and more convenient regimens for patients and, most importantly, the development of cheaper combinations of drug treatments making them affordable to patients in less affluent countries. This recognition by the MRC of the responsibility of developed countries to devise feasible regimens for less wealthy parts of the world was far ahead of its time. In these studies, much was learnt about international medical cooperation and the modifications required to overcome cultural as well as economic differences. The impetus towards international co-operation in medicine on a global scale was immense; indeed, it led to the MRC setting up research centres in a number of developing counties to investigate and treat many infectious tropical diseases.

Whilst sulphonamides were available in the 1930s and penicillin was discovered serendipitously in the 1940s, the 1950s were an era of rapid expansion in the range of antibiotics, transforming the 'natural history' of a large number of acute and chronic infectious diseases – either by primary cure or preventing infective complications.

Prevention as well as cure expanded and there were flourishing immunisation programmes on measles, diphtheria, whooping cough, tetanus, tuberculosis and many others. The concept that medicine involved treating populations as well as individuals was beginning to transform the face of public health medicine. In order to organise the expanding opportunities of preventive medicine, the new disciplines of epidemiology and statistics burgeoned. However, there was a sting in the tail: tensions emerged between those promoting the value of programmes shown to benefit populations and those recommending their value for *individual* people or patients. This dilemma still continues as a major ethical and economic issue. How far decisions on these issues should be left to professional clinicians' judgement of the evidence and how far they should be decided at a political level is another major debate for the NHS in the twenty-first century. An interesting outcome of this debate is the setting up of the National Institute for Health and Clinical Excellence (NICE), an independent body with a medically qualified chairman, to assess whether the evidence of efficacy and cost-effectiveness of new treatments warrants making them available within the NHS. NICE is potentially of great value provided that everyone understands clearly that, because of the usual incompleteness of the evidence, the judgements of NICE should be used as guidance and not in a prescriptive way (under most circumstances) for regulatory purposes.

At University College Hospital (UCH) in the late 1940s there was a strong emphasis on academic medicine both within and outside the Professorial Medical Unit. There was, for example, a somewhat elitist Thomas Lewis Society where students (by invitation) were encouraged to present papers for discussion by their peers and selected consultants. The rule was that the chosen topic must be outside the common run of clinical medicine. I presented a paper on paleopathology looking for the earliest evidence of disease in man: I received great help from the Wellcome History of Medicine Museum and the Natural History Museum. The galaxy of brilliant teachers at UCH was outstanding and some of them I remember particularly well. The Professor of Medicine, Harry Himsworth (later director of the MRC), was exploring new approaches to liver disease with the recently developed technique of liver biopsy. Dr Max Rosenheim (later Professor of Medicine, President of the Royal College of Physicians and Baronet in the Upper House) was making major advances in the understanding and treatment of hypertension. Professor Eric Pochin, a nuclear physicist and clinician, introduced radiolabelled iodine into the treatment of thyroid disease. Professor Charles Dent was exploring new areas in metabolic and bone disease. Dr John Stokes (later Senior Censor and Vice President of the Royal College of Physicians), a broadly based physician who was also interested in liver disease, and Dr John Hawksley, a gastroenterologist, both conducted some of the most popular ward-round teaching because of their clinical talents and breadth of knowledge. Clinical neurology was led by Dr Francis Walshe, of international fame; he was followed by his son, John, renowned for his innovative work on treating Wilson's disease with penicillamine. Dr Blake Pritchard was another outstanding teacher of neurology who preferred to demonstrate the various neurological signs we needed to learn, not by showing us patients but by imitating them himself, because he found that in this way he could illustrate the particular features more clearly. Dr Andrew Morland was considerably underestimated in my view – he had more difficulty in relating to students, but he had consummate skill in eliciting abnormal signs in the chest, predicting in an uncanny way what the chest X-ray would reveal. Dr Howard Nicholson had an immense knowledge of both medical and surgical diseases of the chest, enhanced by his experiences working with the cardiothoracic surgeon, Mr Andrew Logan, while on active service during the war, and by his logical and analytical approach which made him an outstanding diagnostician and teacher. He was an extremely kind man and demonstrated, with superb skill, how to deal with difficult colleagues, troubled patients and truculent students. By contrast, I found Dr Nabarro (later Professor at the Middlesex Hospital) the most intimidating because his inquisitorial approach towards junior staff and students seemed to me to be unnecessarily traumatic. He was undeniably a great lecturer and a fine diabetitian. In later years he mellowed and, while retaining his clinical excellence, he adopted a much more humane approach. He worked excessively hard and expected his research fellows to do the same. Even fifty years ago, UCH asked the students to provide feedback and evaluation on their lecturers. 'Nab' was the most popular because of his systematic approach, which was particularly useful for examination purposes. This caused me to wonder again what lectures were for. Were they simply to reproduce facts easily obtained from other sources – I think not – or were they to stimulate ideas and perspectives often from a personal viewpoint and experience, which were not obtainable elsewhere? Clearly my background of undergraduate training at Oxford preferred the latter.

The fundamental educational question of whether students respond better to a confrontational approach from their teachers or a more sensitive one is still debated. Educationists today generally have a strong preference for a less aggressive attitude and I personally agree with this. However, many students, especially those with a more robust temperament, will often say that they remembered more when the points were rammed home to them with some force, even if the process was painful. Thus again different methods suit different people, and the job of the teacher is to identify the right approach for the right student.

Many of the great teachers at UCH had only just returned from four or five years service in the front line or as prisoners of war. They too had to make major adjustments to convert into civilian life as clinicians, undergraduate teachers and clinical researchers. Part of the excellent supervision of students at the time was due to the number of outstanding supernumerary registrars who had recently been demobilised and were waiting for consultant posts around the country. Among those I remember especially were Ian Gray, Peter Arblaster and Mike Atkinson, but there were many others besides. It is often not recognised that one of the reasons why the NHS, set up in 1948, got off the ground with a remarkably high quality of service distributed throughout the country, was because these excellent supernumary registrars were pleased to obtain any consultant job available and they spread their experience and quality widely across the north and south of England, into teaching and non-teaching hospitals.

The format of clinical training was very different from that of today. Two or three students, rarely more than five, were allocated for three months at a time on to a clinical firm led by a consultant, who was supported by a registrar and houseman. As new patients were admitted, each was allocated in turn to one of the students on the firm and this allowed them to get to know their own patients very well. The student's notes were part of the formal patient's record and often augmented those of the hardpressed houseman. The quality of students' records was closely supervised by the registrar and woe betide the student who did not know about the detailed progress of their patients, the results of the most recent investigations, and the patients' treatments. All the students on the firm attended the working ward rounds of the clinical team, as well as the special teaching sessions for more senior students. They often took on the role of the patient's confidante, and in this way learned about their attitudes and fears in a 'holistic' way. The strength of the clinical firm system was that the student was a working member of it, had a clear role and so learned much about continuity of care and professional commitment from their seniors, most of whom took a very personal interest in the progress of their students, as well, of course, as in their patients. To ensure that students saw a full range of patients, senior students signed up to attend other consultants' ward rounds where they volunteered to 'clerk' and present cases before the group. Some students liked demonstrating their skills in this way to the consultants; others preferred to watch, ask and sometimes answer questions. In this way there was much flexibility in the ways in which students learned. This apprenticeship style of training was taken very seriously by the great majority of consultants, who of course regarded it as part of their job, without (or in some hospitals no more than nominal) remuneration.

There are many reasons why these admirable methods of training are no longer practicable. Not only have the numbers of students suddenly and dramatically increased due to a serious and avoidable miscalculation in medical manpower in the early 1990s, but also most patients now spend such a short time in hospital that this form of teaching has become virtually impossible. The range of topics to be covered has also expanded considerably, so that students have less time to spend on each component of their training course. All these problems conspired to make apprentice-style learning impractical. The substitution of robots, video and interactive computerised presentations, distance learning and the like are much promoted by educationists and, of course, have many real advantages. In any case, there may be no obvious alternative. However, in spite of the valiant attempts to help students get some first-hand contact with patients, the inevitable consequence is that many seem to spend increasing amounts of their time as more passive onlookers, rapidly herded in large groups through various parts of the clinical services. Those who design some of the new and exciting courses should bear in mind that the apprenticeship approach produced some of today's outstanding and much sought-after physicians. Students played a much more active part in the clinical team, caring for the patient as well as acquiring professional attitudes and commitment. This had some real advantages which are now, *force majeure*, being lost. We may have to face the consequences of this in the future.

Another feature of undergraduate life at UCH which has now completely disappeared was the compulsory attendance at a selected autopsy every day at 1 pm. This was regarded as so important that Professor Rosenheim himself and a senior pathologist expected to be present whenever possible. It was the one opportunity for physicians to 'see' and discuss what they had been trying to treat and how they might do better. It was very salutary. My lifelong interest in trying to match clinical medicine with macroscopic and microscopic pathology stems from this experience; it was probably reinforced by taking Richard's advice and reading Boyd's *Textbook of pathology* from cover to cover while incarcerated in Switzerland. The dramatic decline in autopsies in recent years has been a backward step in terms of our understanding of the underlying pathology in every fatal case. The relative neglect of pathology in some of the newer medical school curricula is, in my view, sadly misguided. The best substitute for autopsies is to promote as many sessions jointly attended by both clinicians and pathologists on whatever material is available and, as far as possible, to make this part of the regular routine – not just a selective exercise focussing on the occasional 'interesting case' presented at a clinico-pathological conference.

In the late 1940s, all the blood for various tests was taken by the students. Syringes and needles were simply boiled for an unspecified time in a water bath in the centre of the ward. Needles were also re-used and in some hospitals it was the students' job to re-sharpen them. I do not know what happened to the lethal blood-borne microbes in those days or how many were simply missed. Sterility has certainly improved out of all recognition since those primitive days. It is a pity that in spite of so much progress on sterilisation procedures and the exhortations from infection control officers, hospital infections still seem to be in the ascendant and general lack of cleanliness in hospitals is currently a cause of great concern.

There was a good range of systematic lectures in the 1950s for which we had to be signed up by the porter in attendance. Some were outstanding. Unfortunately I missed most of them for two reasons, one of which was very silly. First, we had had virtually no systematic lectures at Oxford and my memory patterns were trained to rely more on written sources than verbal ones. Second, because they were compulsory I found such 'nannying' offensive and I eschewed them deliberately. I, of course, was usually the loser. In spite of this gross lack of judgement, I was fortunate to get many of the student prizes including the Tuke Medal in

Chemical Pathology, the Filliter Exhibition in Pathology, the Magrath Prize in Medicine and the Atchison Scholarship for the student of the year. Not everyone realised the importance of these prizes but Richards's father had made it clear that to win these was vital, especially for women and particularly in the very early days of one's career, in order to help gain a place at least on the shortlist for house jobs. I strongly advise all medical students to enter whenever there is an opportunity. The internal competitive clinical tests are also very good practice for the clinically orientated postgraduate examinations, such as the Membership of the Royal Colleges, which come later.

During our final year in 1949, the Department of Psychology at University College asked for volunteers to answer a questionnaire because they believed they had solved the perennial question of finding the best way to select medical students – a problem still much debated fifty years later. As a first step, they wished to correlate the results of their new test with our performance in finals and later in our careers. Most of our year agreed to take part provided that the results were posted on the notice board for us to share. The examiners were very reluctant, but in the end were forced to agree. To our great amusement and their chagrin, the eight people gaining the highest marks were those who chose, as was possible in those days, not to attend the clinical sessions, but preferred to pass their time playing bridge in the common room! Of course I realise this proved nothing until the long-term study had been completed, but I do not think that this was ever done.

In the early 1950s, 'shadow' house jobs were introduced for the first time. This allowed senior students to cover for house physicians who also, for the first time, were allowed to take a week or so off at the end of their appointments – a welcome innovation which had not existed before. These shadow posts were closely supervised by the long-suffering registrars and provided a wonderfully easy introduction to one's first official house physician appointment.

Although I have focussed on medicine in this chapter, we proceeded in a similar way with surgery clerking (as dressers) and a series of shorter rotations through paediatrics, obstetrics and gynaecology and other specialties including mental health and psychiatry, eyes, ear, nose and throat, anaesthetics and other things; but, sadly, no time was spent in general practice. Indeed, I remember one consultant declaring with some pride that 'UCH did not expect to train general practitioners'. I am afraid that this attitude says quite a lot about elitism in medicine at the time. Even so, many contemporaries in fact went into general practice and were highly regarded.

In the 1950s, Oxford students went back to their alma mater at the end of the third year to take their clinical finals, entering the wards in

51

traditional style in full *sub fusc* (black suits, bow ties, gowns, rabbit fur hoods and all). The patients seemed to accept this tradition easily enough but at least one of the surgical external examiners from London at the time expressed amazement, finding it both unhygienic and bizarre. However, as far as I remember, we all passed.

7. Continuously on call:
House jobs, 1950–53

Selection for housemen posts at UCH in 1950 was a democratic exercise in advance of its time because it took into account the candidates' preferences as well as that of the chiefs. In addition, in order to give all candidates an equal chance and to show that justice was seen to be done – how very modern! – all candidates had to sit a one-hour written examination, set by the relevant consultant. When I applied for my first job, the paper included two questions: 'What would you do about a seven-year-old boy who continued bleeding following a simple tooth extraction?' and 'How would you give symptomatic relief to a patient dying of congestive heart failure, cancer or a severe stroke?' Two very perceptive questions to be answered by a newly qualified doctor with no clinical experience. The Atchison Scholar was expected to get the job of their preference and the most sought after were normally those on the prestigious Professorial Unit. However, I asked to work on Dr JC Hawksley's firm because I knew it offered a far wider range of experience. The Professorial Unit tended to have a focus on patients with specialised problems but in my first job I wanted to get experience of patients with more common conditions, although in the event some turned out to be extremely rare. For example, I remember a man of 36 who had devastating episodes of 'collapse' with a very slow pulse rate due to intermittent heart block. The interesting thing was that his mother had a similar history and another member of the family had died young of 'a heart attack'. Sophisticated investigation and treatments including pacemakers were not, of course, available and sadly, in spite of our efforts, he did not survive. Dr Hawksley encouraged me to discuss the problem with Dr Maurice Campbell, senior cardiologist at Guy's Hospital who, it was thought, had had a similar family under his care. He was extremely helpful and was intrigued because we had been able to obtain, with the relatives' agreement, very useful histology. Although I was only a junior houseman from another hospital and he was very senior, he generously suggested that we should publish a joint paper together in the *British Journal of Cardiology*. This in fact appeared some four years before the paper which is now often quoted as the definitive reference on familial cardiomyopathy.

As housemen, we were resident for six months without a break, being continuously responsible for the patients on our firm. For several reasons this was not nearly as arduous as it sounds. First, one knew one's patients very well and what one could and could not do for them. Secondly, the options for therapy in those days were much more restricted, so the pressure of decision-making was much less. Thirdly, the experienced ward sister and housemen worked very closely together and she took on much of the burden of decision-making and indeed knew what should be done. Fourthly, the registrar by day and the resident assistant physician at night provided instant senior support. Fifthly, the majority of consultants insisted on being informed by telephone if anything serious developed at any time, because they felt continuously responsible for their own patients. Sixthly, and not least because we were resident, it was easy, with the agreement of sister and other members of the team to slip away for sleep at odd moments if this was obviously necessary. Lastly, there were plenty of other people in the residents' 'mess' to share problems with over meals and thus relieve much of the stress associated with inexperience.

A diversion into some of the factors which have more recently created stress in junior doctors may be relevant, before it is assumed that the problem can be resolved by the simple expedient of reducing the hours of work, although this is of course very important. From the 1960s to the 1980s, the introduction of emergency admission rotas between firms meant that the numbers of patients being admitted at night by a small number of juniors increased dramatically, so they usually worked all night but in spite of this they were still expected to work the following day. These factors together contributed greatly to stress of overworked, often exhausted and inexperienced junior doctors. Further, there was a trend in hospitals for junior doctors to be left largely unsupervised to care for the patients outside daytime hours, and the on-call arrangements for more senior doctors from home was often unsatisfactory. Although recent attempts have been made to ensure that more experienced medical staff are actually in the hospital around the clock, it is questionable whether this is yet giving sufficient back-up for some juniors. Over the last ten years there has been a progressive move to radically reduce the hours of work for junior doctors, and the only practical way of achieving this was to introduce shift work. Although this has many obvious benefits, there is no doubt from various national systematic questionnaires that pre-existing teaching opportunities have been dislocated and that continuity of patient care has been seriously compromised. Since these two components are indispensable factors in the provision of professional medicine, some more satisfactory solution has to be found.

There are several other fairly complex reasons why stress levels in junior staff still seem to remain unacceptably high. In particular, they no longer have the advantage of knowing all the patients in their charge, and they are often therefore required to make decisions about patients on whom they have no background information. The nursing systems have also changed so that much advice and wisdom from experienced ward sisters is no longer available. The manpower shortages have become so great that there are simply not enough consultants to give individual cover for the large number of emergency admissions. Junior doctors' time is further eroded by all the other duties now expected of them. Changes in the training requirements have meant more senior trainees (specialist registrars) are not available (for better or for worse) to carry the service load they used to. Other factors also contribute to the stress of junior doctors. In particular, the success of medical advances in acute medicine has vastly complicated decision-making, and the burden of responsibility without experience is very much greater. The increased threat of litigation has added still further pressure. All these need to be addressed before assuming that simply reducing junior doctors hours will solve the problem.

As housemen in 1951, we earned £150 per annum with full board and lodgings. Since we were resident continuously we had no time to spend any of it. However, I read that it was possible to commute for life one's personal indemnity insurance with the Medical Defence Union for £25. Although this was a substantial slice out of one's earnings it seemed sensible to obtain such cover once and for all. The following year the sum had doubled to £50 and Richard did the same. As a result of this investment, the combined cost of indemnity insurance for our complete working lives has been the grand sum of £75. Not a bad bargain by today's standards.

At University College Hospital our resident quarters were quite grand. We each had two rooms – a bedroom and a study. The Resident Medical Officer, Peter Heaf, was in charge of the proper behaviour of the junior doctors but had a sensible liberal attitude, much in advance of his time. To ensure moral propriety, his strict rule was that he expected to see only one pair of shoes outside any one door (those were the days when our shoes were cleaned for us early each day). Since we each had two rooms, this allowed satisfactory flexibility especially for those of us who were married.

In the early 1950s, the clinical laboratories were very accessible even to the most junior doctors. All the chemical pathology results of the day were put out in trays in the department. It was the houseman's job to check these each night and telephone the chief about any significant results. Uniquely, and sometimes frighteningly, Professor Maizels, Head of the Department, was often there until late in the evening. He would quiz us on what the results meant, what we should be doing about them and why we had ordered the test in the first place, especially when he thought it was unnecessary. Cost-effective considerations are not therefore an entirely new concept in the NHS. Our usual and truthful answer was that we did not wish to be caught out if the chief asked for them. However, this type of 'one-upmanship' was not considered an adequate reason for wasting hospital money. It was a great way to learn.

The microbiology laboratory was run impeccably by Dr Joan Stokes, wife of the consultant Dr John Stokes. We were expected to use this laboratory to do our own emergency Gram and Ziel Neilson staining for various types of bacteria including *M. tuberculosis*. I remember one Saturday afternoon when a very sick patient was admitted with pneumonia. Within the hour, I had had the opportunity to do the appropriate staining test and was able to ring the 'chief' to report that we had just admitted a patient with tuberculous pneumonia and wait for him, I fear with some self complacency, to ask why I was so certain of the diagnosis. These were great moments. I am not for one moment suggesting that we should return to these practices, which have now become so much more complex and refined, but they did provide wonderful 'hands-on' experience.

Today, direct computer links between the laboratories and the wards, and indeed GP surgeries, have greatly speeded up the delivery of results, and automation has vastly improved quality control. However, it still surprises me, especially in general practice, that the reports on results can still take several days before they filter through and are available to be discussed with the patient. This is not so much a fault of the laboratory or the clinicians as the communication systems between primary and secondary care.

It is not uncommon to find that pathology laboratories and their staff have become distanced from the clinicians, due to centralisation policies, created in the interests of cost and efficiency. This can not only compromise a very rewarding personal partnership between clinician and pathologist, but it promotes an erroneous belief amongst patients – and sometimes staff – that a single investigation, performed in the laboratory, and reported on in isolation, has a high chance of providing a secure diagnostic label. Sometimes this can be true, but much more often it is no more than an indicator or pointer to be fitted together with other clinical factors. Unless this is explained carefully to patients, they become confused and lose confidence. The dangers of working in isolation are equally great for radiological investigations, especially when modern pressures make it difficult for the radiologist to find the clinician who has knowledge of the patient. Radiographs are no more than pictures and often open to a variety of interpretations; they need to be read in context. Once again, dogmatic diagnostic statements based on a single investigation, without reference to the whole picture, can be dangerously misleading and also establish bad habits amongst trainees. These problems are very relevant to telemedicine. This system of long-distance consultation and investigation offers huge opportunities for raising standards of practice and accessibility to many more people, especially where manpower and equipment are in short supply and distances from hospital are great. However, it can become seductive if this starts to bypass those with integrative skills.

In order to foster such an integrative approach to investigations, we as junior trainees at the Brompton Hospital (see page 66) were encouraged to read our own X-rays – which were kept on the wards, not in the X-ray department – and not simply rely on the report, although it was crucial of course to check this as soon as it was available. The clinical context of a radiograph was considered so important by many that Dr Ian Kerr, one of our best radiologists, refused to report on X-rays unless the whole clinical file was available to him. In addition to his radiological qualifications, he himself had trained as a physician and obtained the Membership of the Royal College of Physicians. This was quite common practice, not only for radiologists but for many other specialists including surgeons. Today this broad training across specialist fields is becoming much more difficult.

This raises the whole question of trying to reconcile the desirability of extending both the breadth and depth of knowledge in medicine at a time when subspecialty fields are expanding so rapidly and when there is also strong pressure to reduce the length of training. With the increased sophistication in all fields of medicine, there is an inevitable and proper need for greater specialisation and in consequence we are moving steadily away from competence in breadth. Some indeed argue that it is no longer necessary, because day-to-day practice of subspecialists is apparently so focussed. With this trend, the opportunities for lateral thinking are inevitably diminished. Oddly enough, in trying to resolve rare and complex problems, the solution often lies as much in the breadth of their experience as in the doctor's greater depth of knowledge. Good doctors require both. There is still so much in medicine that remains unknown and unexplained. Fresh ideas are badly needed and this requires innovative thinking; those with a broader understanding are more likely to have new ideas on addressing problems than those working from a very narrow and limited base.

Of course, larger teams of specialists working together can provide a collective breadth of experience and this can be complementary, but it does not replace individuals whose wisdom is developed from a breadth as well as a depth of knowledge and experience.

Normally, a medical house job would be followed by one in surgery. However, it was considered that in view of my recent history of tuberculosis this might be too arduous and that compromises were still necessary. I therefore obtained a paediatrics post at the West Middlesex Hospital with Dr Dinski Klein. She had trained in Vienna and had a special interest in eczema and its treatment with milk-free diets, which were often successful. We had several small children with tuberculous meningitis treated with life-saving intrathecal injections of streptomycin. This required daily lumbar punctures. If sister held the small patient firmly, it was considered quicker and relatively less painful for the poor child to deftly insert the needle without prior local anaesthesia; even so, we all hated doing it but there was no practical alternative at the time. Modern techniques have now found ways that have transformed these procedures in children.

This paediatric post in 1951 gave me my first experience of shift work. There were two housemen and the consultant insisted that we left the hospital at a strict changeover time, irrespective of the condition of our patients. I particularly remember a boy of three years with acute haemolytic anaemia causing a major diagnostic and therapeutic dilemma at the time. I felt quite unable to leave the hospital until we understood the problem better and had a treatment policy worked out for him. I was seriously reprimanded for undermining the shift system. I know many junior doctors today feel as I did then. The perils of continuity of care for patients using the shift system is with us again in a major way today, due to the European Working Time Directive on junior doctors' hours of work. We are all expendable, but the problem of continuity of care has got to be resolved in a better way than at present.

My third post was back at UCH as casualty medical officer. This was an invaluable training. It was in fact the equivalent of a general practitioner post in a hospital setting with hospital back-up. It was a great experience for rapid assessment, diagnosis and treatment of a full range of trivial and serious acute medicine.

After 18 months in junior posts and with my tuberculosis well behind me, it then seemed a good time to start a family. I had the advantage of having three months maternity leave and used this to study for, and successfully pass, the Membership of the Royal College of Physicians, an advantage not open to my male colleagues – a fine example of inverse discrimination. I also did some locum sessions mainly at the well run Edgware General Chest Clinic, particularly helping with the large number of patients with tuberculosis still requiring weekly or fortnightly refills of their artificial pneumothorax or pneumoperitoneum. On one occasion, when we were particularly hard pressed, I screened and refilled 82 patients single-handed. This gives an idea of the sheer volume of work involved in treating tuberculosis in the pre anti-tuberculous drug era.

Four months after the birth of Gillian I went back to work. I obtained a house physician post at the Brompton in 1953. These posts were very sought after and this was my third attempt. At the interview Dr 'Ernie' Lloyd, the Senior Physician, addressed me very critically and in a way that today would be quite illegal, about the iniquities of leaving a child of only four months at home (looked after, I must add, by a remarkable Swiss *au pair* called Rosli, who was quite superb). However, in retrospect and on principle I am not sure I would do it again and Dr Lloyd may well have been right. I am sure that the rather longer period of maternity leave taken by many 'professional' mothers (and now fathers) is a much better option. However, at the time and hard as it was, it was an opportunity that simply could not be missed. Once I had been appointed, Dr Lloyd informed me – I think with some glee – that he had selected me to work on his firm, that his outpatient clinic was on a Saturday morning and his ward round on a Saturday afternoon, and asked, did I still want the job? The experience of working for him at a turning point in the history of tuberculosis was unique. He was a great teacher and cared for his patients in a paternalistic, but totally dedicated, way. He had an amazing way of listening to his patients' views but at the same time persuading them that, if they wished to recover, they should follow his advice. They nearly always did.

In 1953, the first successes of anti-tuberculous therapy were beginning to indicate that control of this world pestilence might be a reality. However, much was still to be learnt on how to avoid the emergence of drug resistance, how long therapy would be needed to establish a cure, and how far it could deal with advanced cases.

In the meantime, patients were still being treated in very large numbers with various forms of lung collapse therapy. It was known that it was essential to close cavities if tubercle bacilli were to be eliminated from the sputum. Where, because of adhesions, artificial pneumothorax could not be established and pneumoperitoneum failed to close cavities, disfiguring thoracoplasty with extensive surgical removal of ribs was standard procedure. This was a long operation often performed in two or three stages, usually under local anaesthesia because it was thought for various reasons to be safer. It was a very traumatic and often painful procedure and the patients were fully aware of the disfigurement that it would cause. Their courage to return for a second and third stage was quite unbelievable. Their determination to recover and survive, their incredible bravery and their remarkable morale were humbling for all those looking after them. In attempts to avoid this horrendous surgery, a system of postural retention was introduced where patients were confined to bed for months with the foot of the bed elevated, in desperate attempts to close cavities. The philosophy and patience of these young people, who were often otherwise feeling relatively well, still fills me with tremendous admiration. Through caring for these patients, one learnt a huge amount about what the doctor–patient partnership, in its fullest sense, really meant.

Lung resection was just becoming established and this held great promise of providing a much more humane treatment, offering a definitive cure for selected cases with localised disease. This surgical treatment continued to be used for several years because there was a reluctance to attempt to rely on drugs alone, which at this time was often not preventing relapse, owing to the fact that they were still being used in relatively short courses.

The development of other antibacterial drugs was also transforming conventional thinking on other acute and chronic chest infections and the idea that much more might be done for patients with cystic fibrosis was just emerging. Pulmonary medicine was beginning to develop as an exciting field and the Brompton was at the centre of it all. But first there was the need to increase the breadth of my training in general medicine, so I applied for a registrar post back at UCH.

8. Clinical training:
Registrar and senior registrar
training posts, 1953–61

In 1953 I competed for a three-year registrar post at UCH. Although women were in a tiny minority at this level of training, I do not think that there was any prejudice in the appointing process. These posts rotated through three different specialties, each linked with general medicine. This system of rotating training in medicine was established at UCH long before the nationwide GMC-approved system of rotations set up in the 1960s and supervised by the Royal College of Physicians. The system at UCH, which was unusual for hospitals at the time, was quite flexible and although the final decision was made by the consultants, the prospective registrars put in bids for the posts they wanted; they could expect to get two of their own choice and one where there was an unmet service need.

I elected to work initially for Dr Howard Nicholson and Dr Andrew Morland. The respiratory medicine service was run on today's lines by a multidisciplinary team, in that all cases presenting diagnostic difficulties and all those where surgery was to be considered were discussed at a joint meeting of thoracic surgeons and physicians; the physiotherapists and almoners (today's social workers) also attended. Not only was a patient accepted for surgery after joint discussion, but also the most appropriate operation was agreed jointly. Woe betide the surgeon or a member of the surgical team who deviated without very good reason. This system worked especially well because of Howard Nicholson's enormous surgical experience from the war years he had spent in the Middle East working in close collaboration with Mr Andrew Logan.

We still had a large number of patients requiring refills of their artificial pneumothorax. These were undertaken at special clinics at which the whole team, including the consultants, attended. Many of these clinics were run in the evenings to meet the needs of patients who were working by day. During my time only one member of the team was exempt. He was the houseman, Dr Jonathan Miller, who had to leave by 6 pm to get away to his evening job in one of the London theatres, which we all respected. It is interesting to reflect upon these evening clinics of 50 years ago in the light of the current heated debates about whether it is reasonable to expect consultants and others to accept flexible working, including evening NHS sessions.

Patients were still being sent for prolonged convalescence extending over many months for strict regimens of graded exercise – a precursor of respiratory rehabilitation. Part of the job was to accompany the chief on three-monthly visits to Frimley and Midhurst Sanatoria on a Saturday morning. These were two extremely well run but very disciplined hospitals where the patients showed tremendous patience and acceptance of these prolonged periods of incarceration and regimented lifestyles. It was a wonderful example of trust between patients and their doctors working together to overcome a long-term and potentially lethal disease.

The year 1953 was the turning point between the pre- and post-chemotherapy era, and the full potential of anti-tuberculous medication was beginning to emerge. There was a window of opportunity to determine objectively whether these new drugs were powerful enough to overcome the devastating and often fatal complication of tuberculosis in diabetic patients, who commonly had acute and rapidly advancing disease. This clinical situation seemed to be a naturally occurring opportunity in which to test the real effectiveness of these new drugs. With the support of my chiefs and those running the diabetic clinics, I set up the study which I felt was not only important in its own right but could also form the basis for a doctorate thesis. With tremendous cooperation from many consultants at a large number of hospitals and clinics in London, I was allowed, as a fairly junior registrar, access to their clinical records. Looking back, this support some 50 years ago from so many physicians from different hospitals whom I had never met before was quite remarkable. In part, it was a retrospective study of all the cases with coincidental tuberculosis and diabetes at UCH, the Brompton, the London Chest Hospital and many of the chest clinics in the London area treated before anti-tuberculous chemotherapy, and a prospective study of outcomes following treatment with the new anti-tuberculous therapy. Although I recognise that the study was designed poorly by modern epidemiological standards, I learned a great deal besides the medical aspects. It allowed me to get a feel for different clinical services including the record keeping in chest clinics, which was often of a high standard and included meticulous follow-up details. The conclusion of this study was that the risk factor of coincidental diabetes for an adverse outcome in tuberculosis disappeared when patients were treated with adequate courses of anti-tuberculous drugs. I wrote the work up as an Oxford Doctorate of Medicine thesis in 1955 during maternity leave with my second daughter – another example of taking advantage of inverse gender discrimination. Not only did I learn a great deal in all sorts of ways from this study but it also enabled me to obtain a doctorate degree quite early in my career. This was important at the time in the highly competitive environment for a woman aiming to work at a teaching hospital in London. However, I must admit that in those days it was much easier to select a topic for a doctorate thesis which could be undertaken in parallel with one's clinical training than it is today.

Oral and intravenous corticosteroids had been recently introduced as a useful treatment for asthma and in 1953 the UCH Respiratory Unit became a collaborating centre for two Medical Research Council (MRC) controlled trials. The asthma service was led by two remarkable people: Professor Herxheimer and Dr Monica McAllen. They were both commit-ted to clinical research and were developing bronchial challenge tests to induce mild asthma in patients on which the effect of various treatments, including inhaled solutions of hydrocortisone, could be tested. These studies were done long before the development of the inhaled modulated forms of corticosteroids, which are the mainstay of treatment today. Thus, patients with well documented records were available to study and they cooperated most willingly. Participation in these MRC studies taught me a great deal about collaborative research and the methodology and analy-sis of clinical trails. At that time we were able to make only occasional measurements of airflow using a cumbersome 'wet' spirometer, because the Wright peak-flow meter and the more portable dry spirometer had not been introduced. However, the results were conclusive in establishing the place of corticosteroids in the treatment of asthma.

In the mid-1950s, Professor Rosenheim had the remarkable idea of converting a small room close to the wards into a basic laboratory in which any registrar could set up their own laboratory study. In discussion with Monica McAllen, I wondered innocently why there were so many differ-ent oral compounds containing different derivatives of theophylline in the treatment of asthma. It seemed interesting to look at serial blood levels after a controlled dose of five different preparations and attempt to corre-late these with any relief of asthma reported by the patient. Rather primi-tive apparatus was collected together from various departments to set up the Waxman method to extract theophylline, and the Professorial Unit allowed me to use one of their spectrophotometers. With virtually no pharmacological experience and minimal supervision but a lot of encour-agement, the study was launched. To my great surprise, it became clear that only those patients achieving a blood level greater than 10 µg/ml reported relief. This was duly published in the *British Medical Journal* in 1955 and is still often quoted as one of the first reports to establish a therapeutic blood level in asthma – now recognised as 10–20 µg/ml. A remarkable piece of good fortune from a study conducted, I must admit, under very amateur conditions.

These anecdotes illustrate the encouragement given in the 1950s to individual trainees at UCH to undertake their own clinical research concurrently with their clinical work. For those students who had been through the Oxford and Cambridge training system there was nothing unusual about this, but for the majority of students with different preclinical experience it was very special.

Grand rounds, known as the 'circus' because of the way various trainees were put through their paces, were well established and took place every Saturday morning. While they were under the personal supervision of Professor Rosenheim, all the medical firms participated and the circus was not the exclusive domain of the Professorial Unit. Such grand rounds are, of course, now routine at most teaching hospitals, but they are not usually conducted on a Saturday morning! They set a standard for case presentation, including the deductive steps in diagnosis and systematic review of the literature on selected important points, and were excellent training grounds for later presentations at national and international meetings. The circus also emphasised the importance of evidence-based medicine 40 years before it became *de rigeur* in the late 1990s.

The next part of the rotation was to cardiology under Dr Kenneth Harris, a traditional cardiologist and general physician, and Dr Arthur Holman who introduced cardiac catheterisation to the hospital, having studied in the USA. Cardiac catheterisation was a critical development in cardiology because it allowed more accurate diagnoses of congenital and acquired heart disease. This was essential to surgical correction which was being pioneered in a number of centres including UCH under Professor Pilcher and his outstanding female First Assistant, Doreen Knightingale – one of the exceedingly few women cardiothoracic surgeons at the time.

My return after maternity leave for our second daughter was not to UCH as I had hoped. I was allocated to the Geriatric Unit under Lord Amulree (also the chief Liberal Whip in the House of Lords) at St Pancras Hospital, about half a mile from the main hospital. Although bitterly disappointed at the time, it turned out to be one of my most rewarding and valuable training posts. I was able to consolidate general medicine and the special problems of the elderly. In particular, I had to revise my views on the received wisdom of trying to fit all the signs, symptoms and results of investigations into a single diagnosis. This dictum simply does not apply to the elderly. As Lord Amulree said with his very pronounced stammer, which he deliberately accentuated when making an important point, 'If you have f-f-f-failed to make s-s-s-six different d-d-d-diagnoses in an elderly p-p-p-patient, you have m-m-m-missed one.'

He also taught us many aspects of medicine never normally covered in a premier London teaching hospital. Every afternoon, Dr Peter Helps, the Senior Registrar, and I undertook domiciliary visits to the elderly in their homes. Together we saw the real conditions behind the Regency and early-Victorian facades of the houses in the St Pancras slums, recognised to be worse than the East End of London (which had been demolished, mercifully in some ways, during the blitz). This gave us great insight into the appalling living conditions in the heart of London in the 1950s and the attitudes of patients and their relatives surviving under these conditions. Peter achieved national notoriety by being stabbed by one of his patients – it really was a rough area. Fortunately he survived – Peter always did.

Lord Amulree took delight in broadening our education, which he felt was sadly deficient in the rarefied atmosphere of academic UCH. Over coffee he would discuss the important health issues being debated in the House of Lords and one afternoon he took the whole team to Redhill to visit the only British leper colony in England. I recognise, however, that this expedition was somewhat contrived because of his special desire to ride in Richard's new drop-head Austin A40 that I had borrowed!

As Liberal Chief Whip, Lord Amulree shared with us his views on the role of the medical profession in political debates, as the new NHS (created in 1948) was coming to terms with all the managerial, financial and social problems. At that time and for some decades later, the medical profession tried to keep itself aloof from the 'dirty' world of politics but Lord Amulree was far in advance of his time and taught me much that was to come in useful nearly forty years later when I became President of the Royal College of Physicians. One of the most interesting facts of life is that the relevance and value of some information may only become evident many decades later.

He recognised the importance of continuing education and openly declared that he relied on his registrars to keep his medical knowledge up to date – a principle I have believed in ever since. However, with his shrewd judgement he was quick to pounce if he sensed that we had not got our facts absolutely straight, or that we were getting carried away with our own erudition.

Thus, the cloud of disappointment at being relegated to geriatrics at St Pancras had much more than a silver lining – it was golden. Not least for a domestic reason: we lived in Highgate only about ten minutes away and, with two tiny children of two and a half years and four months old, a less demanding job close to home was very suitable for a young mum. I am sure all those apparently remote academic consultants at UCH were fully aware of these domestic aspects when making their allocation for the registrar rotations. This illustrates once again the insightful support given to a young mother and woman registrar so long ago. I am ashamed that I did not have the maturity to see just how supportive my chiefs were being until much later.

After three years in these rotating posts the time came to consider how specialist training for my eventual career should develop. A career in chest medicine was a natural decision. The network of well-established chest clinics throughout the country, and especially in London, gave many convenient opportunities. London was the best place for us to be if Richard and I were both to find jobs and live together with our young family. The predominantly daytime hours of chest clinic practice was an added attraction and, although it was perhaps less intellectually exciting than mainstream hospital medicine, it was obvious that compromises had to be made. In any case it was exceedingly difficult for a woman to get a consultant physician job at a London teaching hospital. Many women at the time were in fact carrying consultant responsibilities but few were recognised with a consultant title. Even UCH, with its liberal and advanced views on women doctors, failed to give consultant recognition to Dr Peggy Morgans (diabetes), Dr Monica McAllen (allergy and asthma) and Dr Joan Stokes (bacteriology) until much later.

The specialty of respiratory medicine itself was exciting not only because there was a huge clinical need but also because there were interesting established investigative techniques including radiology, bronchoscopy, bronchography, physiological measurements and, of course, microbiology. Thus, precision diagnosis was possible and there were plenty of opportunities for clinical research. There were exciting advances in treatment for tuberculosis and lung surgery and for a wide range of infective conditions including pneumonias, bronchiectasis, cystic fibrosis (mucoviscidosis at that time) and the beginnings of a better definition and treatment of asthma. Beyond London, many fine centres with many good people were being developed throughout the country – at Edinburgh, Birmingham, and Cardiff with the MRC Pneumoconiosis Unit. Thus, the potential for respiratory medicine in the UK was exciting and there is always a particular challenge of working in an important but 'Cinderella' field – as lung disease certainly was then and, up to a point, still is when it comes to research funding.

The next step was to return to the Brompton as a registrar. Having worked there before and with the Doctorate of Medicine thesis in place, this was somewhat easier than the earlier struggle to get a foot in the door as a houseman. Already, female appointments were not quite so difficult to obtain and the post-war 'bulge' of ex-servicemen which had created a large, competitive pool had by then eased – having been absorbed into hospital posts and chest clinics throughout the country.

The Brompton training was an outstanding experience although not organised as formally as today. There were about 12 consultants, most of whom had joint appointments as general physicians at London teaching hospitals and practised specialist respiratory medicine at the Brompton. This provided the opportunity to learn widely differing approaches to problems. Working initially for Howard Nicholson and Clifford Hoyle was quality time. Howard was a very highly regarded diagnostician with a meticulous approach. Clifford Hoyle would have liked to have led a professorial team – he had strong interests in clinical research and had many innovative ideas. His work on sarcoidosis led him to identify what he initially believed was a benign form of miliary tuberculosis. He developed this into a lifelong study, often in competition with and rather under the shadow of Dr (later Professor) Guy Scadding, who had a somewhat different approach to the same condition.

Clifford was perhaps the originator of the idea that if tuberculosis relapsed as soon as relatively short courses of anti-tuberculous therapy were stopped, then the logical step was to continue for much longer, although to use antibacterial drugs of any type for prolonged periods was an entirely untried approach. He and Howard collected in an uncontrolled way their results of long-term treatment, mainly with streptomycin and para aminosalicylic acid (PAS), but some patients received additionally the newly introduced isoniazid. Dr John Batten, Chief Medical Assistant, and I had the difficult job of collating all these uncontrolled data. The paper was difficult to get published because by then (1956) controlled trials were rightly becoming the accepted method to prove drug effectiveness. This, of course, was not the case when this long-term treatment was first started. Clifford was so convinced (rightly as it turned out) that the policy of prolonged courses of treatment was the correct one that he believed that a controlled trial would be unethical. Thereafter, this ethical problem was overcome by using comparative trials of different types of unproven drug regimens. These were conducted by the MRC under the guidance of Dr D'Arcy Hart, Dr (later Professor) Guy Scadding, Dr (later Professor) Wallace Fox, Professor (later Sir John) Crofton and many others. They clarified many details of dosage schedules using different drug combinations and durations of treatment. These were extended in a series of multi-centre trials in many countries throughout the world and established the ways in which new treatments could be introduced and developed from the beginning using scientific validation. The pharmaceutical industry has now adopted these controlled trial methods and transformed the evidence base of medication ever since. It is a curious reflection that the much publicised 'evidence-based medicine', promoted almost as if it was a new idea over the latter part of the 1990s, gave such scant recognition to the well established principles introduced in the 1950s.

During this time at the Brompton there was a special opportunity to observe the progress being made in understanding the scientific basis of respiratory disease in the new Institute of Diseases of the Chest, the University postgraduate academic school associated with the Brompton Hospital. Professor Guy Scadding developed this academic base almost single-handedly despite considerable resistance from some of the 'old guard' of hospital physicians. Guy Scadding was Director of Studies and within his domain appointed Dr Lynne Reid (later Professor) to set up her life work on experimental pathology, especially on the anatomy and development of the lung and, jointly with Neville Oswald, the clinical and pathological correlates of chronic bronchitis. Dr Francis Prime developed lung physiology and Dr (later Professor) Ian Longmuir focused on respiration at a cellular level. Dr (later Professor) Jack Pepys, who had been in general practice in South Africa and retrained in pathology at Guy's Hospital, joined Guy Scadding initially to read the chest X-rays in some of the MRC tuberculosis trials. He then set up his own laboratory to study lung disease related to fungi, especially *Aspergillus fumigatus*, with Dr Joan Longbottom. Later, he turned his attention to Farmer's Lung, working with Dr Lacey at Rothamsted Plant Pathology Research Station, and demonstrated the causal agent as *Micropolyspora faeni* in mouldy hay. His later work was particularly focused on occupational asthma caused by organic and chemical agents, and he introduced some innovative methods of simulating various industrial exposures. His world reputation as allergist and immunologist all began from work in a single lab in the one-storey temporary building which was the original institute. Guy, in collaboration with his senior registrar Dr Kenneth Citron, pursued his ideas on the causes of sarcoidosis and its relationship with tuberculosis. Dr Citron also supported the clinical aspects of Jack Pepys' work on extrinsic allergic alveolitis.

Perhaps Guy's particular contribution, apart from bringing together this extraordinarily talented core group of laboratory-based researchers to explore new aspects of lung disease, was his profound thoughts on the use of words and nomenclature in disease. He banned the word 'disease' and the concept that each lung condition (especially those defined in only descriptive terms) was caused by a single agent – or 'devil' as he used to say. Rather he saw causation in a much wider sense as an interaction of multiple components and risk factors. He was also careful to emphasise that many conditions had overlapping features rather than seeing each as discrete and separate entities. In particular, he distinguished those conditions which were defined in descriptive terms where the causal agent or agents was unknown from those having a clearly defined 'causal' external agent, as in some infections or occupational exposures. He used the term 'cryptogenic' to indicate that the cause had not yet been identified, but still allowed scope for study without prejudice as to whether the condition was an 'entity' (an anathema to him) or a final common path of pathogenesis derived from a more subtle host/agent response which might involve genetic, immunological or other interactions. Wise as the concept behind the use of the word 'cryptogenic' was, it never caught on in North America. So much for countries divided by a single language. Guy's conceptual approach was in many ways the forerunner of the now widely accepted approach to pathogenesis, in terms of interactions between genetic and environmental factors where the new molecular and genetic tools now allow each to be measured and studied separately.

In the 1950s, every registrar aspiring to an appointment at a teaching hospital was expected to go to the USA to gain a wider and more scientific experience. This was referred to as BTA or 'been-to-America'. This experience was as important to one's curriculum vitae as possessing a doctorate. Looking back, this was a very *avant garde* approach to clinical training, appreciating as it did the value of gaining experience from other countries. Unfortunately, this emphasis on overseas experience has largely disappeared in today's more restricted vision of training programmes. For me, the opportunity of experience in America was out of the question. Richard was progressing through his own surgical training in London and I could not leave him and the children, then aged two and four.

As a rather contrived attempt to travel outside the UK, I somewhat cheekily wrote to a number of departments in Scandanavia and, armed with their enthusiastic replies, I was able to arrange a three-week tour of Norway, Sweden, Denmark and Holland where interesting approaches to lung physiology and radiology were being developed. The Brompton had not had a similar request before and generously gave me study leave, which was an innovative idea at the time, and £75 to help with expenses. The tour included Oslo and Stockholm – where I managed to hear Elizabeth Soderstrom at the Opera House – and Copenhagen, Groningen and Amsterdam. I stayed in inexpensive but excellent 'hotelets' which were similar to sophisticated youth hostels. I was treated royally by every department I visited and was invited to many homes. This wonderful welcome was, I believe, due in no small part to the fresh memories of British liberation following the war-time German occupation, as well as, of course, to traditional Scandinavian generosity.

The worrying part of the venture was that the day before my departure both the children went down with 'flu' in the very severe epidemic of 1957.

However, so many people had supported this expedition that I could not cancel it at the last moment. The conflict of guilt was extreme, but the admirable Noodle was certain I should go and in the event all was well, but it certainly tested my continuing inner conflict and guilt to the limit.

After two years as registrar I was appointed Chief Medical Assistant (CMA), the equivalent of a senior registrar at the Brompton in 1958. At first I worked for Dr Lee Lander (also at the Royal Free Hospital) and Dr Brooks (also at St Mary's). Every now and then the Medical Committee tried to even up the workload amongst the registrars and, because these two consultants had only a small number of patients, the firm was amalgamated with that of Dr Reginal Bignall and Dr John Batten. John had a large number of patients and was developing his life-long interest in cystic fibrosis. Working for four different chiefs provided a remarkable opportunity to compare their different approaches, but the logistics of covering all their ward rounds and outpatient clinics allowed no time to get to know any of the patients or do any other productive work, so the scheme was rightly abandoned.

Another duty of the CMA was to cover any outpatients if for any reason the consultant and his team were away. This even included deputising for Sir Russell Brock (later Lord Brock), the cardiac surgeon, although I had not even held a house surgeon post. It was a remarkable experience to see the outcome of his post-operative patients with heart and lung disease in those early days of cardiac and thoracic surgery.

Another serendipitous opportunity arose in 1958. Sadly, a patient died who had an unusual fibrosis of the lungs of quite unknown cause, but which is often associated with vascular changes in the fingers – 'clubbing'. First described by Hippocrates, the condition remains unexplained. The lungs receive a double circulation: the pulmonary and the bronchial or systemic circulations. It occurred to me that the changes in the fingers might be associated with an abnormality of the systemic circulation in the lungs and that this might play a part in the pathogenesis of the condition. The bronchial circulation had not been studied extensively in either health or disease, although a small number of studies had been done including those by Professor Averil Leibow in Yale and Dr Cudzkowitz then in Chicago. Professor Lynne Reid had previously made some elegant observations by injecting the pulmonary circulation with a radio-opaque material mixed with gelatine so that radiographs could be taken to visualise the vascular patterns, as well as facilitate later direct macroscopic dissection of the vessels. This seemed to be a good method to use to study the systemic circulation. With the explicit agreement of the patients' relatives, we were able to remove the lungs and Lynne immediately put aside her other work to help me set up the injected preparation. The results were quite dramatic and showed a massive proliferation of the finest blood systemic vessels of the lung that had not been seen before.

Observations from this single case provided the beginning of a much bigger systematic investigation to explore the link between clubbing of the fingers and the systemic circulation of the lung, which eventually formed the basis of my PhD thesis.

It so happened that for various personal reasons, our excellent pathologist became reluctant to undertake autopsies himself and the service had lapsed. From my earlier training at UCH I was convinced that the only way to learn more about the patients we had not been able to save was to ask for an autopsy whenever this was possible. Although I had seen a large number of post-mortems during my UCH days I had had no formal training in pathology, but the pathologist was quite willing for me to learn from the post-mortem technician and thus restore the service, which was also badly needed by the surgeons. In those very early days of open cardiac surgery, autopsy examinations, with the relatives' agreement, on patients who had died was the only way to learn vital lessons for the future. It was indeed unethical to continue to operate unless every effort was made to find ways to improve the success rate. The surgeons and physicians were therefore pleased that this vital autopsy service was restored. They and the patients' relatives were very cooperative and allowed me to study the lungs in a whole range of heart and lung disease. In return for doing the pathologist's work for him, he allocated to me a laboratory; the X-ray department loaned me an old but functional X-ray machine and was helpful developing the films.

Once again the opportunity to undertake research quite outside one's clinical training demonstrated a remarkably flexible attitude in the 1950s, and the support from all the consultants was outstanding. The experience was quite exceptional. I very much doubt whether the much more rigid training programmes in place today would allow any of this to happen.

Most of the research work was done in the evenings and once again the hospital gave their support by giving me four months paid leave to finalise the project. After about two years further work I tried to write up this remarkable series of observations, which were largely pictorial and therefore difficult to publish in detail in the specialist medical journals. Richard had the splendid idea of submitting it as a PhD. As he said, this had the added advantage that a second doctorate would help to put me ahead of other candidates when applying for consultant posts, and women needed to have additional qualifications to get onto a shortlist. The thesis containing the details of the work was awarded in 1961 and the essential findings were published in peer review journals. PhDs can also have some practical uses: three times in the past few years these systematic studies undertaken some forty years ago have come into their own. The first occasion was to help certain transplant surgeons to understand more about the abnormal vascular patterns in the lungs of their patients with congenital abnormalities of the heart; and the second was to help a group of molecular biologists at Ann Arbor in the USA, who were trying to explore new ideas on angiogenesis in various lung conditions. The third was in early 2005 (45 years after the original studies were made) when the findings on patients with primary and secondary lung cancer were used to help interventional radiologists who are developing new techniques to introduce chemotherapeutic agents directly into the blood supply of lung tumours. Like experience, the full value of research is not always evident at the time, and the tendency today to expect an instant return on a research investment is a sad reflection of our times.

Much as I enjoyed research, by the end of the project I knew I could never abandon clinical work with patients, and the problem was what to do next and how to strengthen my position still further to compete for a consultant position in London. I had been in training for 11 years since qualification at both an undergraduate and a postgraduate hospital, and with consultants who were both general and respiratory physicians. I had acquired two doctorates and I had had several publications. The original plan of working in a good chest clinic had to be revised completely because, with the successful demise of tuberculosis, these were beginning to close down and other job opportunities for women in London teaching hospitals were very limited.

Dr Paul Wood, who ran the Cardiac Department at the Brompton, suggested that I went to the National Heart Hospital to do more cardiology and Clifford Hoyle suggested that I went to the Hammersmith Hospital to get more training in general medicine, but I failed to get either of these posts. Paul Wood then suggested a research post looking at lung function in congenital heart disease, but delays in funding from the newly formed British Heart Foundation caused this project to fail. Dr Margaret McPherson came to the rescue and as an interim measure gave me a part-time job in her follow-up clinic for children recovering from tuberculosis.

It looked as if I was really stuck. I had done all I could to take advantage of all the opportunities available during training, and the chiefs for whom I had worked had given me unfailing support. I could not leave London because Richard was well on his way to a consultant job at the Middlesex Hospital and I was virtually unemployable. This was certainly the most depressing point in my career. Had I hit what today would be regarded as a glass ceiling? I can identify well with the other women in medicine who, in spite of all their efforts, find themselves unemployable because of conflicts between home and professional life. One of the most stressful aspects of this dilemma was that so many chiefs had been so supportive in ways that were well ahead of the times during my training years. Richard and the family had given me so much freedom and understanding and now I was about to let them all down. It was all very depressing.

9. Clinical team leader: Consultant posts, 1961–72

Never let it be forgotten that support from the female medical sorority came to the rescue at a critical time for me and this was combined with a little good fortune. A consultant post as general physician came up at the Elizabeth Garrett Anderson Hospital (EGA) which was linked with the Royal Free Teaching Hospital. Because it had an almost exclusively female staff, I was at least eligible. Although not as systematically required by today's standards, I had in fact continued to train in general medicine fairly broadly because all the physicians under whom I worked were general physicians at their undergraduate hospitals as well as respiratory specialists at the Brompton. In the 1960s, one was certainly expected to cover all aspects of care of one's patients, and chest physicians, as today, were also expected to be generalists. I had always enjoyed the scope of general medicine and was keen to get back to it. I was lucky enough to get appointed, taking over from Dr Doris Baker, a general physician with an interest in rheumatology. So began my interest in this specialty which became especially relevant later when I returned to respiratory medicine and developed a particular interest in the lung and connective tissue diseases. An incidental great advantage of this appointment was that the hospital was only ten minutes from home and the children were still young.

I was also asked to care for pregnant patients with hypertension and so I started a special service to improve the management of hypertension and eclampsia. I was worried that the hospital had no defibrillator at the time but, with help from the Brompton, we introduced this and my registrar, Dr Mary Horn, supervised the training programme for staff. The morale at this small hospital was very special, the range of patients was fascinating, the undergraduate teaching programme was very rewarding, and the post was thoroughly enjoyable. The teamwork amongst the consultants was close and it was a privilege to work with very skilled pioneering women colleagues. However, it soon became apparent that the EGA was coming under increasing threat. Our back-up facilities were fairly limited, we had no intensive care unit and I was increasingly worried that our care of seriously ill patients was not as good as that which could be provided either at the Royal Free in Gray's Inn Road or at UCH just round the corner. I felt bound, in the patients' own interests, to transfer a number of my sick patients to these hospitals, but was severely reprimanded by the nursing staff and the medical students for depriving them of their most 'interesting' patients. This posed a dilemma.

I therefore favoured the proposal of integrating the EGA with the Royal Free Hospital when it moved to Hampstead. This was fiercely resisted by the more senior consultants at the EGA, not least because it would deprive women doctors of one of the few chances they had of being appointed to a teaching hospital in London. These reasons were very persuasive, especially as I personally owed the hospital a special debt of gratitude for my own appointment at a critical point in my career. However, I found this difficult to reconcile with the overriding consideration of what was best for patients at a time when rapid improvements in the care of very sick patients were developing.

These debates dragged on and the future of the hospital remained in the balance because, as so often happens in medical politics, difficult decisions are left unresolved.

However, in 1967, out of the blue, another quite unexpected opportunity arose. Professor Guy Scadding was expanding his Professorial Unit at the Institute of Diseases of the Chest and had obtained funding for a part-time senior lecturer post. A remarkable advertisement appeared in the press to the effect that they were seeking to appoint a man or a woman, preferably with experience in respiratory and general medicine, who had limited sessions at a teaching hospital but who wished to develop clinical research in lung disease. There were rumours that the wording indicated that they might have had a particular person in mind, but be that as it may, the post certainly suited me particularly well. Thus I was privileged to re-enter the Institute of Diseases of the Chest as a part-time Senior Lecturer with Honorary Consultant status at the Brompton, while I continued general medicine at the EGA.

The question arose about what type of research I should do, because no laboratory or desk space was provided and of course no resources. The latter did not bother me much because I had experience of scrounging equipment, but to have no base at all did seem to pose a problem.

Yet again it was a senior consultant's generosity that came to the rescue. Dr Reginald Bignall had taken over from Guy Scadding as Dean and he occupied a small office measuring about nine by twelve feet. Few Deans today would be satisfied with such accommodation even for themselves but fewer still, if any, would offer to share it with a new senior lecturer – but this is just what Reg did.

In the 1960s, new techniques were heralding a re-emergence of immunology. Jack Pepys was developing some of these and I sought his advice. He suggested that I should look at the experimental skin window technique to study inflammatory changes following local challenge by various chemicals and antigens. This was a practical suggestion under the circumstances and Dr Alex Kuper, who was in charge of the Haematology Department, allowed me to have space in his laboratory. However, these studies were far removed from the clinically related questions in which I was more interested. I was still fascinated by the problems of patients with serious forms of progressive fibrosis of the lung, initially in relation to finger clubbing and later because many of them had associated connective diseases including systemic lupus erythematosus, rheumatoid arthritis and systemic sclerosis. These clinical associations suggested that 'lone' fibrosing alveolitis too might have an immunological basis. Professor Deborah Doniach, working with Professor Ivan Riott at the Middlesex Hospital, had proposed two categories of autoimmune disease, one characterised by organ specific autoantibodies (such as autoimmune thyroiditis and pernicious anaemia) and the other by non-organ-specific antibodies – such as antinuclear antibodies and rheumatoid factor, as were found in systemic lupus erythematosus and rheumatoid arthritis. I believed that natural experiments derived from observing disease in man were a better basis for hypotheses than the creation of artificial models in animals – which were so often no more than a pale reflection of the real thing – or constructing them from purely theoretical considerations. Here we had an opening to explore.

Deborah Doniach taught me the techniques, Reg Bignall most generously moved out of his office into an even smaller one, and the hospital gave me a small grant to equip the tiny laboratory, including an ultraviolet microscope behind a black curtain (which little number I ran up myself), in lieu of a darkroom. Professor Scadding kindly offered me access to all his patients and they were wonderfully cooperative. This was the beginning of a career-long interest in this extrordinary condition of progressive fibrosis which had a prognosis as bad as some neoplastic diseases. My first MRC project grant allowed me to appoint a young graduate from Birmingham, Dr Patricia Haslam, who was both talented and long suffering. She worked with me and later ran the lab for over 20 years until I retired from the Institute in 1987.

The guiding principle of most of our work was to identify an important question from clinical observation, to create a tenable hypothesis, to look back again at the clinical database to test its plausibility (a very important step) and only then set up the appropriate study. Oddly enough, such an approach led us to study the lungs in patients with chronic active hepatitis who, we postulated on a clinico-immunological basis, should occasionally develop fibrosing alveolitis – although this association had not yet been described. In a joint study with Deborah Doniach, our prediction proved correct and this study formed the basis of a paper delivered to the Association of Physicians of Great Britain which opened the way to my election to that august body.

Although the EGA offered virtually the only consultant physician post available to me as a woman at the time, it turned out that my experience there in general medicine and rheumatology provided me with magnificent opportunities to range broadly across clinical medicine whilst exploring very specific lines in respiratory research at the Brompton. Together these posts formed an ideal combination. I shall always be grateful to the EGA, not only for giving me a job at a critical time in my career but also for the chance to bring together two branches of medicine which provided a major research interest for the rest of my career.

Other research opportunities also arose at the Brompton. It seemed that long-term clinical trials that were so badly needed in asthma could be undertaken much more expeditiously if all the consultants at the hospital agreed, with the patients' permission, to contribute suitable patients who would be treated according to a set protocol. This meant that they had to be supervised for the duration of the trial by a single specially appointed clinical coordinator. This of course cut across the conventional pattern of care at the time, when each consultant used his own treatment scheme and ran his own autonomous firm. At first there was considerable resistance to joining such a study from some of the senior part-time consultants. However, they soon disliked being left out when so many others were collaborating. In this way we were able to set up some of the earliest long-term trials (over one or two years) on the treatment of asthma, including those on sodium cromoglycate and inhaled corticosteroids. We took advantage of the MRC Tuberculosis and Chest Diseases Unit which had relocated at the Brompton in 1965 and, under the direction of Dr Wallace Fox (later Professor), had a team with great experience in the design and conduct of clinical trials and with strong statistical back-up. We all learned a great deal from this most productive collaboration, which continued with many other trials throughout my professional career at the Brompton and Institute.

A side product of these early asthma trials was a series of Anglo-French meetings arranged by Guy Scadding and later Sir Geoffrey Hardy Roberts. The first was held at the Brompton, the second at Rheims and the third at Midhurst Sanatorium in Sussex. It was at Rheims that Dr Neville Oswald who, at least superficially, seemed particularly chauvinistic about women doctors, gave me a long-remembered backhanded compliment after I had delivered a rather obscure paper intended to impress our French colleagues. 'That was splendid,' he said, and then added, 'You know, Margaret, you and I have one thing in common – we are really at our best when we are completely out of our depth!' I suppose one of the most exciting things about exploring ideas in new fields in medicine is coming to terms with this fact and trying to take steps to make amends.

The environment at the Institute of Diseases of the Chest and the Brompton was interesting because it was beginning to bring together clinical and laboratory researchers in a number of fields where clinicians were starting to work together as teams, rather than in isolation within their own conventional 'firms'. This also allowed the differentiation of physicians, allowing them to take a particular interest in different subspecialty fields.

Thus John Batten (later Sir John), working with Robert May in the Department of Bacteriology, developed his interest in cystic fibrosis and created, by the time he retired, the largest special clinic for adult cystic fibrosis patients in Europe. Guy Scadding with Ken Citron developed his interest in sarcoidosis, and Neville Oswald, in collaboration with Lynne Reid, led a joint clinic for chronic bronchitis. A multidisciplinary shared team between the Royal Marsden Hospital and the Brompton was years ahead of its time in setting up a joint management clinic for patients with lung cancer. This was attended by a thoracic surgeon (Mr Bill Cleland), the Professor of Radiotherapy (Professor Smithers) and the Professor of Medicine (Professor Guy Scadding). Although many other hospitals developed similar multidiscipinary teams over the years, it is only very recently, after some forty years and a stimulus from Sir Kenneth Calman, former Chief Medical Officer in the Department of Health, that such multidisciplinary teams for cancer management are being established as the norm throughout the NHS.

In 1967 Mr Oswald Tubbs, the Senior Surgeon and Chairman of the Medical Committee at the time, asked me whether I would be interested in a consultant post shared between the Brompton and the London Chest Hospital (LCH). The intention behind this was to build up a closer liaison between the two but, at the same time, to allow me to continue as Senior Lecturer at the Institute. Since by then the writing was clearly on the wall for EGA as a general hospital and, much as I had enjoyed my time back in general medicine, I felt it was time to be more focussed on respiratory disorders. I was extremely honoured to be asked to join the staff of a specialist tertiary referral postgraduate teaching hospital and was delighted to accept. Simply for the record, I believe I was the first female full-time chest physician for adults at the Brompton Hospital, although of course Dr Margaret McPherson – a highly respected physician – had preceded me with a more limited remit on a part-time basis caring for children with tuberculosis. We may have been 'firsts' in a sense but I do not think that either of us felt there was in any way or at any time a gender prejudice. It was our great privilege to work in such an egalitarian and supportive environment in those early days when people at other hospitals were often still hitting glass ceilings and having other difficulties. I would go further and say that for the next forty years and in spite of working in a largely male-dominated environment, gender descrimination did not play any part in my professional story. I have always experienced non-partisan fair play, with great support, courtesy and tremendous friendship. It is true that quite recently and at the end of my time working for the NHS I have occasionally felt that perhaps my nomination to various committees was more on the basis of the 'statutory woman', but that could not be helped. On one occasion, in about 1994 I refused to attend a meeting called exclusively for women chairpersons of hospital trust boards (for heavens sake why?) because, as I argued with the senior politician at the time, if this was called, no-one could subsequently object if a complementary all male chairmans' meeting was called and this would have been regarded as outrageously discriminating. Thus, in all sorts of curious ways it seemed important to uphold a strictly non-gender-related orientation, whenever there was the chance.

Following my consultant appointment to the Brompton and LCH, together with the continuation of my research in the Institute, I had an ideal job combining clinical care of patients and the opportunity of laboratory-based clinical research in a tertiary care environemnt. Interestingly, the Medical Committee decided that as a hospital consultant I should join Howard Nicholson and John Batten on their medical firm, rather than the Professorial Unit. This decision reflected the degree of integrated thinking between the Institute and Hospital at the time.

The very special experience of this joint appointment was the chance to look after patients with largely similar chest complaints but coming from very different social backgrounds – one group from the largely indigenous population in the East End of London attending the London Chest Hospital, and the other from the more sophisticated 'flat-land' of Chelsea and Westminster, attending the Brompton. In addition, there were many special referrals, particularly for uncommon lung diseases from other parts of the country. There were fascinating contrasts between the two populations of patients about what they wanted from their doctor, what they wanted to know about their condition, as well as what compromises they were prepared to make in their lifestyles and jobs. The West End population may have had the good fortune in some ways of a 'better' education but when it came to tackling their ill health they were not necessarily wiser. The contrast underlined the importance of a holistic approach, understanding that patients require highly individualistic management and that this extends far beyond the variables of their disease, to their whole philosophy and attitude to ill health (see Chapter 18). In 1991 the Department of Health was quite right to emphasise in the 'Patients' Charter' the need to give priority to patients' expectations and rights, but it was quite wrong to believe that all patients wanted the same thing. The Health Commission and the primary healthcare trusts would be wise to bear this variation in mind when interpreting the results of their important patient questionnaires. As we all know, one of the most important elements in a good doctor–patient partnership is to recognise the compromises needed to meet the perceptions and priorities of the individual patient. Protocols relating to evidence-based medicine are of course very useful guidance, but there are many occasions where good medical practice requires flexible adaptations and compromises, if individual quality of life is to be allowed to enter the equation. Only in this way will trust between doctors and patients thrive.

Working at the London Chest Hospital was a most enjoyable experience. The staff were fiercely loyal and all worked in remarkable harmony as a corporate team. The surgeons and physicians worked very closely together and there was a special *esprit de corps* within the hospital. Dr Max Caplin not only had a very special interest in community tuberculosis and ran a superb service, but he extended this to special care of those down-and-outs, alcoholics and socially deprived patients living near the hospital. Dr Leslie Capel took a particular interest in the junior staff and their postgraduate education; he ran a very efficient physiology service and was an excellent editor of the *Journal of diseases of the chest*. All the consultant staff shared huge enthusiasm and determination to improve the hospital and the facilities for patients. Linked with this, the clinical staff led the way in the management of the hospital. Indeed, the elected Chairman of the Medical Committee was for all intents and purposes the equivalent of the modern clinical director of the hospital. In a remarkable pseudo-democratic way, this post rotated between Mr Jack Belcher, a cardio-thoracic surgeon, Dr Max Caplin and Dr Leslie Capel. Their motivation and selfless work for the progress of the hospital and its patients were remarkable. Because of this strong tradition it was well tuned to the appointment of their first formal Clinical Director, Dr Duncan Empey, who had the unenviable task, much later in the 1980s, of merging the hospital with The London Hospital. The strength and tradition of the hospital was such that, under Duncan's leadership, it successfully became the tertiary referral cardiothoracic centre for East London.

Back at the Brompton and the Institute, the clinical work and research continued productively. In addition to this, it was interesting to observe the contrasting styles of hospital management. The lead in this case was less from the doctors and more from an outstanding House Governor – later Hospital Secretary and later still Chief Executive – namely John Plant, who was first appointed in 1964. Over the years the title of his job changed by NHS decree, but the increasing work he did remained essentially the same. He and his small team believed that the way to improve standards was to facilitate the ways in which doctors could look after their patients within the resources available. He believed in close cooperation but not in domination. He had a remarkable capacity for ensuring that the many individualistic *prima donna* physicians and surgeons more or less toed the line and at the same time he relied on their talents to move the hospital forward to keep ahead of the changing medical and political scene. He always worked through the Medical Committee and was hugely respected. The mutual respect and trust between his very small management team and the doctors was great. It was a good model which, if it had been used more widely in the NHS in the 1980s–90s, might I believe have allowed some of the necessary reforms to have been introduced far more wisely and efficiently. It might also have avoided some of the soaring managerial costs and domination which has contributed to the demoralisation of the profession. It is interesting to observe that after some fifteen years of central managerial domination, a 'new' idea is emerging – to create a closer working relationship between clinical directors and managers both generally and especially at Foundation Hospitals, which are to have far more individual freedom and greater medical leadership. If these can create a better more trusting partnership between management and the professions, which we know worked so well in the past, then Foundation Hospitals will certainly have much to offer.

A special example of the doctor–management partnership at the Brompton was the Steering Committee set up to design and build the new hospital. This began in 1967, shortly after I had been appointed to the staff. It was a small committee of about ten people which was chaired by John Plant and included five doctors: Mathias Paneth (cardiothoracic surgeon), Tony Rickards (cardiologist), Margaret Branthwaite (anaesthetist), myself (respiratory medicine) and Michael Joseph (paediatrician). The idea behind choosing the more recently appointed doctors was that they would be more likely to actually work in the new hospital. There was also a nursing officer, representatives from the Department of Health and the University of London, a project manager and the architects.

Once again the mutually respecting partnership between the medical staff and management maintained the confidence of virtually all the staff and the small core committee proved a very efficient way of working, provided they remembered that the mandate they held depended upon very close communication with the wider management and professional structures at all stages, with frequent consultation with relevant individuals on specialist issues. There were, of course, problems as in any major venture anywhere, but the model of an even balance between key professional and managerial staff which was given the authority to take major decisions was certainly vindicated and could be emulated with advantage more often today.

The Planning Committee met every Thursday evening at 6 pm. There was no question of management requiring it to meet during conventional office hours. Everyone had their day job in the hospital and it did not cross anyone's mind that this was an unreasonable burden. Planning proceeded relentlessly in spite of huge difficulties imposed centrally by the Department of Health who were unable to move, for very good reasons, until the University agreed to invest in the Institute and *vice versa*. Their representatives did their best and were extremely helpful but the complexity of policy decisions were exceedingly hard to resolve and move forward. Sir Reginald Wilson was Chairman of both the Hospital and Institute by this time and one of his great contributions was to encourage us to believe that if we continued to work and kept all our plans in place (even at times temporarily relegated to the bottom drawer) the tide would turn eventually and our time would come. And so it worked out. When the final detailed commissioning got under way, Margaret Branthwaite, an anaesthetist and physician with a huge intellect, turned her talents to masterminding the detail in partnership with John Plant. After a delay of 22 years the new hospital was opened shortly after I retired. This building programme could be regarded as a huge success as well as a considerable disgrace. It was a gigantic success in that we had achieved a wonderful new modern hospital, but it was a public disgrace that the central authorities were responsible for such avoidable delays which added considerably to the costs.

Money for the hospital was, of course, always short but the administrators balanced the books as well as they could and explained to the Medical Committee when improvements could not be afforded. Choices had to be made about where the most urgent need lay for new staff appointments. Of course it was frustrating to see the affluence of North America with all its new hospitals, equipment and staff, but in general there was an atmosphere of tolerance, confidence and above all trust. We trusted our management and they trusted us to be working for patients and not for our own interests. As a specialist tertiary hospital, our funding came directly from the Department of Health. We were 'audited' in robust annual debates by a series of hard-hitting but fair Permanent Under-Secretaries with their teams who kept us on a tight rein but who also had the interests of patients at heart. Many others in the NHS felt that we received unfair privileged funding. Although the process of accountability for us was undoubtedly more straightforward there is, I believe, no evidence that the system was in any way unfair to others.

The fact that the hospital could continue to develop under the continually changing organisational restructuring was due to the fine leadership of Sir Reginal Wilson, followed by Mr Tom Meyer CBE and later still the Rt Hon Sir Philip Otton QC, together with an understanding Chief Executive Officer and some hard-working medical leaders, all of whom had huge tolerance of outside pressures and were equally motivated to improve the quality of every aspect of care and conditions for patients and staff alike.

In the late 1960s, the relationship between the academic Institute for Diseases of the Chest and the specialist Brompton Hospital became much closer. In spite of considerable suspicion by London University Senate, it was eventually agreed that both organisations should be headed by a single chairman and chief executive. This unification encouraged the hospital consultants and senior academic clinical staff not only to come together on collaborative research but also to allow better rotations and training of junior staff. This unification helped greatly to facilitate the changing patterns of postgraduate training which was also undergoing radical but very necessary reform.

Thus my years as consultant physician at two contrasting specialist hospitals were not only rewarding from a clinical perspective but they provided an introduction to understanding NHS and university management which turned out to be invaluable later.

It was at this time, in the mid 1960s, that another completely different opportunity presented which gave me my first experience of Board chairmanship and of fund-raising. I was asked to become the Chairman of Bedales School. There had been a long tradition of association with this school through Richard's family. His mother had been one of the early pupils before the First World War and it was there that she met one of the maths masters whom she subsequently married. Both became doctors and he eventually became Senior Surgeon at the Middlesex hospital. Their four children, of whom Richard was the eldest, all went to Bedales. In the early 1960s, Richard had served on the Board of Governors and suggested that I might succeed him. After a few years I was elected Chairman when Tim Slack was headmaster. He realised that the school had to enlarge if it was to remain competitive and for this we needed to expand the accommodation. This had to be done as economically and as quickly as possible. We employed professional fundraisers who taught us a great deal about the disciplines of fund-raising and these have been very useful on many subsequent occasions. We also had to convince the loyal alumni that enlarging the school was an absolute necessity and that we could only afford prefabricated buildings if the school fees were to be kept down as far as possible. Neither of these appealed to many of the older Bedalians who treasured the intimate family style of the school and its elegant traditional buildings. However, to their great credit and open-mindedness they accepted the rationale and in the event both decisions proved justified. It is interesting to observe that today the school is once again embarking on a major building programme but with far more ambitious aspirations for the style of the buildings. I believe this reflects the lifestyle change which has taken place in England over the last forty years. No longer are the post-war economies acceptable even when financially they may make good sense at the time. The school and its pupils expect much more and I hope it will not cause too great a rise in school fees. The eight years of Chairmanship taught me a great deal about teamwork and inter-disciplinary understanding and I am for ever grateful to Tim Slack and the Board for this training opportunity.

In 1972 Professor Guy Scadding retired from the Chair of Medicine at the Institute and the post was advertised. The post was one of the most exciting in respiratory medicine in the UK, and would provide a wonderful opportunity to develop the clinical, research and teaching activities which Guy had done so much to establish. Although competition would obviously be tough and I was not at all optimistic it seemed too good a chance to miss and so I applied.

Top: The Brompton Hospital in the 1840s.
Bottom: The hospital in 1989, before it moved. The facade has remained largely unchanged, apart from the day room added to the front entrance.

Top: A ward round in some style in the Brompton Hospital boardroom with visitors and students. For historic reasons the room housed an art collection which was open to the public.

Bottom (left to right): with Sister Jenny Hunt, Sister Haines, Sister Assa Awward and Staff Nurse Josie Donkin from the Brompton Hospital.

Top: Tom Meyer (Chairman) of the Brompton and the Institute.
Bottom: With the postgraduate students at the Cardiothoracic Institute, and (on my right) Dr Ken Citron and Dr Margaret Hodgson.

Top: A reunion in 2002 of key personal assistants at the Brompton and the Institute: *(left to right)* Cathy Ambrose (my PA when Dean), Heather Rolls (my PA when 'Prof'), Beryl Varley (PA to the Chief Executive).
Bottom: The Royal Brompton Hospital, Sydney Street, opened in 1989.

Top left: Guy Scadding, first Professor of Medicine, Institute of Diseases of the Chest.
Top right: With Hans Weill, Tulane University, New Orleans.
Bottom left: With Moran Campbell, McMaster University, Ontario, Canada.
Bottom right: With Sol Katz, Georgetown, Washington DC.

Top: Joint Meeting of the Australasian and British Thoracic Societies, 1984.
Bottom: Visiting with Dr Peter Rothwell (second from left) in New Zealand, 1984.

Top: Sarcoidosis Conference in Nana, Japan, 1979; Dick de Remee (front row, third from left); Jacques Chretien (front row, sixth from left).
Bottom: In Bangkok with colleagues.

Dual Fellowships. *Top:* As Honorary FRCS (1993) with Richard FRCS.
Bottom: Fellowships of the Royal Colleges of Medicine and Surgery in Australia.

Part 3

ACADEMIC MEDICINE: A ROLE IN TEACHING AND RESEARCH

10. 'Prof': Professor of Medicine at the Cardiothoracic Institute and Consultant Physician at the Brompton Hospital, 1972–87

On appointment to the Chair my first task was to find a personal assistant. I was most fortunate to appoint Heather Rolls, whose long-suffering and patient loyalty I will never forget. She remained with me throughout my years as Head of the Department until I became Dean.

The next problem was to consider the fundamental question of the best way forward for an academic department of medicine in a tertiary referral specialist hospital and postgraduate medical school, particularly identifying important clinical problems and translating ideas into practical and affordable research projects. The obvious strengths of the organisation were the large numbers of patients with a wide range of chest diseases cared for by some twelve specialist chest physicians in the hospital, the flourishing teaching programme and the core of more basic laboratory departments in the Institute. Our main weaknesses were our extremely limited funds and facilities which prevented us from operating on a scale that could compete with the basic scientific programmes in North America.

The existing strengths together with my own clinical priority led naturally towards a focus on clinical research. The NHS patient base gave us a unique opportunity to do this and indeed we were already establishing a place on the international scene, complementing North America with our strong clinical orientation of applied research.

On review, there seemed to be five areas in which the Department of Medicine could play a significant role:

1 To develop laboratory research fields with a clinical emphasis to complement the existing Institute departments.
2 To develop new areas of research, especially those where new laboratory techniques were emerging, that had been little explored in respiratory medicine.

3 To foster, in various ways, productive clinical research in the hospital by other physicians as an integral part of a tertiary referral postgraduate hospital. This entailed developing the philosophy of integrating hospital and Institute activities as far as possible.

4 To use the developments to foster MD/PhD programmes for both clinical and laboratory staff in training in the UK and from overseas.

5 To continue to develop our own particular Unit's clinical and research programmes, taking bedside ideas to the laboratory and back again.

Developing laboratory research fields with a clinical emphasis

The first priority was to develop a number of research units within the Department to explore areas which had so far been under-exploited in respiratory medicine. As soon as we were able to generate the funding, we appointed Peter Cole (later Professor) to explore host defence mechanisms and protective immunity of the lung linking with microbiology and pulmonary infections. In the 1970s relatively few people in the world were working in this field. With funding from the Asthma Research Council obtained by Neville Oswald and Guy Scadding, they appointed James Patterson (later Professor) to develop new ideas in the clinical pharmacology of asthma at a time when new approaches to the pathogenesis of asthma were emerging. Dr Geoffrey Laurent (later Professor) came over from Australia via France to develop collagen biochemistry, especially with a view to applying laboratory techniques to study fibrogenesis of rapidly progressing fibrosing lung diseases. Dr Pat Haslam (later Reader) focussed on broadening the basis of autoimmunity and exploring techniques in cell and molecular biology as the new method of lung lavage became available and living cells could be obtained from patients with lung disease.

This very broad-based research programme could certainly be criticised for not being focussed enough. However, it was a deliberate strategic policy which was appropriate at the time because so many new basic science opportunities were becoming available. I believe there are times, perhaps particularly in clinical research, when it is sensible to shake off the fixation on well established research fields and cast the academic net more widely for a period before deciding which of the narrower areas are the most productive. Today the exacting criteria of the Research Assessment Exercise (RAE) makes this approach much more difficult.

Currently, very strong pressure is being brought to bear on research departments to be highly focussed in order, it is alleged, to compete internationally – and of course there is much sense in this. This restrictive policy is certainly having a strong influence on both research and university funding bodies. While there are of course good arguments in favour of focus, there are times in the evolution of knowledge, especially in more clinical fields, when it is appropriate to follow research ideas through into a range of fields to identify at a fairly early stage which will turn out to be the most productive. There are in fact many good precedents of multiple wide-ranging programmes, usually with a central theme, which have been spectacularly successful. The Institute of Molecular Medicine under Professor Sir David Weatherall and the Department of Academic Surgery under Professor Sir Peter Morris at Oxford are just two outstanding examples. On the other hand, there are many examples in the evolution of research when a field has been focussed in one area for too long, such as the dominance of physiology in respiratory medicine, where it is appropriate to get out of the mould and take a fresh look at what urgent questions need to be asked and where practical opportunities lie to answer them.

I hope that the ever narrower research base that is often advocated in academic circles today, triggered by the ever more rigorous funding assessment exercises, will not totally eclipse the idea that at certain times there is also a need to stand back and review the scientific opportunities from a much broader perspective, before once again picking up the best and refocussing. I appreciate that this approach is unfashionable and that many people will disagree. In defence of our programme we managed to get many new ideas off the ground quite quickly, at a time when new laboratory techniques were becoming available to apply to clinical questions. I hope that the record as far as it goes helps to vindicate this policy. Members of the department were certainly in considerable demand at prestigious international meetings. Another advantage of such an approach is that it limits quite quickly the chances of people progressing too far in less productive areas and coming belatedly to a dead end. In other words, there are dangers of focussing too narrowly too soon as well as failing to do so for too long.

Fostering clinical research in the hospital

In the mid-1970s it so happened that several of the older physicians retired in fairly quick succession. These included WDW Brooks, Frank Lee Lander, Neville Oswald, Frank Scadding and Howard Nicholson. This led to a cluster of talented young chest physicians being appointed within about five years, each having substantial academic inclinations and training. They included Timothy Clark, Stuart Clarke, Malcolm Green, Duncan Geddes, Antony Newman Taylor, Steve Spiro, John Collins and Margaret Hodgson. These appointments coincided with the early years of my own appointment as Professor of Medicine. All of these people were not only very well trained as general physicians and respiratory specialists, they also had strong research interests and this gave us the opportunity to encourage them to sub-specialise and lead in special areas. The idea of sub-specialisation had been resisted at the Brompton some years earlier on the grounds that it would narrow the range of diseases being seen by individual consultants and would compromise the training of junior staff. However, it was agreed that if the Brompton was going to stay at the fore-front of respiratory medicine as a tertiary referral centre both in the care of patients and research, then subspecialisation was necessary. Thus Duncan Geddes (later Professor), after a period of major research in a number of clinical fields, joined John Batten (later Sir John) in cystic fibrosis, Tony Newman Taylor (later Professor) was appointed to specialise in occupational and environmental diseases especially occupational asthma, Malcolm Green (later Professor) pursued his interests in respiratory muscles, Steve Spiro (later Professor) developed clinical trials of lung cancer in collaboration with a number of other London hospitals, Stuart Clarke developed fibre-optic bronchoscopy, and John Collins later took this over and also had a special interest in the lung complications of HIV infections. This plan did not prevent them in any way from seeing and caring for patients with a full range of respiratory disease but it did allow cross referral of patients to ensure their best possible care. Ken Citron had already had a particular interest in tuberculosis and Tim Clark (later Professor) in asthma. I focussed on the spectrum of interstitial lung disease and asthma. Thus by cooperative planning over several years the range of lung diseases was well covered and each physician had a special 'place in the sun' with opportunities for clinical research. This avoided some of the tensions which had been experienced by some of the older physicians and led to much collaborative teamwork. It also enhanced the reputation of the Brompton where something new was happening in most areas of respiratory medicine.

In the 1980s it became increasingly attractive to care for patients and undertake research in one location. This led to joint appointments with a London undergraduate teaching hospital becoming less attractive and the younger physicians preferred to concentrate their clinical and research energies in one place, often spending less time in private practice. Thus, in due course Duncan Geddes, Tony Newman Taylor and Malcolm Green became whole-time at the Brompton. Steve Spiro elected to leave in 1994 and became whole-time at University College Hospital.

We were also able to appoint Margaret Hodgson (later Professor) as Senior Lecturer to the Professorial Unit and Honorary Consultant at the hospital. She was exceptionally well trained, having had experience in anaesthetics, immunology, as well as general and chest medicine. Before Steve Spiro took over, she had coordinated the programme of clinical trials in lung cancer. However, her real wish was to focus on cystic fibrosis and it seemed sensible to encourage her to join John Batten's team. I am pleased that the integrated atmosphere between the Institute and the hospital was such that it mattered little whether individuals were on the University or hospital payroll and this allowed the flexibility for a senior lecturer in the Department of Medicine to work largely with another hospital team. Margaret continued to pull her full weight as an academic and, besides her phenomenal work on cystic fibrosis, set up in 1984 a remarkable one-year training course in respiratory medicine which became accredited as a University diploma for overseas students. This not only enhanced our international contribution and reputation but also helped to rescue us from insolvency when University funding reached a crisis point.

Because of the extent of common ground between the University- and NHS-paid consultants, we decided to mix whole-time and part-time consultants on each medical firm. This was done to improve the training for the junior staff and balance the clinical load. This was an unusual idea in the 1970s when professorial departments tended to remain somewhat aloof from the rest and were apt to promote a 'them and us' feeling. All the hospital consultants were made honorary senior lecturers and this consolidated their position as University lecturers in the teaching programmes. This plan paid off and currently the great majority have been recognised through appointments to personal Chairs. The fusion of interest between clinical and academic staff complemented the fusion of the Institute and the hospital at governance and managerial level.

Thus we achieved what we believed was a fundamentally sound, albeit unusual, model for a tertiary care organisation (see also page 297, tertiary care). The planned coherence between the tertiary referral hospital and its Institute was clearly helpful in some of the endless rounds of reviews both by the NHS and the University which have gripped London over the last 30 years. The strategy was vindicated in both the 1996 and 2000 Research Assessment Exercises where the top grade 5-star ratings were obtained for clinical research.

The recent restructuring of the training programmes, together with the constraints of the new consultant contracts and the constraints imposed by the Research Assessment Exercise, are now making it much more difficult for clinicians to continue to combine patient care and contribute in an important way to clinical research.

An overview of the Professorial Unit's research programme

Although the work of the Department as a whole is more important, my own personal team also continued its particular interests and this seems a good place to summarise the main thrust of this. The full integration between the hospital and the Institute was especially suitable for our own research. It allowed us to care for a large number of patients with a wide variety of interstitial lung diseases and act as a major referral centre for many complex and often very rare conditions. We were able to investigate them fully, to keep in touch with them over long periods of time (which gave the patients confidence and allowed us to learn much from them), and to monitor their long-term treatment using controlled protocols, which would not have been possible without the full NHS support which was then available. I was also able to continue with the Asthma Assessment Clinic, started when I was a hospital consultant. In the 1960s this was innovative in a number of simple but effective ways. From the beginning we set up a systematic detailed pro forma on every patient. This gave us a good database for many studies, which in those days was transferred to punch cards. In today's terms the service would be called a 'one-stop' clinic in that all patients had simple lung function tests, a chest X-ray and routine skin tests for common allergens on the same day and before their detailed clinical assessment. We also took a holistic approach and ran the clinic in collaboration with one of the social workers with psychiatric training (Miss Malloy) to whom patients could be referred (we sometimes saw them together) and be seen on the same day if they had social or domestic problems which needed to be resolved. In a very simple way, we also developed a systematic scheme to improve patients' understanding of their problem. As I was describing it to them I also illustrated the nature of their problem and its treatment by free-hand drawing on a separate notepad. I gave this to them at the end of their visit, to act as an aide-memoire, knowing how difficult it is for patients to remember everything that has been discussed during a single consultation. We took this a step further by keeping a carbon copy in the notes, so we had a diagrammatic record of exactly what explanations had been given. This helped continuity of care if another member of the team saw them on their follow-up visit. All these very simple measures of outpatient practice were introduced more than 30 years ago to facilitate consistent data collection as well as patient convenience and understanding.

Having established this firm and systematic base, we continued to use the special facilities of the Brompton to undertake long-term asthma trials, believing that the success or otherwise of treatment could only be assessed properly if patients were followed long enough to cover the range of external exacerbating factors, including infections in winter and allergies especially in the summer and autumn months. Such studies, although obvious, are in fact quite difficult to maintain in practice. They are expensive to run, and they require particular dedication to retain the commitment of both the coordinator and patients alike. They could not have been undertaken without the support of Professor Wallace Fox's MRC Unit and his team including, especially, Janet Darbyshire, Andrew Nunn, Peter Davis and David Girling and others. In order to recruit the number of patients we needed as quickly as possible, all the physicians in the hospital were invited to participate. The trials themselves were supervised jointly by myself and a hospital physician. This was another deliberate policy, to establish a collaborative responsibility between the hospital and Institute. The trials on inhaled sodium cromoglycate were undertaken in collaboration with Dr John Batten as lead physician and the trial on inhaled corticosteroids was shared with Professor Tim Clark.

When I retired from the Chair in 1987 and my successor, Professor Peter Barnes, who had a special interest in asthma, was appointed, I was able to hand over to him a systematically documented group of patients which ensured their continuity of care as well as helping him with his many new studies for which he is now so well recognised worldwide. However, after my retirement from the Chair I continued in the hospital as a consultant for another two years and over this time I accumulated another sizeable group of asthmatic patients and was able to hand these over on my final retirement to Stephen Durham (now Professor) who was working in Professor Barry Kay's Department of Allergy and Immunology.

Another earlier and rather obvious approach to the problems of asthma was to classify subgroups of patients whose response to treatment and natural progression varied. We did this by studying patterns of airflow obstruction using systematically monitored charted measurements of peak flow readings. This had become feasible with the introduction of the Wright peak flow meter in 1966. This sub-grouping of airflow phenotypes was important in an attempt to study more homogeneous groups of asthmatics, rather than assuming that all asthmatics responded to medication in a similar way. As this was a descriptive exercise, we gave them somewhat 'racy' names as aides-memoire such as 'brittle' asthma, 'morning dippers' and 'irreversible' asthma (an apparent but deliberate contradiction of conventional terminology). It is satisfying that many of these descriptive titles seem to have stood the test of time.

Along with many others, we developed the use of diary cards to monitor closely the patients' symptoms over prolonged periods of time, both in clinical practice and in research. Monitoring how patients feel is quite as important as objective measurements and gives doctors invaluable insight into the impact of disease on the patients themselves. These diary cards highlighted an important point in long-standing asthmatics, which even today is often overlooked. While on the one hand the introduction of new oral or inhaled medications may have shown very significant improvement on what was available previously, less than half of patients even on the best medications and taken meticulously, did not reach the 'gold standard' of reasonably complete control of all symptoms. Thus we should not yet be complacent about the efficacy of current medications for asthma and much work still needs to be done exploring new approaches. This observation remains inadequately appreciated and all too often patients who fail to respond completely are simply blamed for failing to comply with instructions.

Our other main area of work was to explore bedside-to-bench studies on the role of various immunologal factors on the whole spectrum of interstitial diseases from known and unknown causes. These included fibrosing alveolitis with and without associated connective tissue diseases, asbestosis, extrinsic allergic alveolitis (due to a variety of organic dusts), bleomycin lung damage (bleomycin used in the treatment of testicular cancer), sarcoidosis and many rare fibrosing conditions.

We undertook some large-scale programmes on asbestos-related lung disease in collaboration with the asbestos industry and the naval dock-yards, who were extremely cooperative. While lung damage associated with asbestos exposure was well known, the concept that variation in host responses might be related to immunological mechanisms was viewed with scepticism. How could an inorganic substance cause an immuno-logical response in the host? Today's understanding of pro-inflammatory factors and gene product interactions at a molecular level makes our pro-posal seem perfectly logical, but this was not so in the early 1970s. A dose relationship between asbestos exposure and incidence of disease was well known but this dose–response curve also demonstrated that for the *same* exposure some individuals would succumb to lung disease and others not. In other words, a perfect linear dose–response curve not only demon-strates the importance of the external agent but also emphasises the vari-ation in host response due to genetic or other environmental factors. We attempted to explore some of these risk factors.

All our studies on fibrosing alveolitis suggested that if patients were to respond to treatment it was essential to diagnose them early and before destructive irreversible changes had occurred in the lung. The problem was (and is) that because of the large reserve capacity of the lung, patients only develop symptoms when the condition is quite advanced. Why some patients present with symptoms earlier than others is another important question. It was therefore important to study the early stages of fibrosing conditions. One obvious way to do this was to look at patients with sys-temic sclerosis who present with skin changes but who sometimes develop lung fibrosis. We therefore set up a very productive collaborative study with Professor Carol Black at the Royal Free Hospital who had an international reputation in this field. Her patients were wonderfully supportive and we were able to identify lung changes in patients without symptoms and with a normal chest X-ray. These long-term partnership studies continue under the guidance of Carol and my successor at the Brompton, Professor Ron Du Bois. Once again this productive partnership emphasises the value of freedom to collaborate with anyone across London, and the critical importance of long-term studies.

Another compelling question was why the majority of patients with cryptogenic fibrosing alveolitis ran such a rapidly advancing course over an average of five years but a few, especially some of the elderly, had a much slower rate of progression. Why did patients with associated systemic sclerosis, which our earlier studies showed to have identical histological changes in the lung on light microscopy, also have a much slower rate of progression? The answer to this question has now been partly answered by further studies on larger numbers, although the distribution by stage of disease may differ from the earlier series. Overall, the distribution of appearances on computed tomography (CT) scans are now thought to differ in the two conditions and the histological changes in systemic sclerosis tend to be more cellular and less fibrotic.

We examined these clinical questions in bedside-to-bench studies on the role of various immunological factors in interstitial disease of the lung on their natural history, their role as risk factors and defining different phenotypes especially in relation to progression or response to treatment. We also tried to address the difficult problem of whether they played a role in pathogenesis or were simply a consequence of inflammation. This led us, over the years, to explore the rapidly expanding range of techniques becoming available to study autoantibodies, inflammatory cell components, complement, immune complexes and collagen subtypes. We extended our studies from measurements in peripheral blood to the newly developed technique of obtaining living cells from lung lavage as well as lung biopsies when these had been obtained for diagnostic purposes. While many studies in a number of specialist centres round the world were being undertaken to extend basic immunological understanding in humans, as well as *in vitro* and in animal models, our particular interest was to address specific questions in human lung disease and to explore how they related to subgroups of patients, the stage of disease, its progression or resolution and their response to treatments. The measurements were thus used to increase our clinical understanding, to monitor disease and to attempt to predict prognosis. It was the emphasis on the clinical application of these new immunological techniques that distinguished in some ways our programme, and this was made possible in a specialist hospital environment where we had access to large numbers of patients with these relatively uncommon conditions. This large clinical base, where we could look after our patients and follow them over long periods of time made feasible by the NHS structure, was envied by many well known scientific centres around the world including those in North America.

In order to measure the significance of these laboratory findings, we needed to develop new methods to monitor progression of diseases in patients whose cooperation was always magnificent. None of our studies would have been possible without this very special patient partnership. Thus we developed with the Royal Marsden Hospital radionucleotide measurements of lung permeability, fine-cut computer axial tomography (CAT scans) developed by Professor David Denison and the cellular changes using the new technique of lung lavage to help us monitor their disease better. These special methods were plotted on charts against conventional lung function measurements and treatments so that trends of change could be more easily observed. Haematologists have used the same principle to monitor trends of change for decades but I still cannot understand why so many chest physicians are reluctant to do so and rely on lists of numbers, often on separate sheets filed higgledy piggledy in the patients' notes. Not only does graphic documentation make it much easier to correlate changes with other parameters but it forms an excellent teaching base for junior doctors. Trends of change are often much more valuable than individual data taken out of context.

This apparently wide-ranging programme was at the same time focussed. It used naturally occurring experience of disease to establish the relevance of various potential risk factors in the rate of progression and response to treatment. Thus our guiding principle was to identify clinically important questions at the bedside, seek potential components relating to pathogenesis in the laboratory and bring them back to the bedside to evaluate their role in behaviour of disease. In this way we tried to complete the circle of true translational research (ie from bedside to bench and bench to bedside).

Clinical scientists and translational research

In research, ideas and concepts often develop before there are appropriate laboratory techniques to investigate them and thus they remain unproven and sometimes denied until the technology catches up. The fascination of innovative research is to have the good fortune to bring together clinically important ideas in parallel with evolving investigative technology.

It is interesting to compare our (and many others') tentative, small-scale but fundamentally logical steps in designing our own studies over some 30–40 years, in the light of what is sometimes assumed to be a newly created concept of translational research. The new surge in popularity of this concept seems to have stemmed from the marvellous completion of the huge genome project where scientists have rightly been searching for the clinical relevance for their remarkable genetic information. They thus 'invented' the grander term 'translational research' to replace the more humble bench-to-bedside, which many had been exploring for years. It is an even greater pity that the term, as often used, seems to cover only half the true complete cycle. As I have tried to explain, in order to understand human disease one needs to start with the bedside-to-bench stage and complete the cycle with bench-to-bedside. This complete loop is translational research in its fullest sense.

With the emergence of the huge array of laboratory-based information, it is tempting, even for excellent laboratory-based scientists, to publish their findings and declare that these should explain various aspects of disease in humans. However, if the alleged phenomenon does not occur in clinical practice then the claims can be unhelpful or misleading. Let me give just one example. Much laboratory work suggested that the eosinophil blood cell, when activated, can liberate tissue-damaging cytokines and that pathogenesis of certain diseases can therefore be explained on the basis of damage done by this cell. Under some conditions this may well be so, but clinical observation also shows that there are conditions (such as cryptogenic pulmonary eosinophilia) where there are vast numbers of eosinophils in the lung tissue which can be cleared with corticosteroid treatment leaving a completely normal structure without residual tissue damage. This clinical observation has to be explained and presents the more sophisticated question about how and when eosinophils take on tissue-damaging characteristics. Thus clinical observations can pose highly relevant questions to be solved in the laboratory. Indeed, the fascination of cellular and molecular biology is that it is now beginning to unravel these types of observation.

The good laboratory-based scientist is trained to define meticulously the exact laboratory conditions for his experiments and to control the variables precisely. However, all too often when such scientists attempt to study the relevance of their findings to disease in humans, a broad heterogeneous group of patients is recruited on the assumption that because the patients fall into the same general diagnostic category, they represent a homogeneous group. Real advances in understanding of human disease will only occur when experienced clinicians, who understand the huge number of *clinical* variables, ensure that patients are selected to control as many of these as possible. This will only flourish when both clinicians and scientists recognise the imperative to define in equally meticulous detail both the laboratory and the clinical conditions for the study.

In this applied research the clinician has a major role, not simply supplying appropriate patients on which the laboratory scientist can work. This approach leads to more rigorous sub-grouping of patients in laboratory studies to ensure that like is being compared with like. The more meticulously one studies the clinical variables of disease, the more clues to various questions are revealed. In addition to clinical observation it throws up important new questions which can be taken to the laboratory for further investigation. It does require astute observation and the art is to spot what nature, through disease, is telling us. Thus appropriate studies of the *natural* 'experiments' of disease in humans, as revealed in clinical practice, has a great deal to offer and is sometimes a more secure basis for study than more contrived animal or *in vitro* models.

Working on the 'complete loop' of translational research requires real teamwork between clinicians on the one hand, who in addition to their own skills and experience understand the principles of the laboratory techniques – their requirements regarding appropriate material and their limitations – and the scientists on the other, who recognise and understand the subtleties of individual clinical variation and the limits to what can be made available ethically and with the patients' agreement. Successful partnerships between between PhD scientists and clinicians flourish when there is full and equal engagement of both partners who wish to give focussed priority to solving a particular problem and where each respects the skills of the other. If for one of the partners the problem is no more than a sideline, either the wrong patients may be selected or the wrong techniques used, with corresponding poor or irrelevant results.

More thought needs to be given to how to make the whole loop of translational research more successful and how to facilitate the clinician/clinical scientist/scientist interface. Simply putting large groups together in blunderbuss mergers is not, in my view, necessarily the answer.

So many different skills are needed that networking with the right people becomes critical. The concentration of hospitals, medical schools and laboratory-based University groups in London has provided a particularly rich source for such networking but it can only flourish where there are real opportunities for freedom of association (see chapter 21).

There are a number of examples where smaller institutions in which supervision and interpersonal relations are easier can, given the opportunity, free range and forge highly productive selective partnerships with neighbouring institutions. London provides spectacular opportunities for this (see chapter 21). Although the new opportunities for larger institutions must not be decried, the latter can actually risk isolating scientists who need to cross the boundaries of the institution and team up with others. It can also damage the golden goose of the clinical resource by separating in all sorts of ways university-based research from hospital patient care.

In recent years, a large number of factors seem to have made freedom of networking more difficult. Some of these direct and indirect factors include the restructuring of medical schools and the postgraduate institutes within the four much larger University Colleges; the tendency for financial and managerial reasons to separate university and clinical activities (which we at the Brompton and Cardiothoracic Institute spent so much effort bringing together); the regionalisation policies in the NHS and the primary care trusts changing the pattern of referrals so that patients are often simply not referred and the opportunities for long-term follow-up are reduced; the competition between Colleges within London University for funding; the competitive pressures arising indirectly from the Research Assessment Exercise and the tighter more focussed centrally determined research strategies. To all this must be added the increasing lack of funding for clinical research, especially through the MRC and the NHS Research and Development initiative which held such promise a decade or so ago and which seem, as I write, to have been diverted into other channels.

I fully recognise that many of these changes have been regarded as essential for other reasons and some have also yielded substantial advantages – for example there have undoubtedly been some new opportunities for interactive research in selected fields using the larger critical mass of talent within individual Colleges, especially in more basic sciences. However, a way must be found to allow the best work to flourish however unorthodox its shape and size. There is in fact a growing feeling amongst some fine internationally recognised leaders in the field of medical research that some of the most productive work comes from small closely knit groups where there is greater freedom to pursue imaginative ideas.

It is heartening to hear that at least the theory of freer networking across London is now being promoted once more by the University of London Colleges. However, this must be seen to apply not only to large groups but also to much smaller ones and even to individuals. The obvious reason for pressing this point is that this type of collaboration must be the real way to increase the knowledge base as well as bringing benefit to our patients. The fact remains that London has a unique resource and it must be exploited to the full. This can only be done if there is great flexibility and freedom for individual like-minded people.

As a perennial optimist I hope that over the next decade and as things settle down there will be a real drive by politicians and leaders alike to promote the free associations between those with complementary skills and similar interests which we forty years ago found so easy, stimulating and rewarding.

Work with the specialist societies

In 1982 the Thoracic Society and the British Thoracic Association, with great foresight, decided it was time for them to work together and merge to become a single strong national specialist society. Thus the British Thoracic Society was formed and I was honoured to be asked to be its first President. We held our first meeting in York and the enthusiastic support by the great majority of physicians was heartening and showed their willingness to change as thoracic medicine expanded. It seemed to me at the time that one important initiative was to forge much better links between specialist societies and the Royal Colleges if we were to exert our full influence on clinical standards, training and research. To this end, we invited the Presidents of the Royal College of Physicians and the Royal College of Surgeons (Sir Douglas Black and Sir Alan Parkes) to join our celebratory dinner in York and both travelled specially to be with us at our inaugural meeting. This was nearly ten years before I had the broader responsibilities of developing such liaisons more formally between most of the national medical specialist societies and the Royal College of Physicians.

Time for a career change

By 1984 the various units within the Professorial Department were well established and largely autonomous.

When I was appointed Professor of Medicine in 1972, I remembered Professor Rosenheim's principle that an established professorial post should not necessarily be a permanent one for the incumbent. He expressed the view that in the interests of academic medicine, research and teaching, it would be sensible to act as a leader for a period and then at a suitable time pass the baton to someone else. I believe this is often a very good principle and after twelve years in post, in 1984, it was time to review the position.

I was attracted to the idea of heading an Oxford or Cambridge College and two vacancies arose, first at Newnham College and then at Girton. Although I was runner up for Girton I did not get either post. In retrospect these failures turned out to be most fortunate. However, they sowed the idea of looking at ways of contributing on a broader front. This coincided with Dr Eddie Keal's departure as Dean of the Institute and this post offered the opportunity of getting more involved in University affairs, especially the wider London postgraduate scene through the British Postgraduate Medical Federation, the international need to help train overseas graduates, and the improvement of our own research facilities at the Cardiothoracic Institute. It seemed to be an interesting challenge and it was suggested that I might stand. In due course I was elected Dean of the Institute in 1984. This post was of particular interest because of its importance in postgraduate education of UK and overseas doctors. It provided the opportunity to consider how best to encourage basic principles of analysis and synthesis of information which often contrast with the more didactic approach of many countries. It is therefore appropriate at this point to make a detour and indulge in some personal thoughts on teaching and training, as well as recording some of the vicissitudes of international travel.

11. Patients teaching doctors and doctors teaching each other: Clinical practice and teaching

Clinical practice and the teaching of doctors in training cannot be separated. Since the clinical care of patients and clinical teaching has been so important to me it deserves a special section. My own approach (along with many others), learnt as a student from many excellent teachers, was to collect together as much information from the patient's detailed story and examination and, together with a few basic investigations, formulate a likely diagnosis, or at least the most likely shortlist of these. The purpose of further investigation was explicitly to obtain objective confirmation to support or exclude one's preliminary clinical judgement or hypothesis. The satisfying thing about respiratory medicine is that there is so often a definitive answer to the problem if the right tests are done and correctly interpreted, even when the condition is extremely uncommon. This deductive sequential approach seems to be different from that sometimes used under the time pressures of today, where a wide range of investigations are ordered on minimal clinical evidence in the hope that one of them will come back with a diagnositic 'label' on it. These contrasting approaches are analogous to research based either on obtaining evidence to support or refute a plausible hypothesis, or on a more random 'fishing' expedition. Use of the deductive approach requires systematically acquired experience and time. The fundamental process of teaching is to hand on both the intellectual process as well as the evidence-based relevant facts. There were three overlapping teaching responsibilities for us working in a tertiary referral specialist hospital linked with a University Institute. The first was the responsibility to teach junior doctors who were entering the specialty and who were working within the immediate clinical team. The second was to help postgraduate students from home and overseas who joined the clinical ward rounds to gain clinical experience. The third was to welcome senior consultant colleagues to exchange experiences on the diagnoses and treatment of individual patients. Very often one had to combine these three distinctive activities at the same time. All this also had to be combined with the primary business of caring for patients and their problems, discussing these with them and working towards what today is called an agreed management plan. Keeping a tight rein on all these strands simultaneously was a considerable challenge, but it was nevertheless the essence of real medical practice. Much of this simply cannot be left to the classroom or delegated to others.

Teaching is one of the best ways to learn, for those lucky enough to have junior doctors, undergraduate and postgraduate students. Indeed, before the days of formal Continuing Professional Training it was the mainstay of continuing education for most senior doctors. A real clinical team is where everyone can contribute their own bit. House staff have up-to-date basic knowledge which is valuable for the chief, who has been taught these basics in a very different way many years before. The registrars have information from postgraduate examinations fresh in their minds and can supply a different type of knowledge, and they often have more time to read the current literature. The chiefs have the advantage of years of clinical experience, often demonstrating that what is summarised in the textbooks and other learning material is not what happens to many patients in practice. They also often have the privilege of attending national and international meetings, thus gaining a global medical perspective. Thus, provided that there is enough time, everyone can contribute and everyone can learn. One of the saddest things in much current hospital practice is to see the break-up of the day-to-day work of the clinical team, often exacerbated by time constraints imposed upon juniors and seniors alike. A consultant-led service is a fine modern concept, but if it means that juniors are no longer alongside for most of the time to learn the finer points from every patient and to contribute their bit, a huge learning experience is missed by all. If 'patient-centred' professionalism is to flourish as the core of good practice in the twenty-first century, as expounded so elegantly by Sir Donald Irvine (Ref 5, Chapter 19), then professional development at the bedside becomes pivotal. While experience based in district NHS trusts is obviously essential, tertiary and quaternary patient referral centres throughout the country have a particularly important role in adding a different dimension to training the specialists of the future. Upon this depends the quality of patient care.

Hard as I tried to avoid it, I am well aware that some junior staff found our wards rounds at the Brompton rather intimidating. This is sad because I believe strongly that most people learn better through encouragement and by enhancing their self-confidence than by more aggressive approaches. I understand how this happened. I had to assimilate a huge amount of information as individual cases were presented (it is a lot easier to take the initial history oneself, but this is not a privilege that many consultants with large teams usually had). Inevitably, if bits of the presentation were unclear I had to make sure that the information I was receiving was correct, otherwise serious mistakes could be made. We were working in a difficult field with tertiary referred patients, many of whom had problems where the solution could not be found in the textbooks. This in itself could be unnerving for junior staff. It was often the clinical detail that counted because, with experience, one knew that therein lay some of the most critical clues. Thus, my need for detail in the history, the interpretation of the X-rays or the histology was not intended to 'nit pick' or catch the houseman out; I simply needed to be sure of the evidence, if the best judgements were to be made. Likewise, the meticulous recording of all the data and investigations charted against their individualised and changing treatments became critical. The workload this imposed on junior staff, plotting out the serial results prior to the ward rounds, was extremely heavy and I recognise the very onerous hours they spent collating the data. Selecting the X-rays which corresponded to various clinical events was in itself a mammoth and at times exasperating task. We tried to put green stickers on critical X-ray films to simplify the sorting process on future occasions, but some of the radiologists who regarded the films as their property, took exception to this – nevertheless it did save a lot of time and remains quite a good idea. With computerised films this problem should become easier, but I am not sure how far this has yet been done.

Even from the earliest days of my appointment to the Chair of Medicine, we tried to write down outline provisional protocols of management for various conditions which were special to the Unit. There were two reasons for this. First, so that at any one time, we could be confident that we were treating our patients consistently – unless there was a good reason to deviate. In this way our follow-up studies, both in and outside formal trials, were easier to evaluate. Second, it made it much easier for rapidly changing junior staff to know how and when to order follow-up investigations to ensure consistent data. Obviously we changed these protocols from time to time when there was new information from our own studies or from those of others. However, to have written structured programmes ensured that data were collected in a much more systematic way than is often the case in clinical practice, and in this way we could all learn from it and teach our postgraduate students. It is interesting that over the last decade the value of using protocols to help junior staff and aid audit has now become widely recognised. Provided such protocols are handled lightly so that they can be modified appropriately according to the individual patient needs, such semi-structured management plans have great advantages.

These protocols were kept together on the wards so they were always immediately available. Filed with them, as I discovered later, were some other bits of juicy information about my likes and dislikes. These were closely guarded secrets kept by my excellent registrars and I was not allowed to see them!

It is obvious that management policies for every disease and especially every subgroup of patients with the same condition have not and probably cannot ever be subject to effective randomised trials. Thus treatment policies often have to be devised either on the basis of an hypothesis or experience, or preferably both. Commonly, of course, different physicians hold different views for different reasons. A consensus of experienced people may offer guidance but this does not replace systematic evidence. It must always be remembered that many of the recommendations in today's 'guidelines', including those from specialist societies and the National Institute for Clinical Excellence, are at this stage based only on consensus views (sometimes led by a few, for better or for worse, with strongly held opinions) and no more. For this reason, they should be used for guidance and not for regulatory purposes as 'best' practice.

A good personal example of this is in the management of sarcoidosis. A widely held view held in the UK in the 1960s–80s by a number of eminent physicians was that patients should only receive treatment with corticosteroids (usually for an arbitrarily set time), when they became breathless. Our clinical observations suggested that by the time they developed respiratory symptoms, permanent damage to the lung had already taken place. While some symptomatic relief and radiographic and physiological improvement might be obtained, return to normality was rarely achieved. If permanent damage was to be prevented or at least limited, earlier treatment was logical, if unorthodox. We therefore developed a protocol to treat patients with persisting radiographic changes (after allowing a reasonable time for spontaneous resolution), but *before* they became breathless. Further, we monitored our patients to obtain maximum improvement of the physiology and radiographic appearances and then titrated the dose of corticosteroids to the lowest level that would maintain such improvement, irrespective of how long it took. Eventually most patients were able to cease treatment without relapse. However, the controversy between the two valid approaches continued. In 1996 the British Thoracic Society undertook a comparative trial and our protocol was vindicated – by a modest margin. There are several morals to this example. Our state of knowledge is constantly evolving and at any particular time there may be more than one justifiable treatment. The concept of 'best' practice can become stultifying unless it is constantly challenged. A consensus view may be helpful, but does not guarantee that it is right. Protocols in clinical management are useful to ensure consistent treatment and allow much to be learnt, provided that they are changed as more evidence emerges. Chronic diseases usually require careful long-term supervision with appropriate objective measurements. Obvious as these morals are, they are worth remembering in today's highly regulated, 'best practice' and cost-conscious health service.

Looking back, I am afraid my ward rounds took an unconscionably long time. In justification, there were three reasons for this. First, there were a very large number of patients to be seen and it was important to have time to communicate with each one. For this part of the round, and in order to protect the patients from large numbers of students and visitors, only the immediate clinical team was involved. Second, all the data had to be reviewed carefully to ensure that nothing was overlooked. Third, for the houseman and other students this was for them a new patient, even if I had been looking after them for years, and many had very unusual conditions. It was therefore a good learning experience for them to see the whole natural history of each case and the individual responses to treatments as these unfolded. This clinical experience was a good counterbalance to some of the gross generalisations made in textbooks and indeed some of the scientific literature. Thus on a single presentation, junior staff and students had the opportunity to see the whole course of often unusual diseases as they had developed over many years. This is real medicine.

There were usually some 20 people present on the weekly ward rounds and it was no wonder that it took some time. They started at 8.30 am on Tuesdays and usually finished, with a brief break overnight, at about 4 o'clock on Wednesday afternoon. When we had overseas students and senior visitors the ward round took even longer because everyone had to be catered for and given an opportunity to ask their questions and comment about what we were doing and why. To protect the patients from hordes of doctors and visitors, the first part was conducted in a side room of adequate size away from the wards – where we could all sit down. On some occasions, when the side room was not available and to the surprise of visitors, these sessions took place in the board room of the Brompton Hospital which for historic reasons contained an art collection which was theoretically open to the public. This added a certain style to the proceedings. The ward sister or her deputy always attended this part of the round, as well as our social worker and physiotherapists as integral members of the team. There is much talk today about the need for multidisciplinary teamwork in the care of patients. It appears that we, like many other clinicians, have routinely used something very like it over the last past forty years.

We also had the privilege of incorporating a pathology session as a component of the regular weekly round where all the histological material was reviewed. This was led by one of our senior pathologists, including Dr George Hinson, Professor Brian Heard and Professor Brian

Corrin, all of whom spared a great deal of their time to join us. In this way, we could integrate the pathology with the clinical and other investigations immediately and on every relevant patient as part of our routine work. The clinicians learnt a lot of pathology and I dare say the pathologist learned a little clinical medicine. So often physicians who have had little training in pathology have to rely exclusive on the written pathology reports which inevitably come through after some delay and are often written without the benefit of the rest of the data. Many clinical teams in other hospitals are only able to see the pathology in a separate special session 'of the most interesting cases' or maybe at infrequent clinico-pathological conferences. Neither of these are in my view are really satisfactory. Think for instance of the difference between seeing a genuine Van Gogh painting and reading a short descriptive paragraph about it.

I was worried that with so many visitors to look after, some of the domestic detail about patients could get overlooked. We therefore started the second day of the round with a 'social round' chaired by our social worker and again attended only by the immediate clinical team, where we discussed the details of domestic points which might help the patients and their quality of life. This part of the ward round was particularly important on an academic unit where junior doctors all too easily overlook the human aspects, especially when they are under other pressures to focus on the academic minutiae of the case.

Charged with all of this background information, the real part of caring for our patients began. As I have said, only the immediate clinical team and the ward sister took part in the round on the wards so that real communication with our patients was possible. We felt it was unacceptable for patients to be surrounded by huge hordes of doctors, students and visitors like some sort of circus. The visitors sometimes felt excluded, but compromises had to be made and above all patients have to be protected.

Because of the length of the rounds some senior registrars made valiant efforts to take things in hand. One in particular used to declaim at about 11 am, 'If Prof is not ready for coffee I certainly am'. I could not fail to take this most subtle hint.

One of the teaching exercises we used was to review each patient on the ward round and ask ourselves what new thing we had learnt from them, irrespective of whether they had a very common or a very rare condition. There was always something. This led to recording in a little red pocket book all the most baffling cases or those with exceptional features. Using this discipline, as often as not, we would see the same phenomenon again, sometimes years later, and could refer back to the earlier cases for review. In this way, we were able to define a number of new syndromes that had not previously been described. These included obliterative bronchiolitis in patients with rheumatoid arthritis, relapsing cryptogenic organising pneumonia (inaccurately, in my view, described later in North America as obliterative bronchiolitis) and relapsing desquamative interstitial pneumonitis.

Because of the importance of keeping an open mind on cases which did not fit adequately within existing descriptions, we developed a formal policy not to use the potentially misleading practice of attaching the closest conventional label, to classify patients on their discharge, for the national records. Where patients clearly do not satisfy the conventional diagnostic criteria, it simply closes the mind to classify them inappropriately. We preferred to enter the code, 'not yet diagnosed', or better a simple descriptive label such as 'unexplained irreversible airflow obstruction'. The hospital statistics department did not like this but it was the only honest intellectual solution. Avoiding premature labelling of conditions which do not fit the conventional classifications is a good way to keep one's eye open for new things which only later become obvious. This practice paid off; indeed there was a special page in the red book that listed, to my embarrassment, those cases which took us over ten years to diagnose precisely. It is true that some of these conditions had not been recognised at the time of their first attendance, but there were a few we had simply missed.

Another special feature of this clinical service was the extended follow-up programme. Because patients came from such a wide catchment area and needed several 'pre-planned' investigations to follow their progress, they had to stay for two or three days. Often they would only attend annually and they seemed to appreciate the continuity of care by the same team, especially those with uncommon conditions, where they felt more secure under a team who had seen many similar cases before. When our lists became very long we often made attempts to discharge some patients, but usually they asked to keep in touch even if it was only annually or biennially. By and large, the local doctors appreciated this type of shared care and the partnerships worked well. In the late 1980s we were able to convert one of the wards into a hotel-style facility which was less expensive to run and much more appropriate for the patients. As a bonus, of course, this follow-up service greatly broadened the experience for junior doctors and we were able to learn much about the long-term course of some of these conditions – an aspect of medical knowledge which is still very difficult to gather prospectively.

In the 1970–80s we received quite large numbers of requests from Australasia to assist in the training programme for their junior doctors. The Royal Brompton physicians therefore agreed that for each batch of 12 senior house officers appointed, two places would be reserved for

Antipodean trainees. However, because they had to be accepted without interview it was agreed that the physician sponsoring these trainees, on the basis of a personal recommendation from a colleague in Australasia, should 'take the consequences' and be responsible for them on their own firm. Because of my travels, I had the very good fortune to be asked to sponsor many of these talented trainees. After a number of years my colleagues began to complain and asked why I acquired all these wonderful juniors. I had to remind them that it was their rule in the first place. Thereafter, they insisted that they were shared around more equitably. The Brompton's links with Australia and New Zealand go back a very long way and we were delighted to keep up the tradition for many years. Later on, there was an inevitable trend for them to diversify their travels and many of them preferred the larger centres in America and mainland Europe.

In the 1980s we began to see some of the changes in nursing which threatened our team and the pattern of working we had built up so carefully. It was not the fault of the nurses, but part of the central nursing movement towards greater professional independence. The new Director of Nursing (no longer matron) resented 'her' nurses spending so much time off the ward, attending the first part of the ward round. Understandably, she felt they had plenty to do without spending hours on the professorial ward rounds, but she failed to see the very important role they played while off site and she told them not to attend. Fortunately, the ward sisters themselves thought otherwise and continued to attend anyway.

This was also the beginning of what I regret to say now seems to be the norm – that it is not necessary for a nurse to accompany the doctors when the latter are seeing patients on the ward. This we found unacceptable, not only because we respected the ward as the sister's domain but also because we felt it was essential that the doctors and nurses should work together, so that each knew exactly what the other had said and so that both could know how the patient had responded. We solved the problem by simply waiting immediately outside Sister's office until she delegated often the most junior nurse to accompany us (let there be no mistake, we loved it when junior nurses joined the round). After a while the old system was restored and we appreciated the company of Sister or a senior nurse when they came round with us once more. This sort of detailed collaborative working is what real teamwork is about.

The opportunity to teach overseas students was very important because we learnt to try to focus for them on the practical and important principles rather than the seductive academic minutiae. It was humbling to know the considerable financial sacrifices so many of them had made to come to London to learn. We also appreciated how hard it was for many of them to pick the nuances of the finer points of discussion in a second language. One of the problems with clever academic people is that they are apt to talk very fast. Good teachers instinctively slow to give those using a second language a chance. There is no condescension in this; it is common courtesy.

Teaching at the Brompton was enormously enhanced by the steady stream of senior visitors on sabbatical from many parts of the world. They contributed different points of view, they helped the junior staff, especially with their various research projects, and we learned a huge amount from them. This constituted international collaboration at its best. An added bonus was the number of joint papers we wrote when they helped us analyse our data.

12. Out and about in the world: International travel

Medicine is universal and the opportunities to learn from around the world are endless. In many ways, the opportunities of spending time abroad during training have become more restricted than they were in the 1950s–60s. Fifty years ago, everyone intending to compete for a consultant post in a teaching hospital had to have had an obligatory BTA (Been To America), usually to gain experience in laboratory research and with luck to gain some additional clinical experience to broaden their horizons. The opportunities for paid Fellowships in the USA were very considerable and the disciplined supervision of those in the teaching centres was a very different model from the less organised training in the UK, before implementation of the 'Todd' recommendations. In addition, Britain had been relatively isolated by the war and the pre-war medical school research programmes were often quite limited. Of course, the academic departments of anatomy, physiology, biochemistry pharmacology, pathology and others in undergraduate medical schools around the UK were often of international standing but, with the exception of Oxford and Cambridge where a three-year honours degree course in some basic science was obligatory, the majority of students at other medical schools received an eighteen-month to two-year basic course of practical anatomy and physiology before moving directly to an apprenticeship style of clinical training on the wards. While this was the norm, gradually other medical schools introduced a (usually) voluntary additional year to study for an intercollated BSc. By and large clinical teaching was didactic, focussing on bedside diagnosis, and the transfer of experience was largely apprenticeship-based.

Against this background it is not entirely clear how the sea change in attitude occurred to make the experience of the research environment in the USA obligatory for anyone in post-war Britain who wanted to get anywhere in medicine. Perhaps it was facilitated by the number of experienced doctors flooding back into civilian life after demobilisation, coinciding with the introduction of the National Health Service in 1948. A period abroad while the job market shook itself out may have been a stimulus. In the 1950s, it was customary to have to wait for the job one really wanted and even then the chances were slim. An additional experience in research in North America improved the chances of winning for those working in this very competitive environment.

Thus it was inevitable that Richard needed to go to the USA and he obtained a post at the Columbia Presbyterian Hospital in New York for eight months in 1957, while I stayed at home in London with our daughters aged four and six. Although it was simply not practical for me to go too at my stage of training, it seemed a feasible substitute, thanks to Noodle and back-up from long-suffering grandparents and other family members, to join him for the last eight weeks of his time there.

With great help from his mentors, Richard planned a trans-American tour of other urological centres. It was an ideal opportunity for me to visit a number of centres that were working on the systemic circulation of the lung which, as described in chapter 8, was the subject of my PhD thesis. Of course in some ways this was a contrived substitute for a BTA but the plan was much better than nothing, people were wonderfully kind and generous, the experience was unbelievable, and I was able to make many lifelong friends. It certainly demonstrated clearly the imperative need to gain first-hand experience of other ways of approaching problems. It also 'put the icing on the cake' for my PhD which was crucial to ensure that, at least in the ways that I could influence, I had improved my competitiveness for jobs as far as possible. This first USA experience, undertaken during training, certainly opened our eyes to the benefits of international travel to exchange ideas whenever this was possible.

We set off across the States in a battered old red Ford which Richard had picked up for $200. The generosity and the welcome we received as two young trainees was quite remarkable. One of the prime purposes of my tour was to visit Professor Averil Liebow of Yale University who was one of the world leaders on the vasculature of the lung. Not only did he spend hours going through his specimens with me, but invited us both back to his home where he proceeded to teach us how to make a mint julep. As he commented, the neighbourhood always knew when this was happening because of the sound of crushing ice reverberating across the valley as he pounded it up. But this was not all. He then insisted we stay overnight to conserve our very limited funds. What hospitality, and that it was only the beginning.

A few weeks later we reached Yellowstone Park on our way to the West Coast. We expected to find a bed in an inexpensive motel but the proprietors simply could not believe our naivety: 'Did we not know that it was a Mormon Holiday?' All accommodation had been completely booked for months as everyone in the USA would know. Notwithstanding and since we looked so helpless, a kindly motel owner told us to drive on

15 miles to West Yellowstone to a motel where he had a friend who might conceivably be able to help. So we did. He, of course, had no room either, but if we went down the main street we would find a wood yard. We were to enter this and ask for Hank. Hank was charming and asked whether we would mind sleeping in his own house. We were overcome by his generosity and accepted gratefully. We were not surprised to find that while scrupulously clean it was obviously someone's own personal bedroom. The next morning we discovered that Hank was the quite wealthy owner of the timber yard and he and his wife had turned out of their very own bedroom to give it to two young trainee doctors from England. Such unbelievable hospitality offered by complete strangers makes us feel very humble every time we relive the story.

Having reached San Francisco we had to get back to New York to catch our boat, the *New Bremen*, back to England. We had been regaled with endless 'fisherman's' stories of the huge distances people would drive just for an evening meal. Thus we assumed that they would make nothing of motoring the 3,000 miles back to New York in three days or so. Assuming it was common practice and 'while in America...' and all that, we planned to drive continuously to cover 1,000 miles in every 24 hours to meet our deadline. To begin with we did six-hour driving shifts but by the time we reached New York three days later the shifts were reduced to about 30 minutes. Our American friends felt we had rather over-interpreted their travel tales and could not believe that we had taken their stories so literally. Anyway, we resold the car for $200 and considered we had got rather good value from it.

In 1972, I was invited to give a paper to the Australasian Thoracic Society and under the auspices of their Australian Postgraduate Federation I had the wonderful opportunity of lecturing in most of the states. This led to lifelong friendships with many Australian colleagues and, as I have already described, this resulted in the continuation of the long-standing exchange programme of senior house officers with the Brompton and Institute. Two years later I spent a memorable time as Visiting Professor (my first) at the new medical school in Newcastle, Australia, developed along the lines of that at McMaster in Canada. I will never forget the welcome and friendship as well as the hard work and discipline of this visit. Dr Roy Mills arranged the whole programme in meticulous detail with the strictest instructions that although socialising in the evening with faculty members was to be encouraged, my hosts must ensure that I was back in the VIP flat by nine o'clock because there was work to do the next day. The lifelong friendship with Nick and Irene Saltos, Keith Murray Allen and indeed Roy and Wynn Mills themselves will never be forgotten. Both I and Richard have made so many other friends in that great country that it would simply be invidious to attempt to start naming them. They know that they all remain very special to me.

One of the most rewarding aspects of focussing on the clinical implications of laboratory-based medical research is that many people working in major centres round the world, while having vastly better laboratory facilities and greater scientific knowledge, did not always have the breadth of clinical training or clinical opportunities that the NHS had offered to us, to relate their ideas directly to patients. Thus I had the very good fortune to be asked to speak at many international meetings over more than thirty years to bridge the gap between the laboratory and the patient.

Because there were so many invitations, because there was a serious personal clinical commitment to patients at the Brompton, and because it was wrong to leave Richard and the family for longer than was absolutely necessary, it was not feasible to add sight-seeing or holiday time to these trips. In many ways this was a pity because there were so many opportunities to broaden one's horizons around the world. Life, however, is a compromise and I do not regret striking this balance between home and abroad.

On the other hand, it is remarkable how one can get a feel for a place, its culture and indeed its problems even within a short space of time. Over the last forty years we seem to have travelled to almost every country in the world. So much so that we decided to plot our visits with pins on a world map. This gave us quite a surprise. Far from visiting everywhere, our visits were in fact confined to two quite narrow strips in the temperate zones encompassing the world in the northern and southern hemispheres. The reason for this is obvious. It is where most of the academic centres are concentrated. Within these zones, it is true that it has been our privilege to visit a very great number in almost every continent.

Clearly it is impossible and would in any case be boring for readers to list every place I have visited, although I certainly learnt something from every one. Rather I felt I would record a few anecdotes from which I learnt some very special things. Some have serious messages; other are trivial or simply amused me. Each has a moral in some sense, and from each I have a very fond memory. Here therefore are just a few.

◈ ◈ ◈

I was invited in 1975 to take part in a teaching conference, or so I thought, at Cordoba in Argentina. I was to be met at the airport and transported to the conference centre, which I assumed was close by. Unfortunately the plane journey, which involved a change at Madrid, was delayed by some 12 hours. Thus on arrival at Cordoba there was no reception party and in my naivety I had not yet learnt always to get the details of my exact destination and out-of-hours contact numbers. There was very little English spoken and I tried to indicate that I needed a taxi. This caused some incredulity because they, but not I, knew that the conference venue was some 70 km away. They just indicated that a taxi would be very expensive and was out of the question. After some time, a kindly man saw the helplessness of the situation and escorted me and my luggage to the bus stop. After waiting about two hours, the bus duly departed in the early evening. I still presumed it would be a relatively short ride. We travelled through the town and into the suburbs and even early on the environment looked less and less like the venue for a conference. From the suburbs we travelled into the country. At regular intervals I bleated, 'Conferencia respiratoria?' but the bus driver simply shook his head but did not suggest that I got off – indeed I would be even worse off if I did. Gradually most of the urban dwellers got off and more country folk boarded – some with hampers of vegetables and other with live chickens. The conversation became more affable as is the way with country folk worldwide. The evening turned to dusk and still we continued. Even the villages became sparse and the bus started to grind its way up into the Andes. It was clear by then that for several reasons this expedition was getting out of hand. It was obvious that I had been given the wrong instructions at the airport; there was no possibility of an international conference at the top of the mountains; there would be absolutely no way of communicating when eventually the bus reached its destination, wherever that was, and it was now pitch dark. At one or two isolated stops on the road or at clusters of shacks, I repeated my bleat, which sounded increasingly like the cackle of the numerous roosters on board. By now the few remaining passengers were beginning to laugh, or so I thought. Eventually, late into the night we came to a small village with a completely deserted central square with a solitary hand water pump in the middle, but that was all. One or two pretty undesirable looking characters got off the bus and I was relieved that at least they had gone and I relaxed my clutch on my purse slightly.

However, at that point the bus driver indicated that he was not going further and I should leave. So I stood helplessly in the square. There was clearly absolutely no sort of place to stay, there was no one to ask and in any case there was no way of communicating. I stood helplessly for a long time, guarding my heavy case which I could only just carry. The latter did not matter much because there was nowhere to go anyway.

Eventually, one of the very undesirable thickly stubbled characters who had got off the bus sidled up in a rather sinister way, picked up my case, heaved it on to his shoulder and walked off. In my helplessness I simply

followed. After a time we left the village behind for the darkened countryside. It was evident that I had been kidnapped and would probably not
be heard of again. I had made a serious misjudgement between the priority of my work and the fun of travel and the responsibility to my family.
I should not have got myself into this situation.

However, a medical instinct came in out of the blue like a white
knight, because my stubbled escort started to wheeze a little as we started
to climb the hill again. This was the first familiar feeling I had had for several hours and my confidence spluttered to life. With sign language I suggested I should take a turn at the luggage because I sympathised with his
wheeze – as I indicated patting his chest. But no, he continued and as his
wheeze increased somehow I felt a little less threatened. Then suddenly we
turned a corner and there was a large banner saying 'Conferencia
Respiratoria Annual de Cordoba'. My asthmatic 'friend', as he was now,
struggled on into the reception hall put down the case and disappeared.
That was it. Oh ye of little faith!

I discovered afterwards that the Conference was held in this outlandish
place 70 km from Cordoba because it was much cheaper and it was all
that the doctors could afford. Their commitment to update themselves
throughout the days ahead in spite of all their difficulties was wonderfully
impressive.

I had received very special help from several complete strangers,
including an elderly impoverished asthmatic whom I had completely
misjudged. I felt rather ashamed of myself for many reasons.

※ ※ ※

Just before the troubles in Lebanon, I was invited by the British Council
to give a series of talks in that country, and in Jordan. The Lebanese said
there was no problem about making the journey by taxi. I set off happily
enough from Beirut but of course it had not occurred to me that this leg
of the journey would finish at the Syrian frontier. Again things were very
precarious, travelling as an unaccompanied female with no knowledge of
the language. Various signs indicated that my escort could go no further
and that I should get out. I had stood about rather helplessly for a time
when a very rough type wandered up and indicated that I should get into
his ramshackle car. 'Not another kidnap attempt,' I thought to myself,
but once again there did not seem to be much alternative except to trust
him. To make matters worse, I had no idea how to indicate to him that I
was really trying to get to Amman. Thus we set off through Syria and into
the unknown. After some hours we got to the Jordanian border and
exactly the same thing happened all over again. Eventually I was picked

up again and after several more hours and without a word, transported to my final destination. The British Council arrangements through Lebanon, Syria and Jordan had all worked perfectly but there was no way of knowing at the time. The highlight of my time in Jordan was a visit to Petra where en route we got waylaid at a village where a senior government official was paying a ceremonial visit and was being feasted on all the local delicacies, the details of which are better not mentioned.

In 1979, I was asked to go to Japan to talk on asthma and sarcoidosis. Our hosts had gone to a lot of trouble to make the well-attended conference entertaining in two particular ways. They had invited Dick de Remee from the Mayo Clinic, Jacques Chretien from Paris and myself to enter what they hoped would be a robust and aggressive debate 'knowing', as they thought, that we had very polarised views on treating sarcoidosis. Preparations in Japan are always meticulous and they insisted we got together the night before to plan what they believed would be a heated exchange. Out of kindness and to ease our mutual aggression they left us with a bottle of whisky to help us along. Within about five minutes we discovered we were in almost exact agreement on every point. The only problem was what we should do with the debate, which would disappoint our hosts and, more worrying, what should we do with the whisky, which we did not deserve? Somehow we contrived a rather feeble debate. After the conference we were taken to an exceptional traditional Japanese dinner. In addition to the generous hospitality, the tradition was that each guest was asked to entertain the company. I am not really into these things and being a rather serious person I have no funny songs or stories and am no good at prancing around. Somewhat desperately and I think to make up for the debacle of the sarcoid debate, they suggested that I should dress up as a Geisha girl and pay homage in a very formal way to each one of the assembled company. This seemed to satisfy.

Much later, I was doing some collaborative work on silicosis with Professor Hans Weill in New Orleans and we had been discussing the importance of obtaining accurate case histories on different types and severity of exposure to this dangerous dust and the importance of protective clothing. On a Sunday morning he suggested we went for a drive alongside the Mississippi river. As we approached a major bridge he commented that we might be in luck because it was in a haze of dust. This meant there might be some sandblasting underway, where sand under high pressure was used to blast off old paintwork and rust. He was keen to show me the modern precautions taken in the States to safeguard the workforce which had entirely eliminated silicosis from this particular activity. Indeed, this was what we saw – mostly – the sandblasters using the high pressure machines were totally protected with suits and masks. However, as we turned to cross the bridge, holding our breath the while, there was before us a most salutary sight. Sitting comfortably on the bridge we saw through the haze, the supervisor in his ordinary outdoor clothes without any protection whatever, smoking a cigarette. He was quite oblivious of his huge exposure to the noxious dust or indeed the added risk of smoking. Hans and I agreed that if he had been interviewed back at the research base and a conventional exposure history taken, he would have described his job as simply a supervisor and not in any way involved in the actual sandblasting operation. True but utterly misleading to the innocent interviewer who would assume his exposure was negligible. The moral, when investigating occupational exposures, is to see first-hand what actually happens and not assume exposures from the alleged title of a worker's job.

The visiting professorships to the States and Canada over the years are too many to mention individually, but the experience for me was something quite out of this world. Moreover, many have resulted in some very special return sabbatical visits to the Brompton and Institute on one or more occasions. The invaluable contributions from so many senior people to ward rounds, grand rounds, and the personal help and guidance to junior doctors with their research projects, will never been forgotten. It was a great privilege for the Brompton to receive these distinguished people. Perhaps those who I do not mention will understand and forgive me for recording my particular indebtedness to just a few: Sol Katz, John Murray, Gerry Baum, Jerry Kerby, Ben Burrows, Mike Lebowitz, Bill Ruth, Ron Crystal, Moran Campbell, Hans Weill, Tom Petty, and so many more. The pleasure of working with so many on textbook chapters as well as on research projects has been another privilege.

Lack of a facility for languages (unlike my mother and older sister Cynthia who were fluent linguists) has been a great handicap to me. Not that I haven't tried. I was invited by Professor Kreis in Paris to give a paper in French to a specially invited group of his senior colleagues. I prepared this with the greatest care. The evening before Professor Kreis kindly invited me to his home and in discussion asked me to give him a little demonstration of what I would say. He was so appalled by my attempts at French and, more importantly, fearing he would be let down in front of his friends, he suggested it would be better for him to give the lecture if I just rehearsed the contents of the slides (carefully provided in French) with him. My *amour propre* was damaged; I had tried to take so much care and besides I knew he did not really know the subject very well. Rather arrogantly but with much trepidation I said I thought it was better for me to deliver it and with reluctance he agreed. In the event I just about got away with it and to Professor Kreis' eternal credit he thanked me with extremely good grace, whatever he really thought. Professor Jack Pepys, who speaks excellent French, was also at the meeting and also tried his best to be supportive by saying, 'I have never heard French spoken with such an excellent Oxford accent before'.

❧ ❧ ❧

On another occasion I was in Marseilles. After the previous near-fiasco, I had taken even more trouble. My son-in-law, who is a wonderful linguist, had dictated my text on to a dictaphone so that I could imitate the lilt of his rise and fall of the phrases. It took me hours of preparation. In the end I was able to read it quite fluently. However, when I stood up at the rostrum which could not be moved, I discovered that the projection screen was immediately behind me. There was absolutely no way to point at the slides, which of course were a vital piece of the act, and keep a close eye on the written text in front of me, on which I was entirely dependent. There followed a curious contortion act trying to look directly backwards and directly forwards at the same time. After that I felt it was really better to accept my limitations and stick to English.

However, even sticking to English has its problems. I was in Chile at the invitation of Dr Riccardo Sepulvador who had worked with Professor Jack Pepys in London. The audience was Spanish speaking and he, knowing the subject well, agreed to translate. So we started to go through the slides point by point and sentence by sentence. It was very slow and I found it extremely difficult to keep the train of thought. However, when we got to about the third slide, I rather suspected that he had covered all the six points on it, while I had only got the to the second. I said, 'Have you got to the end of that slide ahead of me?' and rather sheepishly he said, 'Yes'. For the rest of the lecture all I had to do was put up the slide and he spoke to it. It was much quicker and more effective, but I did wonder why he had gone to the expense of inviting me to all the way to Chile when all I needed to do was send him the slides.

Even interpreters can have problems. We were in Beijing on a Royal College of Physicians visit. Knowing the potential language problem and the difficulties interpreters can have, especially on technical words, I had carefully prepared my after-dinner speech and typed it out in full. However, the College secretary met me at the hotel and, in his characteristically supportive way, warned me that the dinner was to be very informal – a prepared text would be quite out of place and I should simply say some off-the-cuff words. Knowing how careful I should be about protocol I naturally took his advice and left the prepared speech behind. As soon as I arrived at the dinner, the interpreter came up to me and asked for my text because, as she said very sweetly, she was not very fluent. Of course I had none and much more seriously I had let her down by potentially exposing her weakness. I promised to keep it very simple. I should not have worried because in fact all the guests spoke excellent English. As I gave my speech, the audience translated it into Chinese for the interpreter who then did her job and repeated it back to them in Chinese. Honour seemed to be satisfied all round.

Sometimes speaking English only can help others. I was in Stockholm at the time of the Suez crisis and met a number of Egyptian trainee doctors who were naturally debarred from England at the time. I wondered how difficult they would find my company under the circumstances. I need not have worried. They were having a difficult time because they spoke no Swedish. Out of courtesy to me, the Swedes spoke to me in their fluent English and the Egyptians thanked me afterwards most graciously for being there because they had been able to understand, for the first time for some weeks, what was going on.

These anecdotes are recorded simply to give a flavour of the amount one learns about so many things besides medicine through travel and overseas contacts. I wish I could include stories about so many other countries all around the world from whom I have learnt so much. I have not even mentioned my very special friends in Australia and New Zealand, South Africa, South America, Canada, mainland European countries, Sri Lanka, Thailand, Taiwan, Singapore, Hong Kong, Iceland and so many others.

13. Helping to develop the Institute: Dean of the Cardiothoracic Institute, 1984–87

The job of the Dean of the Cardiothoracic Institute (CTI) covered both internal and external responsibilities. Internally, these included developing the policies of the Institute through its Academic Board, coordinating the teaching programmes, supporting departmental plans to increase their laboratory facilities, and funding and promoting the career paths of academic staff. The external job was to represent the Institute on various committees of the British Postgraduate Medical Foundation (BPMF) and serve the University in a variety of ways through Senate. I will do no more than highlight a few of the major challenges during my time in this post, which inevitably linked with the evolution of the Institute.

When I arrived, the Dean's Office had been run since 1968 with great efficiency by Cathy Ambrose who had served with loyalty and good humour a succession of some eight Deans. The continuity she provided and the knowledge and wisdom she offered was irreplaceable. The Dean's Office door was always open; she received everyone with courtesy and friendliness no matter whether they were a senior visiting professor on sabbatical, an overseas student who was feeling lonely and missing his family or having a financial problem, or an irate departmental head who was furious with the Dean for some unforgivable failing! No-one could manage without Cathy; she retired in 2003, having given 35 years of magnificent service to the Institute.

I took over as Dean as the changes in London subsequent to the Flowers report got underway. Not only did this mean a greater involvement in University politics and management issues but also it became imperative to strengthen the position of the Institute as far as possible. This could only be done if we could obtain more space, but this depended on getting agreement from the NHS for the hospital rebuilding to go ahead; only then would the University help us expand the Institute.

Not surprisingly, the intention to rebuild the Brompton had been on the stocks for some time as the hospital had been in the same buildings

129

since 1842. The original North block had been built in a remarkably short time by a philanthropist, Philip Rose, and his colleagues in order to improve the care of tuberculous patients. The South Block, a much less well constructed building which had to be supported by innumerable pit props (still in place in 2005), was added in 1882. The two blocks were linked by the 'duodenum' – a tunnel burrowed under the Fulham Road with undulations to negotiate the main sewers. It was deliberately flooded in the early 1930s by the great Geoffrey Todd who as a young resident masterminded some swimming races to pass the time – a high spirited exercise which would certainly have incurred instant dismissal and forfeiting a promising career today. It did not seem to do him any harm and he was knighted for other things some decades later. All in all, modernisation of the hospital was desperately needed.

In the early 1960s an imaginative attempt was made to bring together several of the postgraduate hospitals and their institutes to a site in west London. This was to include nephrology, urology, dermatology, thoracic medicine and surgery, colorectal disease and oncology. After several years of planning, the scheme petered out. A revised scheme, recommended by the Pickering Report and referred to by Guy Scadding as that of the 'assorted Saints' because of the names of some of the hospitals, largely covering the same disciplines as before, was developed, based on the Brompton and neighbouring sites. This one progressed well at first but foundered in 1966 mainly for financial reasons.

When the Pickering scheme to merge several of the specialist hospitals and their institutes collapsed, we felt we had to start planning our own new hospital building. There was an old voluntary hospital (St Lukes) belonging to the NHS on a site round the corner in Sydney Street. Progress on this scheme also got caught up in the endless reviews and vacillations around the future of postgraduate medicine, as discussed in chapter 21. In addition to these development plans was the improbable idea of expanding and re-siting the Institute in an old and dilapidated Victorian Convent (St Wilfred's) vacated by the nuns in the early 1980s which was fortuitously adjacent to the proposed new hospital. With considerable optimism, it was felt that this could be converted to provide more space for the Institute. Although there were all sorts of planning constraints, and it was far from ideal, land in Chelsea was very sought after and it seemed to be the only practical opportunity to enlarge the Institute. In some magical negotiations undertaken by my predecessors, especially Eddie Keal, the University was persuaded and agreed to acquire this for us, provided that the Department of Health agreed that the new hospital should go ahead. There followed endless to-ing and fro-ing somewhat akin to the coxes at the start of the Oxford and Cambridge

Boat Race, where first one was ready to go but the other wasn't and *vice versa*. In spite of the pressures to merge postgraduate institutes, it is to the University's eternal credit that they took the lead on this unusual proposal and went ahead and purchased the building, provided that we raised the money for the conversion. While we set about this task the Convent was let out on a short-term lease to a good cause to accommodate homeless people in London on condition that we would have vacant possession as soon as we had raised the funds to develop it.

Thus, my first job as Dean was a fascinating period of intensive fundraising. In this the Chairman of the Institute and Hospital, Tom Meyer, and the Chief Executive of the Hospital, John Plant, both played a major personal role in the campaign. Without their individual efforts the appeal would certainly not have been successful. Lord Rayne provided the magnificent start-up fund of £1 million and gradually other charities and individuals followed. Brigadier (Dick) Vernon, previously Executive Secretary of the Institute of Cardiology, generously agreed to mastermind the Appeal. We decided not to hire professional fundraisers partly to save costs and partly because some of us had had experience of working with professional fundraisers on other projects before and had learnt many of the tricks of the trade from them. While we did the work ourselves, we were very fortunate to be able to check our efforts from time to time with some friendly professionals. Interestingly, many donors appreciated our direct approach and our efforts to save management costs. The principle of do-it-yourself fundraising is worth considering whenever possible, because many donors are suspicious of extravagant expensive glossy brochures and high campaign expenses.

The funds we raised from many charities and other organisations were very generously augmented by the Brompton Hospital Endowment Funds. In addition, the University agreed to cover the cost of some of the furnishing and fees after robust but very helpful discussions led by Ann Widdecombe when she was working at Senate House, before she translocated to the high profile world of politics. We shall always be indebted to her for all her help.

Having overcome the formidable problems of the University, the Department of Health and the funding shortfall, we were ready to go ahead. However, life is never straightforward and the biggest and totally unforeseen hurdle was yet to come. Our temporary tenants refused to quit in spite of their clear obligation to do so. This occurred because of an alleged legal technicality due to a lapse by a day or so of a renewal of the rental agreement. They saw an opportunity to charge us a large sum to vacate and this was both dishonourable and one which we simply could not afford. All persuasive attempts failed and we had to go the High

Courts where our case was made for us by Robert Prior (now a judge) with great eloquence and unsurpassed knowledge of the finer points of tenant law. Thus the case was won for us and, with a devastating indictment of the tenants from the Judge, we regained possession of our own property.

True to form at the Brompton, planning and building were conducted along somewhat unorthodox lines by a small team including the professional construction leaders, the Institute staff and management. Mr King, the Project Manager, the Quantity Surveyor, the architects and the builders met every Monday morning at a meeting which I chaired but which Tom Meyer, Chairman of our Hospital and Institute, often attended. I remember vividly how easily costs were potentially allowed to overrun, I suspect because the professionals must have thought we were 'easy meat' – with an inexperienced medical academic in the chair. I suspect they also thought that the public sector was a soft touch, in spite of the fact that the funding was from charitable sources and for medical research. Overrun of costs was a rather common practice but one that we were determined to resist. However, with Tom's formidable support we held a tight rein. When we disliked the rather poor choice of bricks they had offered us, and after consultation with our maintenance man at the hospital about how to select a good brick, Tom and I went to the Building Centre in Store Street and found ones we preferred. The builders must have found us very tiresome but they tolerated being regularly held to account and it saved us a great deal of money. In turn, I learnt a huge amount about building and the tricks of the trade.

Towards the end of the programme the colour schemes for all the rooms were selected very democratically. The architect, who had a very good eye for colour, put together several sets of floor, furniture and wall colour schemes which toned well. No change *within* a set was allowed, but departments could choose *between* sets. This we felt would ensure an artistic quality for each room. We then invited the Heads of Departments with all their staff to a free sandwich lunch and asked them to select which set or sets they preferred for the rooms in their own departments. Much fun was had by all and it was interesting to see how much common ground there was. The lecture theatre, with the latest projection equipment, was funded by the British Heart Foundation and although it was constructed on a very difficult site it has functioned remarkably well. The common room space was the least satisfactory but it was all that could be spared and the users have been extremely tolerant. In spite of its drawbacks, it has hosted many notable celebrations, thanks particularly to some equally tolerant but very loyal caterers.

And so it was that a derelict Victorian convent was transformed into the National Heart and Lung Institute and Lord Flowers graciously laid the foundation stone. Under the vigilant eyes of Malcolm Green and Tim Clark (the succeeding Deans), and with great ingenuity, a lot more space has been conjured up and the heads of departments have got down to work with great enthusiasm. It has all been vindicated by the achievement of a 5-star grade for hospital-based clinical subjects at the last Higher Education Funding Council for England (HEFCE) Research Assessment Exercise.

A sadder story during my Deanship was the merger with the Research Institute at King Edward VII Hospital, Midhurst, Surrey. The creation of this Institute had been sponsored by a remarkable philanthropist, Mr Halford Reddish, in 1973. An impressive group of talented scientists had been recruited under the leadership of Professor Gordon Cumming and some quality academic work had been achieved there. Because of restrictions imposed on the funding arrangements and through no fault of the scientists, financial difficulties arose which made it impossible for them to be resolved in a way that would allow continuation on the isolated site in Sussex. Their Board asked the Cardiothoracic Institute to take it over and after much discussion this seemed to be the preferred option for the Board and we agreed to do so. We tried to offer jobs to those scientists who wanted to join the CTI but I do not blame them for finding the travel to London too difficult. Some staff were absorbed into the Hospital at Midhurst and others retired. It was especially hard for the Director, Professor Gordon Cumming, who had done such a splendid job creating a fine team and in building up the Institute. Fortunately, he was able to transfer his work to the University of Surrey to continue in his retirement.

As ever, the funding problems of the Cardiothoracic Institute did not get easier and new ways of generating funds had to be found. All our efforts to blur the distinction between the Institute and the hospital became more difficult when we were urged to generate income by cross-charging the clinical service provided by senior staff on the university pay role, library and teaching facilities which we provided for the junior hospital staff, set against all the clinical research opportunities we gained from the hospital. John Plant and I discussed this and, after some back-of-envelope calculations, decided that we gained more from the other than we provided. Thus, at least for the time being, we refused to go down the cross-charging route and saved a great deal of administrative costs. The Academic Board decided to set up one-year Diploma Courses – which later became University Diplomas – in both cardiac and respiratory medicine for overseas students. The overall masterminds behind these were Professor Margaret Hodgson and Dr Graham Miller. Margaret's dedication to the welfare of the students as well as their academic teaching was and continues to be quite outstanding. Not only was this much appreciated by the students but they brought further international recognition to the Institute. It also allowed us to help students from less well endowed countries who would return and lead the teaching programmes in their own homeland. It was a perpetual worry to us that the fees we were forced to charge by Government were beyond the means of so many. This problem has not yet been resolved and it continues to conflict with ideals of globalised further education to help less affluent countries.

Another rewarding job for the Dean was to advance the career paths of members of staff. Academic promotion was a rigorous affair and required strenuous negotiation with the BPMF and Central Office of London University for each one. It was a particular joy to sit through the interview of candidates being considered for Professorial Chairs, and to have the satisfaction of admiring their outstanding performances when they trounced their examiners.

While Dean, I chaired the Academic Council of the BPMF and worked closely with the Director, Sir David Innes Williams. The meetings were impressive gatherings and always lively as the Deans from all the post-graduate institutes joined the debates and were never at a loss for words. This involved trying to promote the interests of all the postgraduate institutes in London at a time when they were under increasing threat, and also attempting to find ways in which the BPMF could help each constituent member develop the quality of their work.

The managerial experience gained during my time as Dean and the insight into the workings of the University and the Department of Health was invaluable later when representing the Royal Colleges and dealing with matters on a national scale.

Up until the late 1970s, the University of London reviewed the work of the individual institutes on a quinquennial basis. This accountability exercise required detailed and careful preparation. The external assessors were rigorous and searching. Each department was interviewed separately and encouraged to air their own critical views. Students and junior staff were also interviewed separately to give their independent feedback. The reports were returned expeditiously and pulled no punches. They often provided important external support for improvements needed in weaker departments which strengthened the arm of the local Academic Board and Dean. Between these visits, the Institute was largely self regulated through the Academic Board, and the Dean ignored its views at his/her peril. The system worked reasonably well provided that departments remained self-motivated, innovative, well run and were able to fund their own research through grant monies. However, the system was not able to respond well if and when individuals became less productive for whatever reason, because their tenured appointments gave them a high degree of job security irrespective of their performance.

The more rigorous assessment exercises introduced from 1986 onwards were certainly fully justified. I had the unenviable experience of serving as adjudicator on the first round of assessments conducted by the University Grants Committee. While I recognise it did its best breaking entirely new ground, I felt very uncomfortable because it relied far too much on our personal knowledge of individual departments throughout the country. The scoring seemed to be particularly biased in favour of large well-established departments and was unfair to young new departments which had not yet had the chance to build up their programmes and staff. To deprive them of further funds seemed very unproductive. However, lessons were learnt and the mechanisms were greatly improved in later rounds when assessment became much more objective.

The day-to-day work within the Institute was very enjoyable. It was a privilege to be involved with the teaching programmes involving huge support from both the academic and clinical staff. It was also very rewarding trying to support individual heads of departments in their endless quest for outside funding; we all felt proud when a department achieved another major programme grant from the MRC or a major research charity. It was an equal joy when we did battle and won, persuading the university to promote individuals to a Readership or a Professorial Chair; these were usually celebrated with an inaugural lecture and party.

The Dean's job normally lasted for three years and at the end of that time it seemed sensible to hand on the job as well as the Professorial Chair of Medicine. I was 64 and wanted just two years where I could continue to look after my patients in the hospital without the continued distractions and responsibilities of maintaining the momentum of the Institute and all that this involved. Before taking up the Chair in 1972, I had taken the precaution of obtaining the agreement with the hospital that, having been appointed as a Consultant in open competition, I could return as part-time Consultant Physician if I wished and now was the chance (or so I thought), to indulge myself. The Brompton agreed and to my considerable relief Malcolm Green took over as Dean and Peter Barnes was appointed as Professor of Thoracic Medicine – two outstanding appointments.

Thus in 1987 I believed that my career was winding down and I was looking forward to real time with my patients before retiring. However, planning is often a myth and I had no idea that after a relatively minor twist to the tale, this would be followed by nearly another eight years in even heavier harness, first as President of the Royal College of Physicians and Chairman of the Conference of the Royal Medical Colleges and their Faculties, and then as Chairman of one of the new NHS Trust Hospitals in Exeter.

Part 4

A CHANGE OF DIRECTION: THE COLLEGE AND A NEW TRUST HOSPITAL

14. Back to the real world of patients: Return to the Royal Brompton and Second Vice President at the Royal College of Physicians

In 1987, I moved back into the Brompton Hospital hoping to care better for my patients and teaching three days a week, as well as attempting to finish up various outstanding pieces of research which had been shelved while helping to manage the new Institute developments. It was fun to continue to serve on several committees including the North West Thames Regional Board and the Council of the British Heart Foundation. In 1988 I was asked by the British Council to head a team to visit Poland to compare experience and opportunities on various aspects of thoracic medicine. We were all extremely impressed by the way Polish physicians had been able to keep up to date so well with recent advances in spite of extremely limited funding and the continued turmoil in that country following the Second World War.

However, this comfortable life was not destined to last. In 1988, I developed a carcinoma of the breast. This was dealt with very expeditiously and since the operation was performed at the weekend, my ward round and outpatients were not interrupted. However, dove-tailing the six weeks of daily radiotherapy would have been more difficult to fit around all the Dean's commitments and so in the event it proved convenient that I had rearranged my schedule and handed on the Chair and the Deanship. In 1988, the duration of tamoxifen therapy had not been established so I and my advisers empirically elected for five years, rather than two. Later published evidence supported this decision. To date all seems well.

Cancer, however, was not the main stumbling block to my best-laid plans and my luxurious wind-down towards retirement. Someone had suggested that my name should go forward as candidate for Second Vice President of the Royal College of Physicians and I was duly elected. This was an interesting post. First, at that time it was the only Officer of the College to be elected by all the Fellows by postal ballot. Second, it was not a very onerous job and was generally believed to be appropriate for some-one who would not be in the running for the Presidency and, in any case, the appointment lasted for only one year. Third, although I had served on the Members' Committee many years before and more recently on the Thoracic Committee, and had given two of the named College lectures – the Phillip Ellman and Mark Daniels – I had not been closely associated with its activities. My clinical, academic and administrative commitments had been quite heavy and building up the Professorial Unit, funding research and international travel had not left much spare time. I had been on the panel of College MRCP examiners for a relatively short time but the dates constantly clashed with other things and I had had to abandon it. Nevertheless, it seemed to be time to do more for the College if that was what the Fellows wished. And so in due course they did.

Thus, instead of a leisurely three-day week, a busy schedule was re-instated. This involved attending Council, all the formal College lectures which were both fascinating and educational, the formal College Dinners meeting many extremely interesting people, and attending what was in effect the President's ('Bill' Hoffenberg) executive meeting which included the Registrar (David Pyke), the Treasurer (Antony Dawson), the Senior Censor/Vice President (Harold Lambert), who was responsible for the College's examinations, and the Academic Registrar (Carol Seymour) who planned the conference and lecture programme. No other Officer of the College or manager was present. Things have changed a great deal since then. This meeting, known as the President's Business Dinner (PBD), took place over a very good dinner. It discussed College strategy, we shared some of the Presidential correspondence, it considered finan-cial issues, the academic conference plans and all manner of other things both internal and external, including our liaison with other Colleges and the Department of Health (DH). We considered our position in relation to politics and politicians in general, as well as our position on major national issues such as the development of information technology, fund-ing of the health service, the future of academic medicine and our role in solving the medical manpower controversy, and any other innovative ideas that the Officers might have. Much useful and serious business was discussed, leavened with a good measure of irrepressible humour from the Registrar and a smidgeon of gossip.

I also learned that each department within the College was effectively left to get on with their own affairs with a large measure of autonomy. The management structure of the College was entirely different from any-thing I had experienced in the NHS or University. This only goes to remind us that there are a number of different ways of doing things, each of which has its own merits.

It was a time when the College was agonising about how far it should become involved with NHS politics and politicians. The latter were becoming increasingly involved not only in strategic matters but also in how individual practical problems should be resolved. This involvement was justified on the grounds that the Minister of State was personally responsible for the NHS. Many people, including myself, were also very concerned at that time (1988) about the critical medical manpower shortages and the increasing restrictions on training numbers in the different specialties, which were going to have a serious impact on adequate staffing of NHS hospitals in the future. There were, for example, many district general hospitals with specialist physicians working single-handedly and in consequence they were either permanently on call to cover serious problems, or the patients had to be managed by a physician with no specialist knowledge in that field. I remember raising this issue at PBD and was told (very firmly) that that was not the business of the College and indeed they were about to disband their Manpower Committee. This and other things once again raised the issue of whether and how far the College should interface with the DH, the NHS Executive and Health Ministers. The organisation of healthcare in the NHS was changing very rapidly and it seemed that the College would have to change too. It was quite easy to consider these knotty problems from the comfortable position of second Vice President where I had no real responsibility – little did I know that within the year my responsibilities would become much more serious. The more so because by then the Government under the Prime Minister (Mrs Thatcher) would have issued its White Paper proposing the most radical changes in the organisation of the NHS since its inception (their words), so there was no option but to engage much more fully with both politicians and the media.

The time as Second Vice President also showed me how enjoyable the College ambiance was, in ways completely different from the equally enjoyable environment of the Brompton and Institute. There was a small loyal staff who ran the College very smoothly and a special atmosphere of confidence of a defined job being well done. There was innovation but this depended very much on the drive of individual departmental heads.

As the end of my year as Second Vice President drew near, it really seemed as if the home straight to retirement had been reached – but not so. Orderly retirement plans were once again frustrated because Sir John Batten asked whether I would allow my name to go forward as President since Sir Raymond Hoffenberg was standing down after seven years in office. Even to be asked was a singular honour, but I was far from sure that I knew enough about the College responsibilities or that I was the right person to try to lead the profession in times that were becoming increasingly difficult, especially in relation to politics. There were, however, several reasons why I was quite confident that I would not in any case be appointed. First, I was a woman. The College had had very few women participating in any type of office or as Councillors and it was inconceivable that one would be appointed a President after 472 years of male predecessors. Second, respiratory medicine was still regarded by many physicians as somewhat of a 'Cinderella' subject and there were many much more distinguished leaders working in more prestigious fields. Third, there was an increasing bias against electing London-based physicians as President. Fourth, it was well known that a Second Vice President was never elected as President.

Thus I was game to enter the lists with a light heart to show willing, if that was what colleagues really wanted, but knowing full well that I would not actually be called on to do the job. Richard and I had already handed over our London home to our daughter, who was a Consultant at Northwick Park Hospital, and we were well set up to retire to Devon. Once again, how wrong I was.

On the first Monday after Palm Sunday, 1989, over 900 Fellows descended on the College to vote. Richard was a Visiting Professor in the States that week, but being a Fellow he flew back for the day to support me and vote. There were seven candidates and every vote was cast into a silver rose bowl. As was the practice, the name on each voting paper was read out verbatim to the assembled company and I did not get a single vote as the first 40 were read out. My first thought at this time was relief, although slightly ignominious, and my second was how badly I was letting down my sponsors and John Batten in particular. However, this turned out to be a quirk in the way the order of votes had been cast – they tended to cluster as friends sat together. At the end of the first round I was actually ahead but not by a sufficient margin to prevent a second round. Thus I and Sir Christopher Booth, who had distinguished himself at the Hammersmith Hospital and as Director of the MRC Clinical Research Centre at Northwick Park, went ahead to a second round. To my astonishment the Fellows elected me by a comfortable margin. I was particularly delighted that Sir Christopher agreed to take up the office of Harveian Librarian and that we were therefore able to serve the College together.

Richard and I retreated to the President's office wondering what we had taken on and our first thought was to ring up and apologise to our trusty lady gardener, Susanne Easterbrook, in Devon to say that our retirement plans were on hold for at least another three years.

The convention at the time was that one was expected to take up the reins immediately – to chair the celebratory dinner on the night of the election and start to work the following day. Tuesday, however, was my ward round and my patients took precedence. My wonderful junior staff decided we should celebrate with a bottle of champagne at coffee time! Richard was on the plane back to Arizona to complete his visiting professorship.

15. A lady President after 472 years: The Royal College of Physicians, 1989–92

The hard work of the College began the next day. The learning curve was very steep, especially because everyone else knew the working of the College so well and this made it difficult for them to understand how little I knew. I was expected to know everyone on all the committees but I did not. I was expected to make informed comments when I knew nothing of the background. Everyone was exceedingly kind and supportive and if anyone had reservations about being landed with their first lady President, they kept this feeling very well concealed. As medical practice has evolved, every President of the RCP since 1518 has had to meet the professional challenges of the time. This chapter summarises some of the major issues during my own term of office.

At the beginning I was supported by a wonderful Personal Assistant, Anne Cowell, who gave me invaluable advice and filled me in on many of the minutiae of the College. She was succeeded by Jenny Thom who had an amazing capacity for work, was superbly organised and able to handle everyone, from Ministers of State to the most junior secretary in the Department of Health, in a magical way. She was never fazed by critical diary clashes and had a filing system that took care of absolutely everything. I could not have managed without Anne and Jenny.

After a few months it became evident that it was simply not fair on my patients or my junior staff that I was constantly cancelling ward rounds and outpatients due to College business – so I had to resign from the Brompton. One of the saddest things in my entire career was that I could not say goodbye properly to so many of my patients with whose care I had been entrusted over the years and who still attended for their annual follow-up appointments; neither could I hand over their care and introduce them personally to my successor, who of course could not be appointed in time for this. Because of the sudden and entirely unexpected turn of events, Sister Haines, one of my most loyal ward sisters, came to the rescue and explained to every patient individually what had happened. Many them sent wonderful messages of congratulations and good wishes. I was so touched by their support and loyalty – and I still miss them greatly. I meet Sister Haines from time to time and we immediately do a 'virtual' ward round together to keep me updated.

In due course, I ensured that the College rules were changed so that future Presidents had time between their election and taking up their appointment to sort out their other commitments in a more satisfactory way.

I shall always be grateful to Professor Newman Taylor who, in spite of his own substantial commitments in the hospital, stepped in at such short notice and looked after my patients so well. I was delighted that Dr Ron DuBois (now Professor), who had undertaken the research for his Cambridge MD thesis with me and had also had further training on interstitial disease at the National Institutes of Health in the USA, was appointed as my successor. To ensure continuity of care for my patients, it was especially important to be able to hand on the complete, confidential clinical records of the patients who were now under his care, so that none would be forgotten. It was a special delight to see that ten years on, and in spite of all the local pressures, shared care is still possible and many return to the Brompton for their long-term follow-up. As I mentioned earlier (Chapter 10), continuity of care over long periods of time for those with chronic lung disease gives them the security that they really need, as well as the opportunity for us to learn. Naturally, we gave them the option to stop attending the Brompton but most resisted this, preferring the security of our ongoing shared care.

There was much to do at the College in addition to getting to know all the people. There were many unwritten rules about how things worked. In fact, I suspect that some of my colleagues positively enjoyed the art form of extemporisation. Mostly the College ran very smoothly. This was due to the commitment of a group of people who had given many years of loyal service. The departments, each headed by a Fellow of the College working in partnership with a senior administrator, had a considerable degree of autonomy. Although the President was responsible to Comitia for the work of the College, the Caduceus, the silver staff of office which had been in use since 1557 and was carried by the President on ceremonial occasions, was a constant reminder, as explained by Dr John Caius in the *Annals* at the time of its presentation, 'to rule the College with moderation and courtesy, unlike those of earlier days who ruled with a rod of iron'. The latter was certainly never needed.

Day-to-day work of the College

Many people are quite unclear about what the Royal College of Physicians, or indeed any of the other Royal Colleges, actually do. This seems to be a good opportunity to summarise some of the important aspects of its work and outline the duties of those who were in charge of the various sections during my time. Essentially the College, as an independent body, carries responsibility for promoting and maintaining the quality and standards of medical practice by consultant physicians in the care of patients. In practice it does this in a whole variety of ways. It is not a Trades Union and is not responsible for terms and conditions of service of doctors – these are the responsibilities of the British Medical Association (BMA).

The everyday work of the College includes responsibility, in an executive and advisory capacity, for many aspects of training of hospital junior staff, the examining of candidates in their competence to practise, and for maintaining the quality of appointments of consultant physicians throughout the UK. It also plays a major part in defining the quality of standards of medical practice. While it is independent of the Department of Health and the General Medical Council (GMC), it works very closely with both. For some aspects of training as well as standards of practice, the GMC is the statutory regulatory body. One of the major duties of the College is running the various postgraduate examinations and diplomas. The Membership Examination (MRCP(UK)) is run jointly with the two medical Royal Colleges in Scotland to ensure a uniform standard throughout the UK. It always ran very smoothly due to the remarkable dedication of a large number of medical and supportive staff. I was hugely impressed by the amount of time spent by the elected Censors not only on maintaining the quality of the exams but also on constantly trying to explore ways in which to improve them. Their work included frequent updating of the examination structure, the meticulous design of the questions and assessments to ensure that they were fair and unambiguous, the quality control of the examiners and of the conduct of the examinations to ensure equality amongst the candidates. As President, I personally attended a special session following each examination where all the marks of the borderline candidates were checked, reviewed and discussed. The MRCP(UK) examination is not only held in London and Scotland but now also in a number of overseas centres. This involves the examining Fellows and Censors travelling across the world to support their colleagues overseas. This is an important undertaking to consolidate uniformity of standards internationally and it contributes to globalised further medical education. There are few more enjoyable tasks than joining doctors from other countries and together trying to ensure the maintenance of a high standard of knowledge amongst the physicians of the future.

The Registrar's Office, which in my time had been run by the inimitable Dr David Pyke for the last 18 years, undertakes a wide range of duties, including the meticulous organisation of the election of Fellows from the qualified Members. Fellows (designated FRCP) hold the ultimate statutory responsibility through Comitia for the governance of the College and David did an enormous amount of background work and consultation on every potential Fellow to ensure that strong candidates were not overlooked. Later in my Presidency we changed the eligibility criteria and nomination methods to open up the Fellowship further, especially to younger consultants. The Registrar's Office also coordinates the representatives from the College who monitor and advise on individual consultant physician appointments throughout the country to ensure that appointments are made fairly, that the job descriptions are sensible and that the appointed candidate has had the appropriate training to work in an unsupervised capacity.

The Training Office, in my time under the leadership of Dr John Lister (the Linacre Fellow), supervised and inspected the posts for senior house officers undertaking general medical training. The junior doctors at the time were often working excessively long hours and their living conditions in the hospitals were often far from satisfactory. We had many robust dialogues with the individual hospitals concerned, sometimes threatening to withdraw College approval of the training posts unless improvements were made. I am afraid we were not always popular and the press coverage generated was sometimes tough, but it was crucial for the College to protect junior staff in training whenever this was needed. John also supervised the specialist higher medical training of senior registrars (now SpRs) through the Joint Committee on Higher Medical Training (JCHMT) set up and shared by the three Royal Medical Colleges of the United Kingdom (London, Edinburgh and Glasgow). This Committee had evolved from the Todd recommendations (1968) for a much more structured specialist training programme. It seemed sensible for the three Royal Colleges of Physicians of the United Kingdom to work together on a single scheme to ensure equality of standards. Teams of Fellows coordinated through the three Royal Colleges inspect and report on every post in the UK. While the formal business of JCHMT restricts its agenda to training programme matters, it also provides a point of communication between the three Presidents on many other matters, although of course today the Scottish Colleges now relate to an independent Scottish Department of Health. More recently, this collaborative thinking has led to the formation of the Federation of the Royal Colleges of Physicians to exchange strategic ideas where it is appropriate to do so.

The Overseas Office was headed by Sir John Badenoch (the Hans Sloane Fellow) and he did a very special job caring for overseas physicians in training. While these doctors were badly needed to fill clinical posts in the NHS, their training needs also had to be carefully monitored. Much attention was given to ensure that they were given equal opportunities alongside their UK trainees. Thus the College was able to contribute substantially both directly and indirectly to the quality of medicine in many parts of the world. This wider practical role of the College (as with all the other medical Royal Colleges) is often inadequately appreciated.

The Conference Office was headed by the Academic Registrar, Dr Carol Seymour (now Professor), who designed and coordinated a very large programme of conferences and lectures throughout the year to augment the College's teaching programme. These covered a very wide range of topics from systematic updating for generalists and specialists to more advanced topics exploring the cutting edge of medicine. Linked with these were major lectures given by individuals of national and international standing who shared with Fellows and Members their knowledge, enthusiasm and experience. It was the President's privilege to attend as many of these as possible and, for me, it was a first-class continuing medical education (CME) programme – it certainly more than covered the obligatory hours that CME requires!

The College's Academic Research Unit, under the direction of Dr Antony Hopkins, was developing in a particularly important way, because it coincided with the formation of the Department of Health (DH) Research and Development Unit. The College Unit focussed on development of methodology to evaluate many aspects of medical practice and the measurement of appropriate clinical outcomes. Thus it brought together in a very timely way the ideas derived from the College Audit Committee on measuring accountability in the profession and the new work supported by the DH Research and Development Unit exploring evidence-based medicine to improve the evaluation of clinical practice in the NHS. This collaboration between the DH and the College is just one example of how trusting partnerships really can work extremely productively.

Advice from specialist physicians throughout the country on many matters was obtained through the College's specialist committees, from the Regions through the Regional Advisory Committees and from various other *ad hoc* committees set up from time to time. One of the problems with the designated structure of the Royal Colleges was that, increasingly in modern medicine, specialist fields overlap the conventional remit of the established organisation of the individual Royal Colleges. To overcome this, a series of intercollegiate standing committees were set up, covering such fields as medical oncology (jointly between the Colleges of Physicians and Radiology), haematology (Physicians and Pathology) and infectious disease (Physicians and Pathology). It was very encouraging to find so many people willing to spend so much of their time to achieve this.

Issues on medical staffing of the NHS were becoming critical and a Manpower Office was set up to collect data from around the country. This has now grown into the Medical Workforce Unit that conducts extremely important national surveys collecting evidence on consultant and trainee numbers, their working patterns and views. The regular national censuses on manpower issues are collated by this department. In the 1960s, the College had set up an Information Technology Committee to explore the development of computerised information in relation to medicine. Serving on this were some very skilled and forward-thinking people but it was criticised for being a somewhat intellectual and erudite body. There was therefore a need to develop information technology in a more practical way to help the DH, which was at the time having considerable difficulty in its attempts to standardise patient information. We therefore restructured the IT Committee and gave it a new remit to develop standards for electronic patient records, working with the DH. The Committee has now become the Health Informatics Unit and has greatly expanded its work.

To ensure the widest possible dissemination of information and ideas, the deliberations of the College on many national issues were published in College reports under the editorship of Professor Robert Mahler supported by Diana Beaven. These well-prepared reports were circulated widely to inform not only the medical profession, but the NHS management, the DH, the media and the politicians more widely. Every College report was launched at a press conference so that we could meet personally representatives from the media and answer their usually searching questions. I was impressed how many senior journalists would make the time to attend. These conferences were certainly a good way to open the College to the press and to foster working relations with them.

The College library, of particular value to historical medical research, was headed by Sir Christopher Booth (Harveian Librarian) and supported by Geoffrey Davenport who was a mine of information. Together they contributed in a major way to the history of medicine. The College Ethics Committee, with non-medical and medical members, had been established over many years and was then and still is a very important College activity. One of my predecessors, Professor Douglas Black, had made a particularly important contribution, and he continued to mastermind its agendas.

Within the College were two largely autonomous Faculties that brought together consultants working in specific areas outside that of mainstream consultant physicians. The first was the Faculty of Public Health Medicine, established in1972 as an intercollegiate Faculty working jointly with the Royal Colleges of Physicians in Scotland. It was responsible for all its Fellows, their training programmes, examinations and standards. The second was the Faculty of Occupational Medicine, created in 1978, for doctors working in industry and other organisations. My predecessor, Bill Hoffenberg, had planned and completed all the foundation work for a new Faculty of Pharmaceutical Medicine, and I had the honour of launching this in 1989. This brought doctors working in the pharmaceutical industry and in academic units under the umbrella of the College, to the great benefit of both. Bill Hoffenberg had also investigated the idea of a Faculty of Medico-legal Medicine, to strengthen understanding between medicine and the law and to provide a homebase for doctors involved with all aspects of legal practice. This was an interesting idea and, although some very useful meetings and conferences were held, we felt in the end that there were not sufficient numbers to justify a viable separate Faculty. With the increasing importance of medico-legal aspects of medicine, it might be timely to reconsider how the College could do more to foster this area of medicine.

In 1990, a new joint intercollegiate Faculty of Accident and Emergency Medicine was proposed by the Royal College of Surgeons. The purpose of this was to bring together the many Fellows of various other Colleges under a single 'roof' to develop this increasingly important new specialty. While this made sense in one way, it potentially opened the door to every specialty to set up its own Faculty and such a fragmentation of the Colleges could greatly weaken the whole, just at a time when it was of the utmost importance for the Colleges to speak with a single voice. For these reasons, I personally felt that on balance it might not be a good development. However, other Colleges were very keen on the idea and our Council felt that it was better to join them.

As in the past, the College continued to undertake a number of overseas visits which served several useful purposes. First, they enabled the College to keep in touch with its 16,000 or so overseas Members and Fellows. Secondly, they enabled the College Officers to discuss medical matters with overseas 'sister' Colleges. Thirdly, it allowed discussions on how the Membership examination could be developed locally, which saved candidates a great deal of expense. Finally, because these visits were open to any Fellow and their spouse or partner who wished to join, they enhanced the corporate spirit of the College and were both informative and enjoyable. During my time there were formal College visits which included India, Hong Kong and China, and I also represented the College in many other countries including Australia, Canada, South Africa, Sri Lanka and Thailand.

This very brief summary, which is by no means comprehensive, gives no more than a flavour of the huge range of practical activities of the

College in the UK and overseas, which contribute in many different ways to maintaining the quality of medicine upon which the standards of care for patients depend. It illustrates the importance of the more routine work of the College which needs constant attention and the very large number of people who contributed their time and energy to make it work. All this needed to continue alongside the major innovations that the College had to develop, some of which are discussed below.

It was evident that as changes in the practice of medicine were occurring, so also the College had to change. Coincidental with my election as President in 1989 the Government at the time was developing its plans for an extremely radical reform of the NHS and this had some profound implications about how physicians cared for their patients. These reforms were needed because of the funding shortages in the NHS which had become extremely serious. The DH had not come up with an adequate plan to contain costs and the patients who used the service, as well as the professionals who were trying to look after them, were both becoming very restive. Because of the enormous scale of the NHS, the Government believed, not unreasonably, that if those in charge of the NHS had failed to resolve the problems, then the only alternative was to seek advice from economists, businessmen and others to develop an entirely new approach. Thus politicians became much more directly involved in the immediate management of the NHS and the role of the DH tended to diminish. The White Paper proposed a very radical reorganisation of the health service, some parts of which could undoubtedly improve services and others which had the potential to be very damaging (see also Chapter 20).

The Royal Colleges had a choice. Either they could continue to stand back and express their theoretical views on standards of practice or they could change their position radically and engage with the politicians to a much greater extent in the interests of the patients they served ('customers' or 'clients' as they were now to be called). The profession itself was understandably very ambivalent and considerable strategic agonising took place. The eventual view from all the Colleges was that, in the interest of their patients, it was right to engage much more closely with politicians than previously. This required a careful balancing act to ensure that as far as possible we focussed only on what we believed was needed for the benefit of patients, so that we could not be accused of acting in our own professional self-interest. Once this decision was accepted, there was a great deal for the Colleges to do, both internally and externally, to handle the new situation. The first and most difficult task was to try to ensure that the views of the College were heard and taken seriously. Unfortunately, many of the ostensible 'consultation' sessions were dominated by a Minister telling us what had been decided. It was also in some ways unfortunate that so many of these meetings included both the Colleges and the British Medical Association (BMA), where our views often became blurred with the perfectly legitimate, but quite distinctive trades union issues. Under these circumstances, one could not blame politicians for assuming that the Colleges were supporting the vested interests of doctors rather than their real concerns for medicine and patients.

Several other external issues were looming very large, including the whole question of the manpower crisis and the DH policy at the time to restrict the numbers of doctors entering specialist training. This was linked with how the College should respond to pressures from the DH regarding a number of EU regulations affecting manpower in the NHS. These required a sea change in attitude to which the Colleges and the profession, as an instinctively conservative body, was not at all accustomed. Nevertheless, they were problems that had to be tackled.

Several internal issues also loomed. These included the increasing determination of the paediatricians to separate from the physicians to set up their own College; the urgent need to improve coordinated working with the national specialists societies who were increasingly involved in matters of standards and quality in their own subject areas; the need for Fellows out in the Regions to identify more closely with the College; and the need to enhance the delegated governing role of College Council through its elected Councillors. All this required urgent major action and in order to make progress a fundamental restructuring of the College organisation was necessary.

External national problems

The first immediate problem was the manpower issue. In 1989, the College Manpower Committee was about to be disbanded because this was considered to be a political and trades union issue and therefore fell within the remit of the BMA rather than that of the Colleges. However, since manpower was crucial to clinical standards and needed long-term planning outside the personal interests of doctors, I believed that the College had a responsibility to play a critical role, not least in the collection of reliable data. By their own admission, the data held by the DH were woefully incomplete and this was adding to the confusion. The numbers of specialist trainees across the whole spectrum of medicine was determined by the DH on the advice of the Joint Planning Advisory Committee (JPAC) which included representatives from the DH, the BMA, the Junior Doctors Committee of the BMA, and the Royal Colleges. This Committee thus became a veritable battleground between those trying to restrict numbers of trainees and consultant posts on financial grounds, those doing the same to protect their own job opportunities and the Colleges trying to take a longer-term view based on the needs of patients. The BMA junior doctors wished the numbers in training to be reduced to equate trainee numbers to the current numbers of consultants and therefore reduce competition for posts; the Royal Colleges saw an immediate and long-term need for an increasing number of consultant posts if standards of medical care were to be maintained and improved, particularly in the light of the consultant-led hospital service being proposed by the Department of Health. This in turn demanded an increase in the numbers of trainees. However, the junior doctors, fearful that the DH would not increase the number of consultant posts, wanted to restrict the numbers of trainees still further to ensure that there was not a surplus of trainees for the definitive posts available. On this they were backed by their senior colleagues in the BMA. It was a pitiful experience where the grinding of axes obscured sensible debate. I was glad that by the end of my time JPAC was disbanded. I have to say that if more notice had been taken of the Royal Colleges' clear warnings at these meetings in the early 1990s, the catastrophic shortage of doctors now being experienced could have been prevented.

It was of course a question of horses and carts. Clearly, if trainee numbers were too restricted it would be impossible to argue for consultant expansion when there were no trainees to fill the posts, however justified the case, in the interests of quality of care for patients. On the other hand, so long as the DH failed to commit itself to a consultant expansion, one could not really blame the junior doctors for resisting expansion of trainee posts, if future consultant opportunities were not guaranteed. The DH had very inadequate manpower data and were fearful about the costs. The latter were not, of course, very substantial if considered in the context of the NHS costs as a whole. The case for increasing the numbers of trainees also had to take account of the anticipated reduction in junior doctors' hours soon to be dictated by EU regulations, the increasing number of women entering medicine requiring part-time training and career posts, an indication that there was already a trend for consultants to retire early, the unacceptable number of single-handed consultant specialists in many district general hospitals and the much lower numbers of specialists *per capita* of population compared to the rest of Europe, North America and Australasia. Put together, these were persuasive arguments.

In an attempt to resolve this major difference of view between the Colleges and the BMA, and to assist the DH, much more accurate data were needed. Our immediate need at the College of Physicians was not only to re-instate the Manpower Committee but to create a Manpower Unit with full-time staff to collect the national data on these various issues. In the meantime, restrictions in trainee numbers continued. Having completed the first call for national data and verified the facts, and with the continued reluctance of the BMA and DH to accept the need for adequate expansion (except in a very small number of sub-specialty areas), the next step was to persuade the Secretary of State to undertake an independent review. In 1991, the Right Honourable William Walgrave clearly understood the arguments put to him by myself and Sir Terence English (President of the Royal College of Surgeons) and he duly set up an independent manpower review under the Chairmanship of Professor Colin Campbell, Vice Chancellor of Nottingham University. In spite of the much improved manpower data, covering all the points referred to above, being submitted in a coordinated and uniform way by all the Royal Colleges through the Conference of the Royal Colleges, which demonstrated that there was already a serious shortfall of around 50% in every subspecialty which was likely to become worse, the Colleges' case for expansion was turned down. I am told that sadly a major reason for this was that the BMA continued to resist such change.

As the 'writing on the wall' on manpower shortages became more apparent, the Campbell Committee was recalled in 1995. By 1997, a 20% expansion in consultant numbers was recommended. This, of course, was too little too late. In 2000 the Government at last realised that there was indeed a very serious shortage of doctors and that numbers entering the profession should be increased by 50% (the figure the Colleges had advised 10 years earlier). It should not have taken over 10 years to reach a conclusion which was (on considerable if not perfect evidence) evident years before. There should be a better way than this of evaluating and implementing non-political issues of national importance in the NHS. In consequence, there is now a dramatic increase in medical student numbers without the time to ensure that the teachers or facilities are adequate and with unproven truncated graduate programmes and other attenuated courses. Time will tell whether too many short cuts have been taken. So long as gaps in knowledge and skills are identified, I am sure ways will be found to compensate. However, it would certainly have been better to modernise medical student programmes without such a pressure on numbers.

There is, however, a more serious and much more controversial issue. If one stands back and looks at the wonderful opportunities for improving the quality of sophisticated modern medical care, this is likely to require greater breadth and depth of knowledge, not less. The implication of this is that it is probable that more, not less, time will be needed if the quality of training for medical practice is to be improved. This view is, of course, in marked contrast to that held by those determined to reduce the length and scope of training on the grounds that modern specialisation no longer requires a breadth of knowledge or skills. It is encouraging to observe that many of the dedicated young doctors now entering the profession realise this and are willing to spend more time in training in order to practise the quality and breadth of medicine they feel they need to fulfil their professional role. Furthermore, patients themselves are increasingly aware of the lack of experienced specialists who have the refined knowledge and skill as well as the breadth of experience to care for them in a holistic way.

'Reforms' in the health service

Hot on the heels of the manpower question was the Government's White Paper of 1989, *Working for patients*, proposing perhaps the most radical reform of the NHS since its initiation in 1948. The background to this is summarised in Chapter 20.

The objective was to find a way of improving efficiency, and to reduce wastage and costs. The White Paper set out the processes to be used to achieve these ends. These were to be based on competitive market forces, later modified to an internal market where hospitals would compete with each other for resources; there would be a split between the local health authorities who would 'purchase' services from competing 'provider' hospitals; some hospitals would become independent Trusts, offering their own terms and conditions of service and pay scales to make themselves more competitive. Where patients needed to transfer for more specialist care, money to pay for this – as extra contractual referrals – would 'follow' them and be deducted from the local budget. Likewise, some GPs would become 'fundholding' practices and purchase the services they wanted from the hospitals. These GPs were therefore both 'purchasers' and 'providers', which was quite inconsistent with the principle of the purchaser/provider split propounded as one of the cornerstones of the reforms.

It was a grand scheme but it failed, amongst other things, to recognise the differences between urban populations with several hospitals (where competition might be applicable) and rural scattered populations where there was one hospital and no choice. It failed to reconcile the Government's desire for central regulation on targets and standards (including various issues such as nurses' pay) to ensure equality of service across all parts of the country – which was understandable and regarded as a very important political issue – with the proposal that some hospitals would have delegated independent powers and others not. It failed in particular to provide the money to follow patients – so patients tended to follow money and many local health authorities openly declared, as a matter of principle, their intention to reduce extra contractual referrals, thus restricting patients' choice. The two classes of GP caused considerable schism within the ranks, not least because many of the fundholding practices received major bonuses to attract them into the scheme.

The fact is that while the NHS needs to be run in a business-like way, it cannot be run simply as a business. This is so for a very simple reason. In business, 'unprofitable lines' can be discontinued, but in medicine patients (especially those with less common diseases or those who can be treated successfully with very expensive medication) cannot simply be discarded in this way.

The Colleges, acting together through the Academy of Royal Medical Colleges, and their Faculties adopted a positive approach and set out a number of suggestions. More particularly, they set out some serious questions which had not apparently been considered. They hoped that providing this professional contribution in a very constructive way before the reforms were implemented would help to ensure its success. It would also demonstrate in a positive way the College's commitment to working in partnership with government on this new venture. The questions included such things as how would the training programmes for doctors be handled in an internal market? How would clinical research, so vital to progress, be supported in an internal market? How would university-based clinical activities interface with a competitive NHS? How would the quality of care be monitored to ensure that money actually followed the patients as envisaged? If different pay scales were introduced in different hospitals, how would this equate with the principle of the need for equality of staffing standards across the country? Would the calculations on medical staffing numbers, as set out in the Government's document, *Achieving a balance,* be thrown into disarray, and how could this be prevented, if Trust hospitals gained much greater autonomy in the type and number of specialist doctors they employed? Would the autonomy of Trust hospitals allow them to 'cherry pick' the most cost-effective and profitable cases and leave the difficult and expensive ones for other hospitals to manage?

Recognising that these were difficult questions, the Colleges further suggested that there was a very strong case for a pilot study of the reforms in a single Region to iron out some of the problems before it was introduced nationwide. This approach was intended to be both constructive and helpful. Sadly, no reply to the questions was received and there was to be no pilot study. Furthermore, for whatever reason it was quite clear that the medical professions were to be excluded from any part of the design or detailed planning. Those masterminding the reforms seemed to have no intention of involving those working with patients at the 'coalface' who would have to implement them. The Colleges have been much criticised for not acting together, or doing more, to ensure 'patient-centred' professionalism (Ref 5, Chapter 19), but it is hard to see what more could have been done under the circumstances.

Many patients were also worried about how all of these changes might affect their care. In 1991, the College therefore gathered together representatives from all the larger charities involved in patient support, so that we could work together and add professional strength to their views. This group continued to meet at the College from time to time and has now been greatly extended by the current President, Carol Black, into a formal Patient Involvement Unit. Patients or their representatives now serve on many of the College committees.

However, every cloud has a silver lining. These major external upheavals concentrated our minds in the College on how we could get better information about what was happening and how we could better support our Fellows who were trying to care for their patients amidst the turmoil. The impact of this massive upheaval caused the College to reconsider how it could improve its relation with its Fellows and Members throughout the country and improve the organisation of its own affairs. We needed to involve many more people in strategic thinking; we needed to be able to collect better data more quickly; and we needed to get involved with the public in ways that we had not done before. Thus the stimulus of the 'reforms' acted as a catalyst for major changes in the ways the College worked and it was a privilege to be involved in the initiation of some of these.

Internal reforms

We realised that if College Council was to have greater influence on strategic issues then the detail had to be prepared in a better way and this required a radical reorganisation of the College structure.

As well as the reviews that were being undertaken by the departments within the College a number of other issues required attention. In particular, the whole process of election of Fellows was reformed and systematic reviews introduced to ensure that no-one was overlooked. We needed to do more about the long-standing complaint that the College in London was too remote from the Fellows in the Regions. My predecessors had done much to address this and we tried to do more. The scientific meetings in the Regions were extended and some of the eponymous College lectures took place at these. Briefing meetings for Fellows and Members to update them on College and national affairs and to get their views were systematically introduced at all Regional meetings. It was very informative and fun to get out and about, away from London, and it was a particular pleasure working with so many leading physicians throughout the

UK. Their loyalty, fair-mindedness, supportive ideas and indeed their long-suffering tolerance was invaluable and certainly made a very challenging, and often lonely, job possible. These meetings were also essential to obtain evidence on how changes taking place were affecting those working in different parts of the country. This empowered us to enter debates with Government based on facts obtained at first hand. My successors have done a huge amount more to regionalise the College activities as far as possible and in all sorts of ways, including setting up Regional Offices, electing many more College representatives at both regional and district hospital levels, improving communications, introducing more democratic election processes for some College Officers and a more rigorous selection and appointment process for others, and a far greater transparency in its work.

In spite of all these efforts over nearly two decades to make Fellows everywhere feel that it is their College, I believe some still feel that it is still too remote and it remains criticised for being too London-centred. However, I hope that most Fellows recognise that in addition to working with and for them, the College also has to have a strong central hub of leadership if it is to fulfil its external roles relating to government and other national and international bodies on major medical issues.

Many wider aspects of medicine also needed further development by the College, including the clinical evaluation of the effectiveness of treatments, the changing face of medical ethics with various medical advances (including for instance genetics and resuscitation), the whole question of communication and confidentiality in the electronic age, the impact of European Directives especially their effect on manpower, the impact of litigation on medical practice, and the ever-rising expectation of patients. It became apparent that the structure of the College was unsuitable to handle these many new problems and something quite radical had to be done.

After much consultation and debate, Council accepted an entirely new management structure for the College. The work of the departments as well as other College activities were to be collected together under the guidance of four Boards.

The *Education Board,* chaired by the Senior Censor and Vice President, included all aspects of the examinations, general and specialist training and the work of the Regional College representatives as well as the College conferences and the publications department.

The *Clinical Board,* chaired by the Second Vice President, included all matters concerning quality and standards of care of patients, audit of medical practice, the improved working of the specialist societies with the College specialist committees, the work of the Research Unit and the Manpower Unit, both of which involved evaluation of clinical standards.

The *Finance Board*, chaired by the President, provided accountability for those responsible for all aspects of the College's financial affairs. Amongst other things, it offered protection for the Treasurer who previously carried the entire burden with virtually no accountability other than to Comitia.

The *Paediatric Board*, chaired by the Paediatric Second Vice President of the College, and handled all matters concerning paediatrics. This was designed to give those concerned an opportunity to lead on how they wanted paediatrics to develop, so long as they wished to remain in the College (see also page 160).

All the Boards were accountable to the Council, referring reports as well as strategic and policy suggestions to it. The role of Council was strengthened and its elected members took on much more responsibility for College affairs. Comitia retained ultimate responsibility for major College strategy and key appointments but otherwise Council had practical delegated powers.

Each Board Chairman worked in close partnership with a senior College staff member, thus bringing the professional (medical) College Officer much closer to senior management. The membership of each Board was handled flexibly so that as far as possible the relevant people attended, and particularly included those from widely scattered parts of the country.

The departments of the College retained their delegated authority to get on with their own work but they were included in an overall structure so that major issues could be debated and refined before going to Council. In this sense there was accountability with a light touch. A quarterly meeting was introduced to bring together all the heads of departments, along with their managerial heads, to bring greater cohesion to the College.

Clearly this new structure needed refining over time and I was delighted that under Sir George Alberti's Presidency the principle of the Boards was retained and their roles developed.

Of course there were lighter moments. During my time, I received a dozen or so rather angry letters about this and that. It seemed that the best way to handle these was to telephone the author immediately. Being the gentlemen that they were (they were all men!) they usually apologised for some of the language – while dissent is very important, plain rudeness is seldom justified. Because the letters were taken seriously they were not thrown away. When my secretary, Jenny, asked what the file should be called I said, without much thought, 'The Young Mavericks'. About 18 months later it seemed interesting to get all these people together over luncheon to discuss the progress, if any, we had made on the various issues which had bothered them. Wonderful Jenny worked on a date and automatically headed the letter 'The Young Mavericks Luncheon'. There followed several good-humoured phone calls asking how young one had to be to earn the title '*Young* Maverick'. Everyone accepted, many important ideas were aired and I believe they remain my good friends.

Academic medicine

One of the major concerns of the clinical professors running professorial departments interfacing with the NHS was the effects of the increasingly prescriptive clinical training programmes set by the JCHMT, run by the three Royal Colleges of the UK, in order to maintain increasingly rigorous standards. These trainees were pursuing academic research often addressing important clinical problems. For this reason, they also needed to be competent and fully trained specialists if they were to hold honorary consultant status to allow them to care for patients in the hospital. They needed a training programme that was not unduly long but which gave them sufficient practical experience to care for patients who often had quite complex and difficult disease. Obviously undue prolongation of the training programme could compromise recruitment to academic medicine and clinical research, which in turn would erode the career structure from which future professors would be recruited. This in turn would also erode the strength of the vital aspects of teaching and research for those working at the cutting edge of medical advances. On the other hand, as training in clinical medicine was becoming more sophisticated, the clinical training of an academic physician could not afford to be in any sense second-rate. The dilemma was considerable and has not yet been entirely resolved. It certainly needs flexibility and this is becoming increasingly difficult with ever more prescriptive demands from the Specialist Training Authority, GMC and our European partners. It is splendid that these issues are now being taken up by the Academy of Medical Sciences.

Naturally, the academic professors were extremely concerned about the proposed NHS reforms, where consideration of their contribution and their role in the NHS was barely mentioned. As I have mentioned, our questions on these issues in the Colleges' response to the White Paper went unanswered. Clinical research, so closely linked with medical education, is vital if the NHS is to remain at the forefront of medicine by international standards. Successive governments need to be constantly reminded of this.

In spite of all its efforts, the College was unable to do enough to support and protect the interests of the academics and there was understandably considerable disquiet. Professor Lachmann (now Sir Peter), President of the Royal College of Pathologists, and I agonised over what could be done to help academic medicine more and discussed this at length. Out of these discussions arose the concept of what is the now flourishing Academy of Medical Sciences, of which I and many other Fellows of the Royal College of Physicians are proud to be Fellows. Its remarkably rapid development is entirely due to Peter's enormous commitment and organisational talent. This is another example of a cloud with a silver lining.

Paediatrics

Another major debate surrounded the question of whether the paediatricians should break away from the RCP and form their own independent College. There was a strong case for this because they had become a multidisciplinary group with paediatric specialists in many other Colleges. They also wished to join with community paediatricians where the Membership qualifying examination of the RCP was inappropriate. The debate had gone back over many years. A Paediatric Membership Examination had been developed by the College adapted to this special field of medicine. The British Paediatric Association (BPA) had worked very closely with the College but was becoming increasingly autonomous on all paediatric affairs. A suggested compromise to retain the best of both worlds was to develop a Faculty of Paediatrics where they could in effect be entirely autonomous but would have some financial protection from the College and additional heavyweight support when this was needed. This sadly was not accepted.

Naturally there was considerable difference of views, some seeing the advantages of staying within the College of Physicians and others wanting to set up their own College. While these debates were continuing and as an interim measure, we created a separate Paediatric Board under the Chairmanship of Professor Dame June Lloyd (now Baroness), Paediatric Second Vice President, who was also President of the BPA, to give paediatricians the greatest possible autonomy within our College.

After a protracted but amicable series of discussions extending over the time of my predecessor as well as mine, the BPA voted to go its own way. Their own College has flourished and I am pleased to say the relationship between the two remains very cordial and mutually supportive.

The specialist societies

Another major endeavour was to develop a much closer liaison with the specialist societies and associations, who were playing an increasing part in all aspects of quality and standards in their own specialties. They had developed very good databases on many things and their advice was increasingly sought directly by the DH. A quarterly standing committee was therefore convened in the College, attended by the presidents of all the national specialist associations relating to medicine, together with the chairmen of the College specialist committees. This created a very useful forum where the College could represent the views which affected more than one society (and often most of them) and the specialists found that their problems were often shared by others. More recently, my successors have continued to develop and strengthen relationships with the specialist societies but there is still more to be done.

These selected examples of new developments in the College, albeit very incomplete, are used to illustrate the very wide-ranging aspects of medicine in which the College has been increasingly involved and the number of colleagues participating in these undertakings. They illustrate the renewed efforts of the College to look outwards to help wherever it can to advise and share responsibility for improving the standards of those caring for patients. This commitment has not changed in more than 400 years.

There was much unfinished business and my successors have made a great deal more progress in many fields. Professor Sir Leslie Turnberg (now Lord Turnberg), Professor Sir George Alberti and Professor Dame Carol Black have all done so much to advance the professional quality of care of patients, as well as doing all they could to build a stronger partnership with those in charge of the NHS as a whole. Thanks to all they have done and are doing, I believe there are signs that we may now be entering an era where mutual interdependence and even trust are beginning to develop.

Conference of the Medical Royal Colleges and their Faculties

At the end of my first year, I was asked to be Chairman of Conference (now renamed the Academy of Medical Royal Colleges – not to be confused with the more recently formed Academy of Medical Sciences). This was an informal organisation in which all the 13 or so Presidents of the Royal Colleges and Faculties of the UK and Ireland came together to identify common ground so that they could speak with one professional voice. Subjects for discussion included such things as standards of care, manpower, European regulations, principles of training, and especially the radical reforms being proposed by the Government.

This body needed to develop a new way of coherent thinking and working if it was to have a greater impact on a Government which was rapidly taking over direct control of the more detailed working of the NHS.

In the past, Conference had been largely a forum for debate and information; collective action was rarely required. College Presidents usually reported back to their own Councils and made their own representations to the DH or Government as they believed suitable. Now there was an imperative need to agree in some detail about the strategy and tactics of working on collective submissions. Adaptation to this changing mode of operation was easier for some Colleges than others, but considerable progress was made. As already mentioned, we were able to put together an agreed response to the Government's White Paper, *Working for patients,* and to submit uniformly collected national and international data on manpower shortages in the NHS for the Campbell Committee. These examples illustrate what can be done as a collective body.

It was agreed that another way to strengthen Conference was to become more proactive. To this end, several subcommittees were established to develop collaborative ideas in various problem areas. These included information technology (which was not well developed within the NHS at that time), European collaboration (to focus on training programmes and EU regulations) and aspects of medical audit (considering the methodology of objective evaluation of better medical practice through improved measurement of outcomes etc).

It became ever more evident that there was a need for coordinated views between the Colleges on many of the major issues. It was equally clear that the views of those responsible for delivering a high-quality service to patients should be seen to be distinct from those who also represented doctors over trade union matters, such as conditions of service. However, making progress was not at all easy and in this the Colleges themselves have to take much of the blame. There were understandable tensions between the smaller and the larger Colleges and between those whose members were more directly responsible for the clinical treatment of patients and those providing the essential 'supportive' services. More importantly, because of the different ways in which the presidents of Colleges were elected, their authority *vis à vis* their Councils varied. In consequence it was difficult to get unanimous or even majority decisions until matters had been referred back and debated at some College Councils. The delays caused by this seriously impeded the practical functioning of the Conference.

In spite of these difficulties, Conference has made very considerable progress over the last ten years. It has changed its name to the Academy of Royal Colleges and established its headquarters in the Royal Society of Medicine buildings with a permanent full-time administrative staff. It has put together a number of important reports and is now asked to represent the Colleges on a number of important Government committees. If the Royal Colleges can demonstrate the integrity of their contribution by providing high-quality data and by working together through the Academy, it will be imperative for Government to become more responsive to their considered views.

However, there is still a great deal more to be done to fully establish the strength and influence of the Collegiate Academy as a recognised organisation which can lead in the collation of good data and wise unbiased counsel to help those trying to find solutions to extremely difficult problems. Indeed, never was a coordinated voice more needed than at the present time when a range of issues concerning training, specialisation, the role of non-medical practitioners and standards are being taken away from Colleges' authority, to be controlled directly by the DH or Government. Taken together, these potentially constitute some very serious threats to quality medicine and they are topics upon which the Colleges collectively must be absolutely clear.

16. The other side of the story: Chairman of the Royal Devon and Exeter Healthcare Trust Hospital

After three and a half years serving the College, there were a number of reasons for thinking it was time to hand on the Presidency. In particular, I believe on principle that leadership is teamwork and can be likened to a relay race where the next leg can be run faster by handing on the baton. There has to be a judgement on the time, in any organisation, when it is better to appoint a fresh leader. Let there be no mistake, the Fellows, the College and all its staff were wonderfully supportive. Making any headway with the central authorities to maintain the quality of care for patients through the period of NHS reforms had been a major challenge and, although we had made some good progress in trying to engage in a better balanced partnership, I felt that it was time for another leader to try to make greater progress. In addition, I was very aware that my life expectancy could well be compromised by the earlier cancer and Richard deserved a bigger share in what was left. Such decisions are always difficult and compromises have to be made. As it turned out, we seem to have had a very good deal! My successors in the College have all made significant progress and Richard and I are both over eighty years old.

We had bought a derelict but rather special Georgian house in a small village in the Exe valley where my aunt had lived. It was about six miles from Exeter, where we had been brought up. One of our principal intentions had been to try to find some small way in which we could contribute to the community where we were now to be resident. No sooner had we arrived than one of the local consultants suggested that they put forward my name as Chairman in the application they were making for their hospital to achieve Trust status. This suggestion was backed by the local MPs, especially Sir Peter Emery whom I knew well from the Asthma Research Council days. Although some of the powers-that-be had understandable reservations about doctors as chairmen of their newly created Trust hospitals, I was appointed by the Secretary of State, the Right Honourable Virginia Bottomley, whose support I have always appreciated.

To the great credit of our political leaders at the time, they gave the Chairman considerable freedom to nominate from a shortlist of about seven people those they felt would form a good team. The chairmen could add their own suggestions but the final decision was made by the Secretary of State. Unfortunately, it seems that more recently chairmen have far less influence on how to achieve a balanced board. Non-executive directors are being appointed with less consideration of the balance of particular skills required and much more to meet certain ideals such as equal opportunities, perceived involvement of the 'public', and other representational factors. While these considerations are of course important, they have to be reconciled with the considerable responsibilities of a Trust board. Like any other well-run organisation, specific expertise and experience are needed, individual members must blend as a team and they must be respected and trusted by the chief executive and other executive directors. Let us hope that appointments to boards of the new Foundation Hospitals will be made in a way to accommodate this double set of criteria.

I therefore spent August 1992 discussing the formation of the Board with the hospital management, staff and others. We discussed what they felt was needed and what individuals could contribute. I felt it was important for the Board to have a strong input from those with first-hand experience of business, finance, law, ethics and, above all, management of people combined with common sense, empathy, a sense of humour and also a capacity to work together. These considerations were also to be balanced against the strengths of the executives, including nursing, medicine, finance and management. We were extremely fortunate that excellent people who met all of these criteria were willing to help the local community they knew so well. Three of them had already been helping the hospital formulate its plans for Trust status and were already familiar with the local scene.

In due course the Secretary of State approved all but one of our recommendations and we were fortunate to have valuable input from Derek Lamb (banking), Bud Wendover (adviser to the then Ministry of Agriculture, Fisheries and Food (MAFF) with knowledge of local farmers and business management), Henry Ball (a background in industry and personnel management), Anne Mayes (university lecturer) and Rose Tranah (solicitor and a member of the hospital Ethics Committee). They were all dedicated above all else to the needs of patients, as well as applying their professional skills to improving the NHS. They were robust, confident and enthusiastic. We greatly appreciated the input from the local Community Council who represented the local people at regular joint meetings, where they expressed their views in very clear terms on patients' needs and on where the hospital could do better.

The executives were equally keen to make the new system work and I certainly enjoyed building the whole team to try to improve the local services for the local people. Among our executives we were fortunate to have Steve Astbury as Director of Finances. He knew the Health Authority Finance Department and staff well and this helped greatly in the smooth transition to the new purchaser/provider split. Sue Sutherland, as Director of Human Resources, also had a background in nursing and this contributed greatly to our understanding of how the Board should give high priority to what patients and hospital staff needed. Gail Greenfield, Director of Nursing, did a fine job trying to recruit nurses at a very difficult time. Tom Irvine and later Patrick Beasley, both surgeons, were our Medical Directors and did a particularly good job trying to bring together the professional and managerial viewpoints. Their attention to detail when factual reports on medical topics were needed was exceptional. The Chief Executive was Bob Bryant, and later Mark Taylor who had wide international experience and brought a broad background to what might otherwise have been a rather parochial rural hospital. It was indeed an impressive team to run the main acute hospital for an immediate local community of around 100,000 people, with wider coverage for certain problems for a population of around 250,000.

The Board was a great team and everyone pulled their weight, sharing the work of chairing various subcommittees including finance, audit, remuneration and a large number of appointments committees. The hospital staff were magnificent and were proud of their own departments, whether it was the post room, portering, laundry, catering or the telephone service – to mention just a few. Although they naturally complained sometimes, I got the impression they did so in the interest of *their* hospital. The nurses did a magnificent job in spite of severe shortages and were amazingly tolerant of the endless changes thrown at them. I wish we had had more time to hear their views, but it was difficult to find a time that we could get together in view of the huge pressure under which they worked. The senior medical staff were extremely supportive and they were great colleagues, but I was surprised to find that they were distinctly suspicious when I, together with the Chief Executive, offered to attend their medical staff meeting. We had not intended to intrude into their professional territory – the intention had been to give them an opportunity to share problems with us directly. The Chief Executive at the Brompton had always attended all the Medical Committee meetings and this had proved a good way of working in partnership – he was there to listen and answer questions and direct our thoughts but he had never lorded it over us. In Exeter it was evidently different. We settled for a compromise – to attend the first half hour of their meetings – and I hope this was useful. Clearly there were some bridges to be rebuilt here. Of course, we spent much of the time discussing the difficulties of the NHS reforms and the new managerial arrangements. The Trust Board had to carry responsibility for implementing these even though we understood that some aspects were often very unpopular. Once again, I was impressed by the great tolerance shown by the consultants, even if we got quite a lot of stick at times.

I was also surprised when I arranged a special informal meeting to find out how the junior doctors were feeling. As I discovered later, it was the BMA junior doctor representatives who took quite an aggressive approach, and the beginning of the meeting was distinctly frosty. They assumed that I was there to put some new pressure on them and complained that they should not be asked to attend a meeting at 5 pm even if it was the only time when the majority were likely to be free. Eventually their colleagues realised that I too was working after hours and that it was an entirely informal affair – to listen to them and learn how things could be improved, including such things as night-time meals, accommodation and out-of-hours professional support. We ended up having a good discussion with a number of positive suggestions and much good humour. The meeting served to remind me that however good one's own intentions may be, they may not necessarily be understood by others. I think they were expecting something more formal. In any organisation there is a place for informality as well as formality; getting the right balance is not always easy. I personally prefer informality whenever possible because it encourages freedom of communication and fosters trust.

I believe that my Trustees and I got our greatest reward from working inside the hospital with its special atmosphere and wonderful staff who really cared for their patients. I just wish we could have done more to lift morale during those years, which were really tough for all of us.

Frankly, I did not find the work of Chairman outside the hospital such fun. The purpose of the next few pages is to record some of the problems we faced at the time and to give a first-hand account of the sorts of challenges being tackled throughout the country at the time of the 1990 NHS reforms.

Of course there were tensions between what the District Health Authority (DHA) as the new 'purchasers' wanted from the 'reforms ' (or were told by others to put in place), and the Trust hospital providers. The DHA held the purse strings. The central concept was for them to define *what* quality of services they required, and for us, the provider, to specify with evidence *how* we intended to meet these efficiently. Of course there was some overlap in this structured separation of function. The DHA would, for example, indicate how many consultants they would pay for in a particular specification and thus intrude on provider function. One could not blame them because they simply did not have the money to do otherwise, but it was frustrating not to be able to persuade the local DHA to fund some of the necessary improvements to the service and then be blamed, sometimes very publicly, for a poor performance. The Board was often in a compromised position when it had to accept contracts which we knew would only provide a limited service. Naturally the hospital teams often found this very difficult to accept. On the other hand, the concept of separating the purchaser and provider function certainly gave more room for an open debate on quality and costs and had the potential for considerable improvement over the previous arrangements where the DHA controlled both funding and provision of the service.

The main purpose of the new purchaser/provider split was to stimulate competition between provider hospitals. This had relatively little impact in our rural area where we were for all intents and purposes the only acute hospital. After 1997 (some seven years later) the internal market was largely abandoned because, amongst other things, Ministers found it to be divisive and inefficient. Trust hospitals were then encouraged to collaborate or merge. It seems odd that the same Government that found the internal market 'divisive' now seems to be recycling competitive practices once more, through the creation of Foundation Hospitals and through NHS versus private tendering.

The purpose of reviewing the past is not to be reactionary, but to learn from previous experiences in order to develop new ideas and not repeat the same mistakes. The history of management of the NHS is strewn with reinventions of the wheel (see chapter 20). Now that the NHS has such a long experience of trying to do things in different ways it might be useful, whenever a 'new' proposal is made, to first ask 'Has this been tried before' (the answer is often 'Yes'), 'Why did it not work? and 'What in the new proposals will ensure success this time?' The money saved by the NHS if this simple logic was implemented would probably go a long way to help our current financial difficulties. More importantly, it would restore a great deal of confidence in those who have seen much of it all before and have been in the NHS for much longer than many of the enthusiastic strategists. The zest for change alone is not good enough; change for the better, backed by good evidence, is what we need. I believe this sort of change would be embraced enthusiastically by a very large number of people.

It was a particular privilege for me to see how the blueprints of the reforms – over which we had debated the safeguard of services for patients with government while at the Royal College of Physicians – compared with what was actually happening at the coalface.

In Exeter we were fortunate in moving into a brand new hospital. This was a happy consequence of a disgraceful piece of earlier building, where the previous hospital, built in the 1960s was declared unsafe due to mal-construction of the concrete structure – alias 'concrete cancer'. We also had the good fortune to have a considerable amount of land which allowed us to develop and streamline our services. The first project was to consider the future of the Princess Elizabeth Orthopaedic Hospital (PEOH) located on an adjacent site. The debate aroused great local loyalties because it was very popular with both the public and the staff. However, it did not meet a number of modern standards including special facilities for children and intensive care for the very sick; the building itself required radical upgrading and it was uneconomical to run. There was just enough space for it to be relocated in purpose-built accommodation on the main hospital campus, although this involved compromising the light in and the view from the existing Intensive Care Unit. Naturally, the local population and staff in both hospitals held strong views, but after months of consultation and revisions to the plans to preserve as far as possible its identity – with for example, its own front door, its own outpatients, physiotherapy, radiographic services and theatres – we achieved its integration on the main site and the intensive care staff (and patients) accepted the plans philosophically.

Some of the rooms in the new Princess Elizabeth Orthopaedic Centre are less spacious and we had great sympathy with those who cherished the old PEOH with its space, gardens and the corporate cameraderie associated with a small independent hospital. However, I understand that the staff have, by and large, settled into the new building quite well. They have been notably adaptable and gracious in recognising the advantages, while naturally missing the atmosphere of the old hospital. They are currently running a first-rate service. Its own flag on its pole flutters aloft.

Today there is considerable emphasis on giving more power to the local population in developing and running their hospitals, especially in the new Foundation Hospitals. I wonder whether local opinion would have prevented us from achieving this sensible relocation and modernisation programme of the PEOH today. If we had failed it would certainly have been to the detriment of quality of care, patient safety and cost effectiveness.

The next directive was to investigate the possibility of getting all the other outlying hospital facilities onto a single central site. Clearly, there were efficiency savings to be made here. We had a fairly large general and maternity hospital a mile away and a special small unit for children with physical and mental difficulties about two miles away. The feasibility review was to be independent but a chief adviser was to be appointed from the Department of Health. He quite openly volunteered that he was operating to central guidelines on a number of things, such as reducing bed numbers and the reconfiguration of certain services. In spite of our data on patient needs at the time, the report presented by the adviser naturally had a very strong flavour of the prevailing central policies. Most fortunately, and through no credit to the Board, the pressures of acute medical admissions throughout the country came to the surface just in time, and the Department of Health had to revise its ideas on radical reduction in the numbers of hospital beds in district general hospitals. The plans for the further reconfiguration of the hospital services were therefore shelved. Even if working on separate sites is less convenient for staff, at least we have been able to conserve the threatened bed numbers, which are evidently so badly needed today.

One of the major debates at regional level at the time centred on the 'downsizing' of district hospitals. This was propounded quite reasonably to encourage care of patients in the community, in order to reduce hospital costs. At much the same time Community hospitals (run by Community Trusts) were being closed (much to the displeasure of local communities) to improve efficiency, save costs and adapt to the serious shortage of nurses. Thus the idea was floated to set up a novel 'hospital at home' service where quite intensive nursing would be provided at home by social services (which did not have the funds) and by nurses (who were in very short supply). Much time was spent trying to devise theoretical plans to accommodate the 'downsizing' directive when evidently, under the prevailing circumstances, alternative accommodation for the patients, on a large scale, was not realistic. The crisis of the acute admissions to district hospitals and its effect on surgical waiting list targets prevented the downsizing plan from being implemented. Today, the very urgent need to prevent bed blocking in hospitals by patients who are not yet ready to go home, but do not need the special facilities of acute hospitals, remains an unresolved problem. Indeed, it is raising once again the question of re-opening the Community hospitals to provide intermediate care.

In spite of these major managerial pressures, the Board took a particular interest in the hospital environment for patients. The Director of Planning, Nigel Walshe, was and continues to be in charge of improving these. He obtained a substantial grant for art work in the hospital and commissioned several works, including a large and very fine tapestry and murals created by local artists. As a member of the national Art in Hospital organisation, the main corridors of the hospital have a range of attractive pictures; there are also ever-changing local exhibitions and a wonderful set of black and white photographs of the old apple orchards of Devon. The mini courtyards separating the various ward blocks have been planted with care, are well maintained and contain many agreeable sculptures and water features. It shows what can be done with limited funds but unlimited enthusiasm and ideas.

Although the duration of stay for patients is now quite short, many activities for patients are well supported. The hospital chaplain, David Walford, who has a professional background in music, in addition to supervising the traditional ecumenical and multi-faith chapel and counselling functions, works with Nigel Walshe (himself a talented violinist) and other local musicians to produce concerts and other relaxing events for the more mobile patients, relatives and staff. All of these non-medical activities are very important contributing factors to the creation of a caring community, employing about 4,000 staff in my time, where, by the nature of things, stress and anxiety abound. In my view, it is crucial for hospital Boards to give strong support to these activities.

The hospital was and is also much in advance of its time in developing its Patient Advisory Service. This is located by the entrance and offers a welcome to everyone entering the hospital. It is staffed by very experienced and dedicated people and works particularly closely with the medical and nursing teams. It also provides information for local GPs when they need it. A good advisory service requires personal communication as well as patient information. The distinction between the two is important. Impersonal information from the Internet or from pamphlets can be helpful but it can also be misleading. Well-informed personal contact with the right people is vital. All manner of personal touches have also been designed to facilitate patients getting appropriate information to augment that given by the professional teams. This is especially needed in today's service, where doctors are put under extreme time pressures and patient 'turnover' in the hospital is so rapid that communication has inevitably suffered. They have also initiated various additional services including a programme of exercises and support for those with osteoporosis, anti-smoking counselling, and healthy eating guidance to tackle obesity. Of the many medical people I have taken to see this service, none have seen a better one in the country. So far we have only been able to identify a very small number of others who are successfully running a similar form of comprehensive personal advisory service for patients and relatives.

I only wish I had been able to generate more interest in this exceptional model which should be available to all patients throughout the UK, particularly because it can be run at relatively low cost. It is an excellent example of how, in a practical way, difficulties of communication with patients can be overcome, and in the process it created something new and better than anything that preceded it. Moreover, it has generated the support and trust of everyone. Last year over 40,000 patients and relatives sought advice from this very personal service. At the time of writing, we have now developed some new ideas supported by the Rayne Foundation about how to spread this good practice more widely throughout the NHS. It is a practical way forward for today's NHS where giving patients choice and responding to individual needs are now priorities.

By and large, the medical and nursing staff worked well with management in the various medical divisions after the formation of the Trust, although I worried that too much time was spent in meetings and the unproductive creation of paperwork, both of which delayed the resolution of practical problems. The compromise between teamwork and consultation, on the one hand, and efficient use of professional time on the other, is a perennially difficult one.

Patient complaints is another area of increasing importance where we devised a new approach. On occasion, patients in desperation would write directly to the Chairman. This was an awkward problem. If I replied formally saying I had forwarded it on to the appropriate department, it would be regarded as passing the buck and simply exacerbate the patient's anger. If I sent a conciliatory personal response, they would assume that I agreed with their viewpoint which would be unfair to the staff who were being criticised. My tactic was to ring them up. Nothing was committed in writing; it assured them that I had received their letter and took it seriously; and it also allowed me to assess their attitude to the issue and give me some feel for whether they were justified in their complaint. Of course, the letters had to be forwarded for official investigation but I kept a personal record of these conversations and on review found that in around 85% of cases where I had been contacted directly, we should have been able to do better for the patient, particularly regarding more considerate communication. I got a strong impression that the patients appreciated this direct approach and this set a more balanced tone to any subsequent formal correspondence. Thus, informal direct and supportive communication from the Chairman was much more helpful than heavy-handed formal procedures involving much time and innumerable people, many of whom were only marginally involved. The latter simply creates antagonism and defensiveness which helps no-one. These more personal approaches do not of course invalidate the need for more formal procedures, which are obligatory in all hospitals *where these are appropriate.*

It was the duty of the Board to be alert to any doctor about whom we received an undue number of complaints or where there was reason to believe their performance was not adequate. We took this part of our work very seriously. I am pleased to say that the numbers of backsliders were extremely small and the huge majority pulled their weight far beyond the call of duty and formed a wonderful professional team. Where we found inadequacy, the reasons for this varied greatly. Sometimes retraining was needed but on other occasions it was a question of communication, attitudes or simply lack of commitment. All needed to be helped, but in very different ways.

Of course we had our share of worrying problems. Sometimes they were our fault and should not have occurred, and sometimes they were due to factors beyond our control. We were fortunate in running a local service needed by local people on a relatively small scale compared to many. Devonians are generous and trusting people and were very supportive of the hospital and the staff. Sometimes I think they may be too patient. It was certainly an honour to be involved in their care.

Being medically qualified, I made it my personal business to visit as many local general practices as I could, to see first hand what they wanted from the hospital and how we could do better. The majority were very supportive and at the same time robustly open in their criticisms. The feedback we received was invaluable and, I hope, helped to bring together primary and secondary care. We identified some evidence where the attitudes of hospital staff towards GPs were not as helpful as they should have been and some of the communications were certainly slow and poor. These visits were certainly very revealing in other ways. I was sad that a few GPs regarded me with considerable suspicion, assuming that I had come to them with some hidden government-generated agenda. This surprised me, but such were their suspicions about what the government wanted to impose on them, that they assumed that I was, in some way, their agent. Some asked directly whether I had come to force them to become fundholding practices, which many regarded with great suspicion. Actually, in my innocence it had never occurred to me. Indeed, I was worried about the divisive effects this was having on primary care. Others had an instinctive reservation about being 'spied on' by a female Professorial Dame from a specialist hospital in London. How important it is to understand how others perceive things. My father's dictum returned. Whether you like it or not 'always look at it from the other person point of view'. Most GPs, however, were enormously helpful and made many extremely reasonable suggestions about how to improve the service, many of which certainly needed a facelift. I enjoyed being among professional friends, talking about real medical things rather than political issues. I was enormously impressed by so much of the general practice I saw and the people of Devon are certainly very fortunate. I do, however, worry about the effects of the new GP contract on both the medical profession and the patients – but more of this in Chapter 20.

When I first arrived I tried to set up a 'Zip Club' – zipping up the seamless services between primary and secondary care. We had some preliminary meetings but this did not get very far because everyone was working extremely long hours and neither party really saw the need. However, I still believe very strongly in a seamless service between primary and secondary care to provide a continuum for patients. The current trend for GPs to be urged to take over what used to be done by consultants, and specialist nurses taking over what used to be done by GPs, in the new world of community care, may be practical in some specific areas, but if it promotes a culture of separation between community and hospital care, this will not be in the interest of patients.

Of particular interest to me was how district general hospitals would fare under the 'reforms' of the 1990s. As Chairman there was a good opportunity to experience how the theory and the practice of the new system really worked. I learnt a huge amount about what the pressures were from the other side of the 'coin'.

The Chairmen of all the hospital and community Trusts in the Region met regularly, supposedly to consider how they could implement the directives coming from the Region or the Central National Executive. Some of the Chairmen were Party members (Conservative at that time) and were therefore convinced, for better or for worse, by the current political solutions for the NHS. Others were non-political and were simply concerned with making a public contribution. The interaction was interesting especially when some of the contradictory directives (through NHS Executive Letters – ELs) from the centre were being debated. Many of the Chairmen believed that the promised independence for Trusts would give them authority as well as responsibility. It became increasingly apparent that while they indeed had responsibility (especially to balance the books) they had much less authority in terms of how this was to be achieved. The financial constraints on the local health authorities gave them very little room for manoeuvre and the central directives became excessive. In a single year, I counted more than 100 Executive Letters from the NHS Executive about what we were to achieve and how we were to do it. This raises fundamental questions about devolution on the one hand and central political control from Government on the other – another recurring topic in the history of the NHS. The problem is that there are very good arguments in favour of both policies. Centralisation facilitates equality of service throughout the country and devolution allows adaptation according to local circumstances.

We all met with the Secretary of State once a year ostensibly to discuss problems, but sadly these often became set pieces where trusted Chairmen were selected to sing the praises of the new NHS while the more controversial topics which needed to be aired were assiduously avoided. This was not necessarily the fault of the Secretary of State. It seemed that the politicians were desperate to hear that their reforms were working well and they relied on compliant Regions to boost their morale.

Of course, it was to the advantage of the Region to give a good impression as they too were under pressure to perform well. In fact, of course, it was the other way round. It was the people trying to work the system at the coalface who needed the morale boost and an open discussion about difficulties and a little clearing of the air at virtually no cost would have been a healthier approach. All that was needed was a little understanding of social psychology.

The Chairmen of the different district hospitals in the area were supposed, according to the 'rules', to be working in competition. In practice our populations were sufficiently scattered for this to be largely impractical. We did, however, feel that we could support the NHS more by working together and sharing problems. Since we were quite remote from the centre we simply got together. Thus the Chairman and Chief Executive of Taunton, Barnstaple, Exeter, Torbay, Plymouth and Treliske Hospital in Cornwall met regularly to exchange ideas. These meetings were enjoyable, sometimes reassuring, and certainly enabled us to share good ideas productively. However, in those early days they were frowned upon by the Region because we were not acting in the required competitive mode. We had formed in effect our own South West Peninsular network which long preceded the later central change in philosophy where Trusts were encouraged to network or even merge.

After a few years, the Regions, of which there were fourteen, were reorganised in an attempt to devolve power to the local DGHs, so that the South West, Hampshire and Wiltshire became a single very large Wessex Region; one of only eight in England and Wales. The headquarters was in Winchester over two hours drive away from Exeter and four hours from Cornwall; the meeting involved over 60 Chairmen with additional Regional managers. It is unbelievable that such a structure could be conceived as viable from any point of view and of course it was not. Within another few years this huge Region was disbanded (after a change in government) and replaced by the South West Peninsular Strategic Health Authority (SHA), one of 28 SHAs. While understanding that changes in government will inevitably result in a change in policies, the cost in terms of disorganisation, disruption, insecurity for staff and distrust, particularly at a time when finances in the clinical services were extremely hard pressed, did little to generate confidence. Constant reformulation of the superstructures of the NHS without much evidence of increased effectiveness has been the history of the service since 1948. We should have been able to learn something from all the experimental variations which have been tried – particularly how not to waste money on constant managerial reorganisation. I do wonder what the history of the primary healthcare trusts will be in ten years time. There are rumours that ideas on their reorganisation are already being floated. What is clear is that a substantial period of stability is needed where all those trying to help make the NHS work can build up trust and corporately work together.

It is all too easy to criticise. In order to be positive we quietly tried our own experiment. Clearly competition within an internal market had for many reasons simply not worked in many parts of the country. It seemed to our Trust sensible to explore our own alternative and we did this by a type of 'benchmarking'. We sought to collaborate with a hospital which we both agreed was comparable in geographic location, size of population, rural/urban mix, academic pretensions etc, to compare the success of our services and try to learn from each other why and how the other was able to do better. We selected Norwich. At first we invited the Chairman and his Chief Executive to meet ours. Sadly, at the time they were very engaged in funding and planning their new hospital and could not find time to progress this. Notwithstanding, we collected together teams of six consultants in key areas from each hospital to see if we could set up a service-by-service comparison. We met at a midpoint between the hospitals by courtesy of the Royal College of Physicians to save time. The approach looked promising but unfortunately it was near the end of my time as Chairman and it petered out. A more widespread attempt at benchmarking has been attempted, but a scheme where individual hospitals choose their own partners for comparability and then approach their problems not negatively as a threat to the less successful, but positively as a helping hand to solve problems in a practical way, seems to have many advantages. If neither can solve the problem then they should not be shamed through league tables and the like. This approach could be explored much further. It would have the great advantage of engaging both the professions and management as an example of a real partnership; its clinical value to patients is evident; and it is relatively inexpensive in both time and money.

During my chairmanship our Chief Executive, Mark Taylor, tried to construct a policy to develop the Royal Devon and Exeter as a 'supra' District Hospital to increase the status of the hospital and the scope of services to patients. His submission for the hospital to become a Cancer Centre was successful. A special purpose-built centre for research and care of patients with diabetes was already thriving, and he tried to strengthen the links between the hospital and Exeter University in a variety of other ways. While these were rudimentary at the time, these beginnings bore fruit later when Professor John Tooke achieved his inspirational plans for the Peninsula Medical School, which received its first students in 2002.

My time as Chairman certainly allowed me to see how the changes in the health service at a local level really worked and gave me ideas on how things might be done differently. If these sound unduly hard-hitting in places this is not the intention. The object is to focus on difficulties openly to find better solutions. I hope it may cause pause for thought so that we can learn from some of the well-intended solutions to the very difficult problems of the health service. One of the major lessons I learnt was that while pushing ahead with change and improvement in one area, one ignores the knock-on effects in others at one's peril. The interdependence of services must be addressed and resolved satisfactorily *at the same time* – they cannot be patched up later. Just as on a world scale, political change may work with brilliant success *quae* politics but it will fail unless economic and social strategies are equally effective. As we see from repeated examples, success will only be achieved where the whole package of change is both satisfactory and workable.

By 1995, the non-executives and I as Chairman had all served for our first appointed term of three years and the Government was clearly looking for some new replacements of non-executives. In their understandable efforts to do this, there had been some unhappy experiences where valued, hard-working Trustees had, without warning, suddenly found themselves at the very last minute arbitrarily not reappointed. Although unintended, this had the effect of implying a lack of confidence in individuals, which was unkind to them and very demoralising for the Board and the hospital. To prevent this happening to us, we needed to develop our own forward plan. It was clearly very unlikely they would reappoint us all. As I was the oldest and the others were contributing so much and keen to continue, it seemed sensible for me to volunteer to retire, leaving a vacancy for a new Trustee. At the same time I sought and obtained re-appointments for all the others for varying periods of time, so that an orderly sequence of retirements could be established.

Top: The Royal College of Physicians, designed by the architect Denys Lasdun.
Bottom: Five Presidents: with Leslie Turnberg, Cyril Clarke, Douglas Black and
Bill Hoffenberg, 1995 *(left to right).*

Top: Portrait by Jeff Stultiens.
Bottom: Helping the Secretary of State, the Right Honourable Frank Dobson, to understand the NHS, 2002.

With College Officers, Censors and colleagues, 1991. *Front row:* Unidentified, Alan Read, John Stokes, Bob Cohen, David Pyke, Leslie Turnberg, M, Alec Cooke. *Second row:* Grant Lee, Peter Richards, David London, Sheila Sherlock, Richard Turner-Warwick, Oliver Garrod, Douglas Black, Bill Hoffenberg, June Lloyd, Unidentified, Ian Murray-Lyon, John Nabarro, John Richmond. *Third row:* Antony Hopkins, Peter Toghill, John Dickinson, Chris Booth, Tom Oppe, Bernard Lloyd, Maurice Lessof, Norman Jones, Robert Mahler, Harold Lambert, John Lister, John Batten, Carol Seymour. *Back row:* Sarah Thewlis, John Grimley-Evans, Michael Besser, Roger Williams, George Smart, Tony Dawson.

Top: With other Honorary Fellows at the Royal College of Physicians and Surgeons of Glasgow. *Back row (left to right):* Robert Kilpatrick, Terence English, John Richmond, Stephen Doyle, William Hederman. *Front row:* Geoffrey Chisholm, Bob Hume and M.

Bottom: Jenny Thom, my PA at the College, with her husband, Robert.

Family support at the College. *Top:* Five grandchildren (Hannah, Helen, Nathaniel, Michael and Tabitha) singing the Calypso Carol accompanied by Lynne, at the College Christmas Service. *Bottom:* The family in the President's flat. *Back row (left to right):* Gillian, Bea, 'Mr Bill', Richard, Lynne, Chris Chapple; *middle row:* Edna Denard (Richard's secretary), M, Tabitha, Thelma Rondel (Richard and my first secretary); *front row:* Nathaniel, Helen, Hannah.

Top: a working holiday at Studland, helped by a butterfly *(bottom left)*.
Bottom: with College staff at my farewell party, 1992.

Top: Honorary DSc (1992), Oxford; with *(left to right)* Richard, Celia Westropp (my tutor at Lady Margaret Hall) and her husband, Francis Price (Worcester College).
Bottom: Three Oxford Doctorates of Medicine: M (1956), Lynne (1989) and Richard (1957).

Top: With members of the Trust Board and staff *(left to right):* Michael Williams, Henry Ball, Sue Sutherland, Anne Mayes, Mark Taylor and Murray French, past Chairman of the District Health Authority.

Bottom: The Royal Devon and Exeter Healthcare Trust Hospital.

Part 5

RETIREMENT

17. 'Don't retire, it's a job for a younger person'

As Dr Alec Cooke, the wonderful physician who taught us as students at Oxford, said to me when he was over 90, 'Margaret, don't retire, it is very hard work. Retirement is for a younger person.' The learning curve for retirement continues to be very steep and there are several reasons for this. The greatest difficulty is that all infrastructure support is suddenly lost. For the first time, I really understand the burden I created for my team of long-suffering secretaries. The post box remains undiminished and piles up relentlessly, the letters have to be processed in all their complexity as well as written – which is by far the easiest bit. The e-mails, which are supposed to solve problems, while a joy for family communication and where quick answers are required, become outrageous with spam and inappropriate attachments which jam up the works and make me bad tempered because they use up time, paper and cartridge ink, when a simple postage stamp with a hard copy would have been so much more efficient and allowed me to read them comfortably in an armchair or in bed. The computer did not think of that! The battle of the computer continues to challenge with all its unpredictable quirks and at the same time it drains one's remaining intellectual resources with a mesmerising fascination. Fortunately, our daughters and grandchildren have infinite patience and are able and willing to come to the rescue, answering the most absurdly simple questions. But worst of all is the filing. The harder one tries to be disciplined the more things get lost. Altogether living becomes a whole time job and proves that the concept of retirement with the vision of those luxurious languid days reading a good book and other gentle leisure pursuits is in fact a complete myth.

During our working years, escaping to the country occasionally was a relaxing joy because all but selected papers could be left behind. However, when living in that idyllic retreat all the time, the daily pressures mount up as before. In consequence, holidays from retirement are as essential as they were before.

This is only the beginning of the make-believe story of retirement. While formal links with medicine are ended, not a week goes by without

189

someone phoning about some fascinating problem where medical networking in various guises can still be helpful. This keeps us both up to date with how the health service is working out, both in the community and in hospitals. Richard and I are both kept busy and I am afraid our colleagues are constantly bothered about even more patients needing their help. They too are very tolerant.

The other aspect of the steep learning curve of retirement is that one is constantly asked to become involved in things completely outside one's own competence but often having wider connotations for medicine. They are all quite fascinating and fun.

Sir Richard Southwood, jointly with John Gummer, then the Secretary of State for the Environment, had set up the Round Table on Sustainable Development and asked me to join. This was intended to draw together people with varying interests, including those from industry, as consumers of energy and raw materials but who also create economic growth and therefore increase world prosperity, those from various 'Green' groups concerned with conservation and the exhaustion of non-renewable resources, and a leavening of those concerned with social and equality issues, as well as, for some reason, one bishop (now Bishop of Exeter), and myself as a medical person. The discussions were wide ranging and fascinating. It was also a model for how an independent group can bring together potentially very divergent views into a constructive synthesis, as well as how such groups can work in close harness with government when there is integrity and goodwill on both sides. Working through subgroups, the Committee was extremely productive and published many reports on a wide range of subjects including the development of brown field sites, integrated transport, energy planning and many others. I was asked to chair a working subgroup on indicators or models of measurement in the evaluation of sustainable success. It was supposed that I had a scientific approach and experience of such things. It was remarkable how even some of the younger members of the group had difficulty with the concepts of objectivity and quantitative analysis. It seems to me that the diminishing interest in science in our schools may be contributing to the failure to teach the fundamentals of an analytical and objective approach to problems for all children, even those who are not going to pursue scientific careers.

Another committee of immense interest was the Nuffield Bioethics Council, of which I was fortunate enough to be a founder member. This was chaired by Sir Patrick Nairne and later by Dame Onora O'Neill from Newnham College, Cambridge, and later by Sir Ian Kennedy. The group was multidisciplinary and included theologians, geneticists and other scientists, philosophers, teachers, doctors and people from the media.

They tackled a number of topics of current interest to the public including screening for genetic defects, the ethics of clinical trials of medication in developing countries, the genetics of mental health, genetic modification of crops and much more. It did not attempt to decide what was right and what was wrong. Rather, it tried to set out the issues without prejudice and in a language which could be understood by non-experts, so that the debate could be taken forward on a firmer basis of better information. It attempted to engage the public with good quality and understandable information. The way it undertook its deliberations was a lesson in itself and the synthesising ability of remarkably talented support staff, making sense out of some very diffuse discussions, was marvellous. Again it showed how much can be done to produce valuable documents on very controversial topics in a very constructive and lucid way to help understanding by the public.

For some slightly mysterious reason, following my time as chairman of the local hospital, I was asked to serve on the National Employers Liaison Committee, now the National Employers Advisory Board (NEAB) to facilitate employer support for the reservists in the armed forces. This was especially interesting because the regular armed forces have been substantially reduced and the service from reservists has become of crucial importance as crises arise. This strategy can only work if employers are supportive and their organisations can survive when potentially key staff are suddenly called up. The success of this national strategy has been tested in the recent conflict in Iraq. Few problems were experienced in the combatant stage but the jury is still out on whether it caters adequately for the longer-term peacekeeping and reconstruction work. Many employers believe that defending the homeland is one thing but that they should not be asked to subsidise non-combatant activities which the government chooses to support. If this view amongst employers becomes widespread, some fundamental rethinking about how the armed forces are maintained and financed will be needed. Moreover, this will have to be done quite quickly if the turmoil in the world continues. It has given me insight into how another important public service conducts its affairs and it has been of great interest working with an entirely different government ministry (the Ministry of Defence) and representatives of industry and business. It was a special privilege to see the medical teams of British forces as part of the peacekeeping force in Kosovo and the way they helped in practical ways to re-establish the main hospital in Pristina in its care of the civilian population as well as the military personnel. It also taught me how to have a very effective shower using a plastic bag of water heated out in the sun during the day, with a drip-feed tubing fitted with a small plastic spray nozzle, hung on the branch of a suitably secluded tree.

As a member of the Advisory Board of Lady Margaret Hall and Green College Oxford, it has been fascinating to learn about the changing scene at Oxford and the medical schools over the last 50 years. It has also given me the chance to throw in ideas and stir the pot a little – the most recent being the suggestion to set up, perhaps in collaboration with a business school, an MSc in 'Understanding Medicine for Managers' to complement the well established courses on 'Management for Doctors'. I believe this could help greatly to bring together the medical profession and managers in the care of patients (see Chapter 20).

Of all the honours I have had the good fortune to receive, one of the greatest privileges was to become an Honorary Bencher of the Middle Temple, through the generosity of Leo Price QC, thus taking me back to the earliest days of my childhood when we lived in the Temple and the legal company with which even as a child I was so very much at home. Their social occasions continue to be great fun and are exceedingly stimulating. Minding other people's business is always a joy. I continue to remind them that when the powers that be tire of regulating teachers and doctors they will turn their attention to lawyers and clergymen.

I also have the great privilege of continuing to work as a Trustee for the Rayne Foundation to help assess the priorities in their support of medical projects. This Trust has over the years given immense support not only to medicine but also to education, the creative arts, social welfare and many other much needed areas, especially those where financial support is very difficult to find. An added bonus to this work is the opportunity to visit the people doing this splendid work.

Likewise, as a Trustee of St Luke's Foundation, it is remarkable how the criteria for assessing applications from clergymen seeking bursaries to help their ministry are in so many ways similar to the assessment of need for bursaries in medical fields. The work of the Trust also covers some of the University Chaplaincy and takes in the whole question of pastoral and spiritual care for the students at Exeter University. This is another area which needs much more thought because it embraces the growing numbers of students of multiple faiths and those with no faith at all, at a time when their need for pastoral and spiritual care is as great as ever.

In Devon, Richard and I have both tried to help the Devon Community Housing Society in their splendid efforts to provide accommodation for the elderly and the disabled. This has given us insight into a rather different aspect of social deprivation and the challenges it presents, as well as some of the problems independent bodies have interfacing with government-controlled regulators. The scenario here, of delegated responsibility with considerable retained central authority, rings a familiar note.

In the village where we live we managed to set up a charity to obtain land and create a five-acre Millennium Green in perpetuity for the villagers of Thorverton for their open air leisure pursuits. We were rather pleased that our village became one of two hundred and fifty such schemes in all England and Wales. Thanks to much local effort we were able to get support from the Lottery through the Countryside Agency, the Landfill Tax Credit Scheme and a number of other national and local charities. The scheme is run by a small team of local villagers and this experience too has been entirely new.

For the rest, there is still time to play the violin badly and have huge enjoyment and learn a lot when I play chamber music with my most tolerant and talented daughter and grandchildren, all of whom play a clutch of instruments and still enjoy playing together. There is still a little time for watercolour painting which is undertaken largely for therapeutic reasons but gives me the chance to learn from my artist daughter. In between, Richard and I struggle with a garden which is too large, but compensated for by the glory of eating and preserving our own vegetables and fruit, raising cuttings and generally pottering around, keeping us fit. The balmy weather of the south west is, of course, ideal.

At the end of the day and what matters most of all, is looking back at the true partnership with so many patients with whom it has been such a privilege to work and the memories of so many wonderful colleagues. Medicine for us has been an unbelievable life and, as I have said before, in the long run gender never got in the way. Many major and dangerous issues will continue to raise their ugly heads and will have to be tackled fearlessly by the profession, but that is part of life. For the rest, but of equal importance, is our family and all the exciting things that continue to go on in the lives of Gillian and Lynne, their husbands and our six splendid grandchildren. Most special of all is the fifty-five years of glorious life with Richard with his constant support, friendship and love. What more need I say?

Top left: Painting by the River Test. *Top right:* A windsurfing granny.
Bottom: 'Reflections', watercolour of the River Culm.

Top: Playing chamber music with Lynne and the grandchildren (Michael, Hannah, Bea and Tabitha).
Bottom: Gillian and Lynne playing duets aged six and eight (in inset photograph) and still playing 42 years later.

At the Palace in 1992 with Gillian and Lynne celebrating Richard's CBE, with my DBE (1990).

In Devon with Honey, 2002.

Reflections

An Unrepentant Apologia

It is now necessary to 'change gear' and take a much broader look at medicine – patients, doctors, healthcare systems and the interface between these and academic medicine.

Some may think that these topics are quite outside and beyond the scope of any individual's memoirs. I hope to show that this is not the case. I believe they are essential aspects of this record, which would be incomplete without them.

As I was writing I realised that this personal story made little sense without tackling the more fundamental issues which impinged on and moulded the progress of events I was describing – and which were moreover of critical importance to my life (and indeed to most doctors' lives). What do patients really want when they are sick? How do doctors meet these needs and at the same time work within a healthcare system determined by others? What is the definition of a professional person and how does this differ from an artisan (artificer) or tradesman? Are professional doctors still needed in medicine? Where has the NHS succeeded, where is it still failing, and what might be done in practical terms to improve its shortcomings? Lastly, and in particular, how far should academic resources and their crucial links with tertiary care medicine be harnessed to push forward the frontiers of medicine and clinical standards for the benefit of patients and enable British medicine and its doctors to maintain their place on a world stage?

A further justification for including a discussion of these fundamental topics is to add a personal and *physician's* perspective to complement those propounded by others such as policymakers, strategists, economists, politicians and planners. In order to understand and explain the issues and gather evidence, it also became essential to set as a backcloth some of the key changes in the NHS and universities which have taken place over the time I have been in medicine.

The real importance of this section is to explore ideas about a better way forward so that, whatever healthcare systems are developed, patients can get the treatment and holistic support they need, medical research can flourish to address the huge number of unanswered questions, and teaching and clinical standards can assume their rightful importance in every part of the health service. Only then can doctors make their contribution through committed service to patients and 'living medicine'. In doing this, they reap their own reward.

Having completed this manuscript, I read Professor Tallis's remarkable recent book, *Hippocratic oaths* (2004), which explores many of the same problems and provides more extensive references for those properly demanding more evidence.

Reference
Tallis R. *Hippocratic oaths: medicine and its discontents.* London: Atlantic Books, 2004.

Part 6

THE SPECTRUM OF HEALTHCARE: WHO SHOULD DO WHAT?

18. The heart of the matter:
What do patients want?

The NHS is, or should be, about meeting the needs of patients and providing the quality of care which reasonably satisfies their demands. As medical advances provide more opportunities, so these demands are bound to increase.

If, as Professor Chris Ham has suggested (see Chapter 20), a gulf has developed between 'policy intent' and 'delivery of care' at the frontline, we need to consider in more depth what that delivery of care to patients actually requires in practical terms. The following is essentially based on what I have learned from patients over the last 50 years and what they have said in a number of recent surveys[1,2] – remembering always that individual patients have their own individual preferences about what they want. This most important subject is not one that can easily be validated in control trials, neither is it readily available in reading material for managers or medical students.

What do patients really want?

What patients want from doctors on the one hand and from the NHS on the other must be separated, because trust in doctors and trust in the NHS depend on very different factors. A distinction also has to be made between what patients want and what the healthy public believe they would want if they became ill. For example, their views on priorities of expenditure on the NHS may be different from patients who naturally have an overriding interest in the availability of treatment for their own particular condition. Further, because the healthy public may have little direct experience of the NHS, they are particularly influenced by the press and other media, as well as various government statements. These impressions, for better and for worse, may be very different from patients' individual experiences.

Various important bodies, including the Patients' Association and the now disbanded Health Community Councils, have made major contributions towards promoting what patients want from both doctors and the NHS. The continuing roles of such independent organisations are vital.

Much of what is summarised here is not new, and indeed much has been well summarised in a recent Standing Advisory Committee report (2001) from the Department of Health.[3] However, in practice, much of what patients want is insufficiently appreciated and is in consequence contributing to lack of trust.

What patients want from doctors in a modern patient/doctor partnership

What patients actually want is a competent doctor who they can trust and who understands their individual problem. They also need someone to advise and support them regarding diagnosis, treatment and management of their condition. The essence of this is their expectation of a real patient/doctor partnership based on trust, understanding, empathy and mutual respect as well as knowledge and skill – in other words quality professional support. This partnership is something very personal, it involves a holistic approach, a commitment to continuity of care for people and, above all, time. With all the hurly-burly of day-to-day life, let us never forget these additional elements, especially the need for time.

Patients want reassurance and a clear idea of what is wrong; even an apparently trivial illness is very important to them and they hope that it is not serious. They now have access to much more knowledge, through the Internet, helplines, pamphlets and other sources, and it is often this confusing surfeit of information which leads to an even greater demand for personal guidance and advice to help them through this maze. They certainly expect doctors to explain things to them (as far as they are able) much more fully than in the past. If they need investigations, they wish them to be as painless as possible, and they want treatments which are safe and have no more than minimal side effects. They certainly want to know what risks are involved. Unfortunately, medicine is not sufficiently advanced to provide all of this and, in consequence, there is an increased obligation for doctors to understand and to explain carefully where these ideals cannot yet be met. Such openness promotes rather than diminishes trust. Patients also want to know whether they have a short- or long-term problem, whether it can it be cured or controlled, and whether bothersome symptoms can be relieved.

The importance of integrative skills in medical practice

A primary role in clinical medicine, of both GPs in the community and hospital-based consultants, is to use their training, knowledge and experience in an *integrative* mode to help sick people. First, by using their skills to arrive at a provisional understanding of what is wrong with the patient. Second, to obtain appropriate supportive evidence through selective investigations to refine their understanding. The situation, including the risks and uncertainties, then needs to be explained to the patient in terms that they can understand, and a mutually acceptable treatment plan devised. It is important to recognise that, on the basis of the same statistical evidence on the results of treatment, a particular risk to one patient may for them be unacceptably high, but for another may be regarded as acceptably low. For example, one patient finds the advantages of corticosteroids in the treatment of asthma outweigh the disadvantages of its side effects, while another finds the latter unacceptable. Indeed, if they have certain coincidental diseases, the risk may be dangerously high. Both the patient and the doctor need an agreed follow-up plan to make sure that the problem has been resolved. If it has not, then the doctor, be they GP or consultant, may need to take the next sequential step in diagnosis or treatment or have the humility to ask the question 'Is there someone else who knows more than I do and who can give the patient more help?' In short, humility and second opinions are vital in good quality medical care, if real trust is to flourish. However, so far, the regulations covering patient choice do not include opportunities for second opinions even when a patient, for justifiable reasons, wants it.

Communication

The full subtlety of appropriate communication with patients thus becomes a central issue and extends beyond any amount of formal student training on the subject. To build trust, doctors must not only be able to listen but be able to convince patients that they have understood and appreciated the individual's needs and viewpoint. If and when there are uncertainties, most patients like to know. They do not like feeling that they are being kept in the dark but, at the same time, how much a patient wants to know about serious illness varies considerably and good doctors are sensitive to this. Given time and experience, it is not difficult to understand how much a patient really wants to know at a given time and when there are aspects they are not yet ready to face. For example, a patient may ask a doctor directly whether they have cancer, when they are really only wanting to be reassured that the answer is 'no'. If the answer is otherwise, overt lying is rarely acceptable; there are many ways of working with patients to help them towards fuller understanding, at their own pace. Occasionally a patient's relatives can be adamant that the patient should not be told the truth even when they – the patient – actually wants to know. The well-meaning endeavour to 'live a lie' can be a very sad conclusion to a loving life. While the priority of the doctor/patient relationship is crucial, the well-intended wishes of relatives must also be taken seriously and resolved if possible.

Doctors must have the skills and knowledge to provide up-to-date information in a clear and appropriate form. Practical and simple devices often help. For example, as explained in Chapter 10, a simple hand-drawn diagram often adds clarity to words when explaining a problem or the action of medications. I believe this type of visual aid is not used enough. It seems that some people, wishing to promote increased patient-power in decision making (which is a welcomed advance), sometimes give the impression that this is a necessary challenge to doctors who, they assume, have the power to dictate treatments without their patients' agreement. Doctors have never been and are not in such a position, except under specific well-defined legally directed circumstances. The fundamental fact remains that doctors cannot force patients to be treated; they can only advise and explain. When a patient declines the advice they are given, they usually still want to know that they will be cared for. This is where real professional skills and trust are most needed. There are, of course, limits to how far a patient can pursue their own course and at the same time take up a hard-pressed doctor's time when his advice is rejected. However, with professional patience, rather than the adoption of an authoritarian attitude, the confidence of patients can often be won and a sensible compromise reached.

Trust based upon personal integrity

The fulfilment of professional responsibilities in society cannot be determined by regulation alone, but also requires trust.[4] To be trusted, doctors clearly need to be trained and certified as competent (and registered by the General Medical Council (GMC)) to take responsibility for extremely important medical decisions, including those on life and death. Whenever possible, action on such decisions is taken with agreement by the patient or their relatives, but there are of course occasions where this is simply not practical and the primary objective is to save life. No amount of managerial or political intervention can overrule this relationship between the patient and doctor. Trust is not automatically included in the certificate of competence. Neither doctors nor anyone else has an innate right to be trusted; trust must be earned. It is closely linked to personal integrity. Every doctor must therefore carry a personal responsibility for this. Integrity in medicine encompasses personal ethical standards, a commitment based on what they can give, not what they want to take, honesty in thought and communication, and the humility to recognise their own limitations. The guide to *Good Medical Practice* published by the GMC[5] sets out clearly many of these professional standards, but the principles have been in place for hundreds of years.

Insistence on these personal standards of integrity should not begin at the time of entry to the profession. It should begin much earlier. Hopefully, it should start in childhood because personal integrity is not restricted to those entering medicine. It should of course begin under the guidance of parents, but when home influences diminish who will guide? The capacity of schools to fill the void may also have been undermined by current external regulators limiting the freedom and opportunities for teachers; too often they feel unsupported, distrusted and overruled. Who then is going to ensure that a sense of individual personal responsibility is nurtured? The current trend in today's materialistic society and much of the content of popular media entertainment is not providing much educational help in the development of these personal moral standards. Against such a background, how is the medical profession to tackle the issue of personal philosophy and attitudes in students at the beginning of their career, especially when the traditional system of apprenticeship training has been largely abandoned? It may be out of fashion to use the word 'apprenticeship' but, in a field where personal attitudes and principles are so important, learning on the shop floor from the experience and attitudes of those who are respected and trusted by the profession and patients alike, remains vital – the actual terminology does not matter. Indeed, this raises the question as to whether more attention should be paid to these personal qualities – as well as the capacity to communicate sensitively with other people – in the selection of medical students?

Awareness of these problems has resulted in new programmes being set up as part of introductory courses for medical students, and this is a welcome beginning. However, attendance over a few weeks of an ethics module is not by any means enough to cover the ground. Far more consideration must be given to professional integrity and this is the responsibility of all of those guiding students through every component of their training. Progress depends on adequate personal contact time between teachers and trainees. It is not something that can be taught in the classroom, or by electronic wizardry. Only by personal example will such attitudes be transmitted. Everyone in the profession therefore bears responsibility.

On the other hand, there is no doubt that the medical profession itself is to some extent to blame for the breakdown of trust because it has often failed to distinguish between self-interest and its responsibilities to others – to patients, the public and government. In addition, trust has been undermined because of a small number of doctors who have behaved disgracefully and by some who have adopted over-paternalistic attitudes and not done enough to encourage open and equal partnerships with the patients they serve – patients who are increasingly well informed and wish to play a much more active role in their medical care than in the past. However, before we lose all perspective, national opinion polls still indicate that the medical profession remains at the top of the list of those trusted by the general population,[6] and the vast majority of doctors work very long hours selflessly for their patients and the NHS. We are in a good position, but we fail to nurture trust at our peril.

The broader context of 'trust'

Once again, clear distinctions have to be made between trust in doctors by the public, by patients and by managers and politicians. The distinction is important because the reasons for distrust are different.

Curious things have been happening in the world today, involving an erosion of trust in the professions and public services by society.[6] The reasons behind this are very complex and are linked with a number of factors. Amongst these is a general sense of healthy egalitarianism in the world today which rejects the perceived privileged position of people in the traditional professions, such as the law, the Church, education and medicine. Another factor is the trend towards greater transparency, which is also welcomed but which at the same time runs the risk of undermining trust in the professions, when the media indulges in unbalanced publicity and trivialised or emotional story-telling on television. Other contributing factors also sadly include the negative attitudes which have been taken against the medical profession by some politicians and the media for their own purposes. This has occurred for several reasons. For example, as the British Medical Association (BMA) undertakes its rightful role in representing doctors' interests on some issues, the medical profession as a whole has been accused much more generally of putting self-interest first. If self-interest is ever allowed to take priority over the interests of patients, the medical profession will quickly disintegrate. The profession has also been accused of resisting change when the record shows that they have in fact been the leaders of staggering change, especially over the last 50 years of medical advances; indeed, they are frustrated that management often cannot keep up. Of course, doctors must accept and support organisational changes where these are for the greater good, but the profession's right to resist proposed changes must be respected when it perceives that it is not in the interests of their patients and when their views can be substantiated with evidence. This promotion of distrust has been used to justify increased regulation, to erode clinical authority and professionalism more generally.[4] It is sad when these trends have caused schisms between management and the profession which are bad for both – as well as for the NHS (see also Chapter 19).

Public changes in attitude have, however, had some useful consequences which can be used to promote trust. There is always a silver lining. Over the last ten years or so, it has led to the introduction of much greater accountability and scrutiny of doctors – of their competence and skills, of their clinical performance, of their judgements especially when these might be influenced by personal interests, of their honesty in research and towards their employers, and their ethical behaviour to their patients. The introduction of various agreed processes of audit, clinical governance, declaration of interests and transparency, provided that they are handled sensibly, must therefore be welcomed. They should be supported by doctors because they help to restore and maintain trust in the profession by the public and their patients. Notwithstanding all this, the truth expressed so eloquently by Reverend Gordon Dunstan should not be forgotten: 'Without the interventions of conscience, the law cannot govern'.[7]

What patients want from the NHS

While the British public are very supportive of the NHS and the majority are grateful for the services it provides, some surveys show that a considerable proportion of patients are dissatisfied.[1] Patients want an efficient, timely service which is accessible. They want kindness, understanding and support. They quickly sense when a person from whom they need help is incompetent, uncaring or simply out of their depth.

Patients want choice within the NHS in two senses: choice in their management once the options have been clearly explained to them and choice in which doctor or team of doctors looks after them. Patients know that particular services are available in one place but not in another. When they know that better care is available at a distance (sometimes in a tertiary care centre), most patients – but not all – are prepared to travel to obtain this, even if it means that it is less convenient for their families to visit. Very recently, the Government has recognised the importance of 'choice' and has promised improvements, albeit in fairly limited terms.[8] This is naturally increasing patients' expectations and they are understandably frustrated when they find that their referral is not permitted outside their own Region owing to the restrictions on transfer of funding. In 2004 there was increasing evidence that much pressure was being put on patients to be treated locally, in spite of specific requests for an alternative referral for treatment in more specialised centres. These restrictions inevitably lead to 'postcode' inequalities of service. Currently, GPs are often not permitted to meet such requests, and can only offer a choice between local consultants at district general hospitals who may have less detailed knowledge than those at specialist centres. These restrictions, which did not exist until the early 1990s, are not good for patients and are also reducing opportunities for clinical research in medical fields where it is most needed. Careful monitoring of the new promises will be imperative to ensure that real choice materialises. It would be a shame if something as important as choice caused disillusionment because the promises outstripped the reality.

When in hospital, patients expect to know who is actually responsible for their management. The replacement of the traditional medical firm, led by a consultant, by large rotating teams of medical and non-medical healthcare workers often results in patients simply not knowing who is ultimately in charge. This causes worry and distrust. Advances in medical knowledge inevitably lead to more specialisation, with doctors knowing more and more about less and less. Indeed, on this assumption there is a groundswell of view promoting an ever narrower and shorter training in greater depth. In consequence, patients in need of hospital management are apt to be handed round from one specialist to another and they naturally feel that there is no one single consultant with whom they can discuss and agree their total care. With increasing patient power, the need to have a defined overall lead consultant in whom the patient has confidence is crucial if trust is to be nurtured. Thus, while narrower training in greater depth may be acceptable for some super-specialist areas, there is an equally vital need for quality people trained and experienced in *both breadth and depth* of medicine, as every patient knows who has had to face multiple common, unusual or complicated problems. So much of modern medicine is in fact quite complex and falls into one or other of these categories. The idea that broad-based experienced physicians can be replaced by groups of super-specialists is unacceptable and is like the five blind men describing the donkey in terms of the only bit that that each can feel within their reach! Important as teamwork is, there is always a need for a leader to take ultimate responsibility.

On the other hand, the idea suggested by some that the patient's GP can subsume this role is inappropriate. These colleagues have many other special skills and indeed are, with added training, covering some of the work of a general physician. However, they simply do not have the experience or the information, without major retraining in more advanced medicine, to handle all these difficult aspects of patient care in adults or children.

There are a number of other reasons why this broader experience at consultant level is still needed in modern medicine. First, many apparently common conditions, as well as rarities, present in individual patients in a wide variety of ways. Second, breadth and depth is needed for good quality medical care because with an increasingly elderly population more people have several different disorders affecting several different systems. Not only will there be several diagnoses, but treating one may have important knock-on effects on the others. Thus breadth of judgement and experience is essential. Third, breadth and depth of knowledge is a crucial requirement for good clinical teachers. Students need to see how different modes of thinking can be applied to tease out a diagnosis or to refine a particular line of treatment and how these can be brought together into a coherent management plan. Such doctors need longer training, not shorter, as is the current trend. There are many young surgeons and physicians who are quite willing to accept a longer period in training to equip themselves adequately with the multiple skills they know they need. The Royal Colleges are now doing their best to set up special programmes intended to compensate for the defects in the new shortened training schemes but these may not be adequate to tackle the fundamental problems which have been imposed by others.

Patients like to know that there is good communication between primary and secondary care teams, because above all they want continuity of care. They also want to feel that they could seek a second opinion without offending the primary team, even if it only confirms what has been said before, or, in the case of serious illness, to be certain that no stone has been left unturned. They also appreciate continuity of nursing staff but they understand that this is not usually possible. The introduction of 'named' nurses has been an attempt to improve nursing continuity, but with the inevitable change of shifts every eight hours this is only partially successful.

Patients are sensitive about apparently minor things and understanding of this should not be considered old fashioned. Many, especially the older ones, feel most uncomfortable about over-familiarity – such as being addressed by their first name often by youngsters less than half their age, who they have never met before. To be asked blandly on admission 'What do you want to be called?' (as I have heard so often) is both ambiguous and crude; it certainly does not show much respect. 'How would you like to be addressed by the hospital staff?' is much better, but not all hospitals provide a space to record this important information on the admission form and in consequence there is no consistency in approach between members of staff. Many patients are intimidated by hospitals and feel very vulnerable and exposed, especially concerning their personal and private functions. Many have not experienced sleeping in a ward with complete strangers, especially when some may be noisy or frighteningly intrusive. Many are embarrassed by their symptoms, especially if they feel that they will disturb other patients. They do not like to be asked personal questions in public hearing. It may be easier and quicker to shout from the 'drugs' trolley 'Have you had your bowels open or would you like something for them?' than come to the bedside – but it is not very dignified. Even modern hospitals could improve their approach in so many practical ways. These are fundamental sensitivities and none should be taken for granted. Doctors in training, nurses and all the other paramedical staff should be taught much more about patients' vulnerabilities and what we ask patients to put up with. All this is a crucial part of professional training and it cannot be learned from books.

The current trends towards greater emphasis on the academic and theoretical content of so many training courses for healthcare workers, including those for nurses, have been driven by the demand to satisfy new standards deemed necessary to keep pace with modern medicine and to raise professional standing. However, if the elements of empathy and care are lost, those who are motivated to enter these professions to help others will feel that they have been let down. In many good centres, sensitive communication is uniformly excellent, but to get it right for everyone all the time is the aim and this costs nothing. The essential foundations upon which to build patient confidence and trust are respect and dignity; this involves understanding the patients' perspective in many different ways.

Ethics of medical research

The principles of personal integrity and honesty outlined above also apply to research as much as anywhere. Fifty years ago when I started medicine, how and when research on patients should be conducted was entirely up to the judgement of individual clinicians. As the possibilities of medical advances grew, the need for proper assessment of the objective value of research became an ethical necessity. It therefore became imperative to set up independent systems to set standards of how and when research involving patients could be undertaken, to supplement the ethical judgement of individual doctors undertaking it. All organisations within the NHS and universities undertaking research that involves patients are now bound by the rigorous standards set by ethics committees throughout the UK.

It is worth recalling that at first, in the 1960s, many excellent doctors found it difficult to accept the need for external evaluation and felt that it was a personal distrust of their integrity. Gradually, however, their confidence in the system has grown and today everyone is convinced of the absolute necessity for external monitoring. Over the years, the composition of ethics committees has widened, first to include nurses, later lay representatives (often a Board member) and more recently patient representatives.

It is interesting to observe that as the authority of ethics committees has increased the personal responsibility of individual doctors can, inadvertently, be diminished. Several years ago, I was worried when a young doctor showed me a proposal for research which I felt contained some ethical difficulties. When I questioned him he greatly surprised me by saying that he had not really thought much about it – he thought that that was a job for the ethics committee. We have to be constantly on our guard to get the right balance between fostering personal responsibility and at the same time ensuring that external regulatory mechanisms (which should not become unduly bureaucratic) are in place to give added value. It is important that ethics committees, in their efforts to cover every eventuality, do not destroy important research. The need for a 60-page submission before undertaking even a small and simple clinical study may be counterproductive. A reasonable balance is required.

The first report from the Royal College of Physicians' own Ethics Committee was published in 1971,[9] and this major commitment by the College has continued since. Through this, it has contributed seminal reports which have now been accepted both nationally and internationally on many aspects of the conditions under which medical research can or should be conducted. Other Colleges have taken up the challenge to cover their own fields. Editors of medical journals have also played a vital role in developing ethical standards. The whole question of ethical evaluation and its monitoring in medical practice and in research has rightly become a key issue in maintaining medical standards in modern medicine.

One of the most rewarding appointments in my whole career was to serve on ethics committees both at the Royal Brompton and the College. This experience was a constant reminder of the great responsibilities carried by doctors and other healthcare workers in the day-to-day care of patients. It also stimulated debates with junior staff on the right path to take for individual patients, particularly when any research or investigation involving patients or volunteers was involved. I was privileged to use this experience when in 1990 I was asked to be a founder member of the multidisciplinary national Nuffield Bioethics Council.

Holistic welfare of patients

It is widely recognised that, especially when quality of life is concerned, both mind and body play an equally important part in what could be described as holistic welfare. Perhaps the most easily recognised 'mind' component in illness is that related to stress, but this is only part of what we need to understand. The interplay between the two is not limited to the domain of psychosomatic illnesses but is relevant to all patients needing care. Attitudes of the mind can have a profound influence on how people cope with their illnesses, just as changes in the physical state can

213

influence, for better or for worse, their psychological attitudes. The importance of this interplay is often overlooked when trying to equate what is best for individual patients against the pressures to adhere rigorously to guidelines based on evidence-based medicine and protocols. There is now at last a renewed and growing recognition of how much the so-called 'humanities' can contribute to good medical practice, because it emphasises the vital importance of the development of perceptive skills discussed earlier in this chapter. This reminds us clearly about how far modern medicine is at risk of pushing rounded care of patients off course. Valuable as scientific knowledge is, it alone is not enough. From earliest civilisations there has been clear recognition that the human state includes far more than just the rational, analytical and intellectual behaviour based on physical objective facts. It also includes the intuitive, the sensibilities and the power of the human spirit. This is often and somewhat coyly referred to as 'the inner self' or 'self within'. In what follows, I shall use the word 'spirit' unrepentantly as a shorthand (OED definition: 'a person's mind or soul as distinct from their body'). This of course has nothing whatever to do with spiritualism. In health, as in dis-ease, the body and spirit are inextricably entwined. Holistic medicine demands the understanding of both, recognising that damage to one may compromise the other, and likewise healing of one may support the other.

Scientific interventions have of course achieved fantastic things in medicine. What follows is in no way intended to denigrate or diminish the importance of some of the remarkable medical advances. Neither is it intended to minimise the very many improvements in medical care which have taken place over the last few decades. However, it is in fact these very successes that have led seductively to a disregard or lack of comprehension of that fundamental reality known to man for thousands of years, namely the importance of the human 'spirit'. The assumption that, with our new scientific knowledge, nurture of the spirit in sickness and in health is unimportant, or at least not relevant to modern medicine, is in my view a serious misapprehension.

Such is the power of our new-found knowledge in scientific medicine that it has now been allowed to seduce the medical world to such an extent that those untutored in the art of medicine and the needs of patients are now presuming to call the shots. Medicine, they suppose, can be conducted exclusively as an evidence-based science; diagnosis and treatment can be computer assisted and protocol driven, and symptoms can be explained in scientific terms without professional interpretation. However, if we are honest, we know that we are still only at the beginning of our understanding. We should never forget that all 'symptoms' (as opposed to 'signs') are by definition what the patient can perceive and describe, and this relies entirely on their cerebral interpretation. A symptom may have its origins in some peripheral part of the body, but its perception is central. What one patient finds intolerable is to another merely an inconvenience; how one patient copes with illness, especially when it is chronic, will be quite different from another.

Paradoxically, at the same time some of those promoting this sterile objective caricature of de-personalised medicine stress that care must be 'patient-centred', evidently without having much insight about what this actually means or how it can be fostered. Patients, on the other hand, know all too well. They instinctively recognise their need for both physical and 'spiritual' support for their problems. The modern emphasis on patient power and the rejection of so-called professional paternalism is not just about the patient's right to accept or to reject the advice they are given – it goes much deeper than this. It is an expression of their demand to be treated as a whole person. Their trust in doctors is dependent on an often unspoken empathy of mutual understanding of these things between the two. All good doctors, be they in primary, secondary or tertiary care, try to provide this within the context of the increasingly skewed system that is driven forward and sometimes mesmerised by science, financial stringencies, statistics, directives, government-speak and targets, in which real understanding of people, including their hopes and their fears, is in danger of being neglected. Such understanding of the human state is far more profound than the frequently used trivialising phrase, 'touchy feely', which is patronising, distasteful and misleading. The pressures in general practice are as great as those on the more specialist services, and delegation of the professional responsibility to others is not acceptable. All doctors involved with patients must play their part. Specialists must not rely on GPs to do the 'spirituality bit' and likewise GPs must not delegate this to other healthcare workers. Everyone must contribute.

The recent focus of publications and research on the power of the humanities in medicine is beginning to remind those caring for patients about the much broader dimension of human care that is needed.[10] There is an appreciation that various art forms, be they visual as in pictures or architecture, auditory as in poetry or music, or both as in drama or opera, can, by enhancing the 'spirit', support the ailing body. Conversely, where the spirit is neglected or damaged, the body may also suffer. All this, however, does not absolve doctors from carrying through their responsibility for understanding the physical and spiritual components of every patient and supporting both as far as they are able. This is the essence of professionalism in medicine and there is no substitute for it. Patients come to doctors intuitively expecting this total support but sadly they often do not receive it any more.

One sees many young aspiring doctors entering medicine with a strong instinct for the whole human estate, not just the physical breakdown – but somehow the pressures of the training, the rigours of practice weighed down by well intended regulators, directives, and academic and scientific overload, often conspire to steer them off course. Some even opt out altogether without perhaps fully understanding the reason for their disillusionment. Others become extremely competent, adapting to the modern materialistic approach, but in the process losing that precious instinct that drove them at the start.

Likewise, many senior doctors are retiring early. They are being driven from the NHS because it prevents them from giving total support to patients. It is tragic to hear experienced and devoted doctors say that they are pleased to be giving up because they can no longer serve their patients in a way that they know is needed. Management, government and the profession itself must take heed before it is too late.

Thus, in different ways we are all to blame. The exciting prospect is that the way ahead is clear. Doctors simply must regroup and reclaim the high ground with a clear view of the care that they know they need to provide. If they do not wish to do so then they should not be in the business of medicine. Time must be made available for patients and doctors to build that partnership of empathy and trust – not by delegating tasks that doctors should be doing themselves, but by freeing them from the bureaucracy, the endless meetings generated by managerial overload, and the frustration of needing to see too many patients in too short a time. Some aspects of a patient's care can be delegated very successfully to different members of a skilled team and the practicality of this will vary according to their competencies and their talents. However, the success of the team depends not only on the constituent members, but also on leadership by someone who can lead with comprehension and inspiration to ensure that all the strands of care can be brought together to create that highly individualised thing, a fusion of compassion with knowledge, which together forms the foundation of real patient/doctor relationships.

A supreme example of what I am trying to describe is the development by Professor Archie MacIndoe of the Burns Unit for severely injured fighter aircraft pilots at East Grinstead after the Second World War. Here, innovative plastic surgery for their serious disfigurement was combined with equally great creativity to restore their confidence as special people in the community. Hopes and fears, sensitivities, attitudes and misapprehensions must be given their full place as well, of course, as the extraordinary opportunities now available to help the physical state. Further, it is the leaders' responsibility to ensure that every member of the team aspires to these principles. The so-called medical humanities are supportive in this understanding and not an add-on; they are central to medical practice because they stress the importance of that dimension of care reaching beyond the physical, of which modern medicine has so often lost sight.

The NHS is at a crossroads. Not, as many think, because there are financial difficulties or nursing shortages, although these are indeed grave limitations, but because unless it is recognised that in the end much of medicine depends on professional doctors – working in partnership with many other splendid professionals – trained to understand the total care of patients, then the whole system will in the long term disintegrate. The recipe is simple and there are no compromises. Modern aids and short cuts can do much to help but they cannot substitute.

Many people will of course try to rubbish these views as old fashioned. Actually, I do not believe this is so. Stress in our modern and changing society is increasing and this is well recognised by the public, by patients needing help, and by those caring for them. The ideas I have tried to summarise are vital in the mayhem of today's world. Conventional religion may be currently out of favour in much of our contemporary world, but there is no option on the importance in both health and sickness of that deeper instinct of spirituality as an intrinsic part of human nature. Some things in life are perennial truths and cannot be sidelined because they are hard to define or difficult to understand. The fact is that medicine must serve patients and it is the responsibility of the profession to know and to understand what those needs are and to insist that these are the standards to which we must aspire. It is the maintenance of all these standards both in breadth and depth that defines the profession (see also Chapter 19).

While all those directly concerned with caring for patients must carry a major responsibility for taking a broader view of their needs, which is so difficult to provide in the pressurised climate of modern healthcare, there are many interesting practical ways in which others can help. I believe that management and Trust Boards should take a much stronger lead than is often the case, and there are several ways in which they can contribute. One is to create a non-threatening and supportive environment where a holistic approach to patients needs is promoted. Attempts at this can come in many forms, including art in hospitals, open-house patients' support centres, appropriate background music in some places (for example where patients may feel claustrophobic), and quiet areas in others. Wherever possible, the creation of garden and courtyard areas can also do much to support both patients and staff. Qualitative and quantitative research is now beginning to validate objectively this approach.[11] All these practical ideas feed the spirit not only of patients but of those who may be under considerable pressure trying to look after them. Hospital chaplains and lay volunteers as well as everyone else in contact with patients, from the tea lady onwards, can contribute, if they have the right instincts, are given the right opportunities and are supported by the right leadership. Whether one is agnostic or not, and whether one likes the word or not, the 'spiritual' aspect of human nature needs support in times of stress as much as any physical help and can play a major part in recovery.

19. Doctors' dilemmas:
The profession of medicine
in the modern NHS

Before discussing the broader changes in the NHS and the gap that has developed between policy intent and delivery of care (Chapter 20), it may be helpful, as a background, to summarise briefly some of the professional dilemmas for doctors posed by the changing trends in medicine and the effects of these on professional standards of clinical practice and training.

Not only do doctors have responsibilities to meet the needs of patients (Chapter 18) but they also have a responsibility to do this within the context of the NHS. This raises challenges because the NHS is controlled by managers and government who, are in the main, not medically trained, but legitimately have legal, financial, political, managerial and other agendas which are sometimes inevitably in conflict with the immediate needs of individual patients. When this happens, doctors face a dilemma between their professional responsibilities for patients and their commitment as employees to the NHS. These dilemmas have to be faced and resolved. To quote O'Neill,[1] ' If we want a culture of public service, professionals and public servants must in the end be free to serve the public rather than their paymasters'. This chapter is about finding ways to preserve professionalism not for itself but for patients, and at the same time trying to help those ultimately responsible for this very special national public service.

Medicine as a profession

A *professional* person not only has particular knowledge and skills, acquired through training and refined by experience, but also agrees to conform to certain standards of personal behaviour and codes of practice.

As we have seen in Chapter 18, because of their responsibilities to patients, professional doctors must also adhere to codes of behaviour which include honesty, ethical integrity, humility to recognise their personal limitations, compassion and empathy. It is essential to the notion of professional codes of practice that they include standards of training and practices set by the corporate body of the profession itself. Inherent in this – and it applies to any profession – is 'self-regulation'. This reflects trust placed in professional doctors to serve the best interest of patients and the public and not themselves. This is not an exclusive responsibility; it must be coupled with 'intelligent accountability based on good governance, independent inspection and careful reporting'.[2] Self-regulation and intelligent rigorous accountability together amount to 'professionally led or shared regulation', in modern terminology.

These personal standards and codes of practice must be essentially independent of politics and government, but professional people must conform to the laws of the land. There may be very exceptional circumstances where a professional medical doctor finds his/her own professional ethical position incompatible with the law (eg where the state demands doctors' participation in torture, or other forms of harm to people). Under such circumstances, s/he has to take responsibility for making a judgement either to comply with the law or declare his/her position, usually endorsed by the corporate view of the professional body, recognising the consequences.

Because of the incompleteness of our knowledge in medicine, personal professional qualities also include the capacity to make judgements, the ability to extend and develop knowledge through innovation and, because of the complexities of modern medicine, the skills of leadership. Professionalism requires all of these.

Thus doctors have a triple responsibility in the NHS which may sometimes be in conflict: responsibility for care to their patients, responsibility for personal codes of conduct and clinical standards to their corporate professional body, and accountability for their performance to their employers. There is a need for everyone working in the NHS to understand more clearly the implications of this three-way accountability.

The distinction between a professional person and an 'artificer' (artisan) is subtle and may vary depending on the particular responsibilities involved. In general terms and as applied to medicine, an 'artificer' may be very skilled and have great personal integrity; they may even have their own representative body, often with an emphasis on trades union functions. Nevertheless, their relationship with their employer is somewhat different in that they do not usually have independent ethical responsibilities for the welfare of their 'clients' defined by their corporate body, and to which they are expected to adhere. Artificers are primarily required to serve their employer and no one else.

With increasing government control of standards of medical practice, there is *de facto* the potential for an erosion of independent medical professionalism. If the case as set out in Chapter 18 for the need for medical people as professionals is accepted, then such a trend will not be in the patients' interests. Of course, modern care of patients is rapidly changing for a variety of reasons. Some are clearly desirable – there are always different and better ways of doing things. Others may be inevitable – such as those due to workforce and financial shortages. Others, however, may be due to government policies – such as the decision to have greater regulatory controls on how and when patients can be treated, how doctors should work and how they should be trained. These are clearly areas of potential conflict.

One of the arguments most frequently used by management and government for justifying the increasing regulatory controls on medical care in the NHS is that doctors, for reasons of self-interest or ignorance, are resistant to change. Such a charge must distinguish between the alleged resistance to change *per se* and a failure by doctors to comply with or support changes which they believe are not in the interests of patients.

The accusation that doctors are resistant to change *per se* is evidently not tenable. In fact, doctors have been the leaders of unbelievable changes in medical practice over the last fifty years, often to their own personal disadvantage. One has only to look at the massive clinical changes over the entire face of medicine to find the evidence. For example, the introduction of drugs in the management of tuberculosis in the early 1950s made the need for an entire nationwide service caring for these patients obsolete, including personnel and property. The widespread practice of medical treatments such as long-term maintenance of collapse therapy was discontinued and major complex surgery involving specialist thoracic surgeons and anaesthetists was abandoned. The service was dismantled with extensive hospital closures and required the retraining and relocation of skilled personnel. Advances in mental health have resulted in the closure of another nationwide network of institutions, with major personnel consequences. More recently, the introduction of keyhole surgery has radically transformed surgical practice and fundamentally altered training requirements. Many specialist surgeons have found that after years of training and experience, their skills are simply no longer needed. Scanning procedures have transformed diagnosis affecting almost every specialty, making other procedures unnecessary. The list is almost endless.

The frustration of doctors is not that changes in medicine have led to the need for them to adapt and change their skills, it is that the healthcare systems in the NHS and elsewhere are often, but understandably, unable to keep pace with them, even when such changes have obvious and proven advantage to patients. Some of the problems attendant on introduction of the new techniques of interventional radiology is just one example. Further, as will be seen in Chapter 20, doctors have shown remarkable adaptability and tolerance to the huge and not always consistent changes in the direction of the NHS made by successive governments over the last fifty years – trying the while to look after the patients.

Of course, it is true that doctors, like others, are human, and not uncommonly resist changes to their established routine, particularly when the reasons do not seem to be compelling to them at the time. However, when the reasons are good and they are handled sensibly by their colleagues and management, the proper professional response must be to comply with good grace.

If, however, the imposed changes to the system are perceived by doctors to be a disadvantage to their patients – shift systems as at present constructed for junior doctors is a good example – it is their ethical right to say so. However, whenever this is the case, doctors must be careful to examine their motivation and their reasoning, to make sure that they rigorously exclude all self-interest.

Getting the right balance between self-regulation and accountability in the NHS

The central issue for a quality NHS is to achieve the right balance between four complementary components of regulation: those determined through legislature, directives set by government or the Department of Health, those depending on 'self'-regulation set through professional corporate bodies, and those imposed by individual professional doctors on themselves. To get the balance right requires wisdom, discipline and mutual trust. While legislation and external controls can be very helpful to ensure that certain standards are maintained, it is crucial to understand that legislation and prescriptive regulatory processes can never regulate *all* practices or indeed *all* human behaviour. This fundamental truth is explored in more detail in Reverend Gordon Dunstan's *Artifice of ethics,*[3] where he stresses, 'The Law cannot regulate all human behaviour which also needs professional and social "conventions" to prevent anarchy and tyranny'.

We must therefore consider some of the ways in which this balance has been set in the past and how it has been shifted by other changes in the NHS more recently.

After qualification, standards of professional behaviour have been largely self-regulated by the General Medical Council (GMC) – a body established in 1858 with statutory powers to set standards of medical practice, medical education, and to register qualifications. It is independent of government and party politicians but it has delegated powers from Parliament. In practice, it has largely concerned itself with the most extreme cases of inadequate performance. Cases of gross misconduct have always been taken very seriously indeed, but lesser misdemeanours have, in the past, not always been dealt with as rigorously as they should. Indeed, some have not come within the remit of the GMC. This body has medical and lay representation and recently the number of the latter has been considerably increased to improve the accountability of the profession to the public. Over the last few years, the GMC has undertaken a major review of its responsibilities and implemented many radical changes. Notwithstanding, in 2003 the Government set up the Council for the Regulation of Healthcare Professionals to oversee decisions made by the individual independent regulatory bodies (GMC, General Nursing Council etc). This is a radical development because it challenges the balance between government and professional-led regulation.[4]

Government has also increased professional regulation at a local level through the introduction of clinical governance to strengthen the accountability of doctors to management. While some aspects of this are undoubtedly both justified and helpful, others require very mature judgement if the service is to work well. Chief executives in hospitals now have certain statutory responsibilities for the behaviour of doctors. They also have the power to suspend doctors where there are indications of inadequate performance. Part of the understandable reason for this increased clinical control is that government, through the NHS, has taken over some aspects of indemnity and are thus not only the employers but are directly liable when things go wrong. Nevertheless, suspension or simply exclusion is a very serious step which, if unwarranted (as has occurred), causes devastating personal and professional damage as well as cost to the NHS.[4]

There have, of course, been recent much publicised examples where regulation has broken down disastrously and a few very serious bizarre cases concerning criminal behaviour or mental derangement continue to remind all doctors that outrageous acts by a very small number of individuals can cause a dramatic loss of trust and confidence by patients and government, and cause irreparable damage to the profession as a whole. There is no doubt that the profession must learn lessons very quickly from these cases and find ways of eliminating all breaches of proper professional conduct as far as possible. They must demonstrate that any backsliding from the highest standards will not be tolerated. This involves vigilance by doctors at all levels within the service.

In order to introduce better controls, by the profession itself, by the GMC or indeed by government, we still need to have better information about the full range of the problems and their size. The public enquiries following recent notorious cases have been extremely helpful in highlighting some of the correctable factors in these extreme cases. We also still need to have more hard facts about the scale and the type of other misdemeanours we are trying to tackle, in order to focus on appropriate corrective measures. Regular formal appraisals should help to provide better information. For example, how many backsliding doctors exhibit their incompetence through a failure to keep adequately up to date? How many are competent but let their patients down through a deficiency in or disregard for adequate communication? How many are simply lazy and not pulling their weight? How many short-change their NHS sessions in favour of their private practice? With more accurate information, appropriate and constructive preventive, remedial or other actions can then be taken. There is a real danger that blunderbuss controls may mollify public opinion or the media while actually failing to address the real problems. These are very serious matters and undoubtedly much more still needs to be done by the profession and management working together.

There are five major trends of change which require intelligent handling, if the advantages of doctors working as professional people are to continue in the NHS. These include changes in patterns of care within the profession, changes in patterns of care between clinically trained and non-clinically trained personnel, changes to improve dissemination of good practice, changes in control of clinical standards within the NHS, and changes in control of how doctors are trained.

Changing patterns of modern patient care within the profession

There are two contrasting trends of care in the NHS which run as counter currents and with conflicting requisites, that have not yet been resolved. On the one hand, as highly developed opportunities for treatment become ever more sophisticated, more patients require more hospital-based resources including more specialist doctors (ie moving from left to right in the scheme of things). On the other hand, there is understandably increasing pressure being exerted by government, for financial and manpower reasons, to keep patients in the community (moving as it were from right to left), believing that the generalist GP can take over many aspects of work currently undertaken by hospital consultants, provided that they have access to various technical procedures.

Clearly, the latter policy has much to recommend it. Thus, if a patient has persisting symptoms, rather than seeking more expert advice and assessment from a specialist consultant, GPs are encouraged to resolve the problem by having increased direct access to a wider range of hospital investigations, including blood tests (and there is an almost unlimited variety of different things that can be measured here), endoscopy (and there are plenty of orifices for this), ultrasound (and there are lots of organs to sound out), and sometimes even computed tomography and magnetic resonance imaging scans. Clearly GP access to standard investigations are entirely appropriate and, under some circumstances, certain special procedures may be all that is needed to allow a patient to be diagnosed and treated without referral to a hospital specialist. However, a further problem arises, because the results of all of these tests, while undertaken by very skilled people in hospitals, are often reported by them in the absence of detailed information about the background history or the context in which the test has been requested. Good medical practice depends on the integrative skills of the practitioner, and it is the context of the results of investigations which becomes crucial. To illustrate this point, an abnormality may be identified which is quite irrelevant to the patient's complaint. This may be quite properly reported back but inevitably is sometimes inappropriately interpreted as '*the* diagnosis'. While investigations ordered by community practitioners can often solve the diagnostic problem and ease pressures on the hospital service, especially when there are long waiting lists for patients to be seen by hospital consultants, a fine professional judgement has to be made as to when another opinion is more appropriate, to ensure the best possible care. This may also actually avoid unnecessary investigation and thereby save costs to the NHS.

Changes in the roles of medically and non-medically qualified personnel

Because of the acute shortage of doctors, government has sought, not unreasonably, to find ways of devolving work that was previously carried out by the medical profession. Once again, if good quality patient care is to be maintained, a fine balance has to be struck between devolving those tasks which are appropriate to those without full medical training, while retaining those which must remain the fundamental responsibility of the profession.

There are of course many sources of useful medical advice to patients other than from doctors. Sometimes it is simply a question of experience and common sense from granny, a parent or a wise friend. The NHS Helpline introduced in 1998 has proved extremely successful, as has the extended role of modern well-trained pharmacists who can often give invaluable advice. In a short conversation they can often undertake a preliminary 'triage' and suggest a first course of action. They are particularly expert on advising on the interaction between medications, which is so often an important issue in modern medicine.

In community practice there are two main categories of people, without full medical qualifications, who could be especially helpful in counterbalancing the shortage of doctors. First, those who could under-take a triage role and deal with minor problems in general practice *before* the patient requires the skills of a doctor, and second, those who can run specialist clinics and services *after* the doctors have made a definitive diag-nosis and set out a broad treatment plan. Practice or district nurses, including those running, for example, special community clinics for asthma, diabetes and hypertension, can not only provide very effective specialist services, but may in some instances actually have greater knowl-edge of the practical details in particular fields than doctors themselves. In 'office practices' in the USA, physician assistants (with a much short-ened training) have also played a successful role in the diagnosis and treat-ment of common or transient illnesses. While it is always useful to seek useful ideas from other countries, it is essential to remember that the structure of community medicine in the USA is very different from the current system within the NHS in the UK. If physician assistants are to be trained and used in the UK, their skills must be tailored and carefully integrated with the existing patterns of care in this country.

In hospitals there are rafts of specially trained individuals including physician assistants, technicians of various types, specialist nurses and AHPs (allied health professionals) without full medical qualifications, who, with appropriate experience, can properly take over many tasks pre-viously undertaken by doctors. They can work successfully in all sorts of areas, acting as surgeons' assistants in the operating theatre or in outpa-tients, and supporting physicians in a wide variety of clinics. Their full value has certainly not yet been fully explored in the UK. Indeed, there is so much enthusiasm for these modern breeds that some very senior peo-ple in the NHS are tempted to ask the question of whether fully trained doctors are necessary at all any more. This raises fundamental and fairly obvious questions about the role of doctors in a modern technological age and what sort of doctors we need. Some of this has already been explored in Chapter 18.

As the Modernisation Agency explores ways to develop new training programmes to enable those without full medical qualifications to take responsibility for certain medical decisions and procedures, new methods of practice and controls will be needed to ensure that standards of patient care are not compromised. If these are not in place, there are many ways in which patient care can be potentially harmed and it is worth considering some of these in more detail, so that obvious mistakes are avoided.

The obvious way to try to ensure satisfactory quality of *treatment deci-sions* being made by those without full medical training is to substitute professional medical knowledge and judgement by greater reliance on more rigid protocol-driven medicine. However, before this can be applied it presumes that an accurate working diagnosis has been made. Who will be responsible for this? Will this also be protocol based? The purpose of ensuring a breadth and depth of medical training is to avoid falling into the trap of making the more obvious diagnosis, when the signs and symptoms are masquerading as something quite different. Those without medical training cannot be expected to identify these and to know the difference. Another trap for the unwary is the danger of over-reliance on written reports of investigations. As already discussed, many investigations have to be interpreted in the context of the whole case and by someone with trained integrative skills.

On the assumption that a reliable diagnosis has been made, the place of protocols in management and treatment must be looked at critically (see also Chapter 20). Treatment guidelines acting as a checklist and support, especially for doctors and others with limited experience, can be invaluable, but they may become dangerous if used by those who are not in a position to know when they are inappropriate. This is inevitable if treatment is delegated to those with inadequate training. It is so because appropriate treatment for individual patients often differs, and the evidence of medical knowledge (on which guidelines are based) is almost always very incomplete. While good guidelines themselves are proving to be invaluable in raising and maintaining clinical standards throughout the country, there is danger in using them as centrally directed prescriptive protocols for performance-monitoring purposes, from which doctors may not deviate and which are to be followed blindly for all patients. On the other hand, doctors must always be fully aware of the guidelines and be able to justify, on very good grounds, their reason for deviating from them. Good local audit procedures should and are being developed to monitor this.

The reason for caution is that these protocols are normally developed from an evidence base and this is often very incomplete. Therefore, before 'guidance' transforms into 'rigid protocols', the quality of the evidence has to be considered critically. Everyone in medicine must constantly remember that we simply do not yet have (and probably never will have) the ultimate answers to 'best practice' to permit total automated protocol-driven medicine. The fact is that what we can offer today will probably be wrong tomorrow. Judgement as well as knowledge as to what is *better for individual patients and for the time being* is therefore critical. Good judgment adapted to individual patients cannot be ensured by legislation. Even attempts to validate good judgement by outcome measurement present difficulties because the optimal outcome may vary from one patient to another. For one, quality of life may be more important than its duration (eg patients with end-stage disease) and for another, the quality of life may have to be sacrificed in the short term, if the long-term survival is the goal (eg chemotherapy in curable tumours). An outcome measurement from evidence-based medicine may indicate one thing, while the patient wants another. For example, open heart surgery may not improve mortality from coronary artery disease very substantially – and evidence of some improvement took very large studies and a long time to demonstrate – but it is extremely successful in relieving patients' anginal pain.

These arguments do not of course imply that evidence-based medicine is not the way forward – quite the reverse. In general terms, evidence-based medicine has been the guiding principle to improve the quality of medical care over the past fifty years, but it has assumed a new importance more recently with the explosion of new medications and procedures. Obviously, it is particularly important when it leads to the avoidance of useless or dangerous practices. It forms an excellent basis for medical practice especially as modern methodology allows far greater scientific evaluation of new and established treatments and management practices.

However, wholly scientific medicine can only be logically applied where *all* the variables have been accounted for and in clinical medicine this is virtually *never* the case. The amount we do *not* know still greatly exceeds that which we do. Thus, judgement is required and this is based on information, training and experience. So long as this pertains, professional humility is crucial. Management and our political masters need to recognise the scientific limitations of medicine and therefore not be seduced by concepts of automated medicine. In addition, patients' individual points of view need to be handled with great respect. Protocols do not allow for this.

Improving the dissemination of 'proven' good practice

Historically, dissemination of improvements in clinical management of patients was left largely to the profession. In spite of tremendous advances in medical care, led particularly by academic departments throughout the country, dissemination of this information depended largely on publications in scientific journals and medical conferences and the efforts of individual doctors to keep themselves up to date. It is important to remember that it takes time to establish how far new treatments are better than the old in the longer term, and whether they are without late undesirable side effects. Confirmatory long-term definitive clinical trials are time consuming; the rigorous standards set by ethics committees often cause delays before they are allowed to start. Such trials are difficult and expensive to fund and they are notoriously difficult to maintain over long periods and require meticulous commitment from investigators and patients alike. Further delays are often encountered before the results are accepted for publication in reputable peer review journals. Thus establishing good practice is both slow and expensive and it has to be recognised that much remains which is less rigorously evaluated. However, in spite of all of this, well validated new treatments are still often slow to percolate into clinical practice around the country and doctors are often cautious about changing from old established treatments, with which they are familiar, to new ones.

Thus, there is a serious gap between the acquisition and the application of knowledge. This problem was increasingly recognised in the 1980s and led to clinical audit, initiated first by the Royal College of Physicians. Their report, *Medical audit* (1989), encouraged review of the performance of individual physicians in the light of modern well-validated medical advances.

Over the last fifteen years, major improvements have been made to extend the knowledge base of many treatments, to develop guidelines of '*best* practice' and to monitor their introduction to clinical practice. The Research and Development Unit set up by the Department of Health helped to encourage the expansion of evidence-based medicine. Based on this, guidelines were developed by various bodies, including the Medical Royal Colleges and specialist societies, who also introduced more formal educational programmes on Continuing Medical Education, Updates and the development of plans for revalidation. Monitoring of the rate of introduction of new proven advances into clinical practice is now applied through compulsory audit across all NHS hospitals.

More recently the Government-run National Institute of Clinical Excellence (NICE) has taken on an increasing role in setting out guidance and guidelines on clinical practice and deciding which treatments have a sufficient evidence-base and are sufficiently cost-effective to permit them to be used within the NHS. The Council for Healthcare and Audit Improvement (CHAI), now renamed the Healthcare Commission, was commissioned in 2004 to review individual hospital performance in the implementation of these standards. The implication of these developments is discussed further in Chapter 20.

So far the discussion has covered the changing patterns of patient care and the practical attempts to ensure that treatments are objectively evaluated and how good practice can be disseminated. This now raises the broader question of who should set the overall standards of medical practice in the NHS.

Who should set the standards of medical practice in the NHS?

In the NHS, there are many stakeholders – government, managers, patients or 'clients' who need and use the service, the public who pay for the service through their taxes, as well as the professional doctors and nurses (working alongside the supporting paramedical staff and technicians), with their complementary skills and experience, who actually care and take responsibility for patients. The fundamental question now is who should hold the responsibility for setting the standards of medical care for patients? Is it government and politicians who are responsible for its funding? Is it the managers holding delegated responsibility? Is it the medical profession, who have responsibility for major decisions, sometimes with life-saving implications, as well as the quality of care for individual patients, in the light of their own knowledge and experience? Is it the patients, in need of care and treatment? They have the right (under most but not all circumstances) of accepting or rejecting advice on treatment that they may be offered. Is it the general public who in the end pay for the NHS through taxation and who certainly have a right to have their say in what sort of NHS they want when they become ill? The answer is of course that each has a key role to lead in different areas but each must recognise their interdependence on others. Unfortunately, putting this obvious conclusion into practice is not as straightforward as it seems. The challenge for the modernised NHS is surely to set up a new order where these distinctive areas are clearly defined, in each case allocating responsibility linked with accountability, but at the same time firmly establishing a balanced collaboration.

The lead role on managerial and policy issues by managers and government at various levels is important and obvious, and must of course be respected and indeed welcomed by doctors working in the NHS.

If the representative organisations of the medical profession are to play a lead role in the maintenance of clinical standards, they must make sure that the views of some of their recent critics are demonstrably unfounded. In 2003 Professor Sir Donald Irvine, General Practitioner and Past President of the General Medical Council, discussed 'patient centred professionalism'[5] and tackled the question of how the professional medical organisations could be improved, to play a more effective role in maintaining medical standards. He contended that while the public retains confidence in individual doctors, the professional medical organisations, including the GMC, the Medical Royal Colleges, the Academy of Medical Sciences and the BMA, were not giving strong enough leadership to demonstrate to government that they can be trusted. He took a critical and broad-brush approach. He referred to their shortcomings: 'their institutional complacency, failed leadership, poor communications, failure to ensure that new medical advances are put into practice; their laid back attitude to accountability and transparency', and their over-reliance on the regulatory functions of the GMC rather than taking a proactive line to identify backsliders.

Such strong words must of course be taken very seriously and some were certainly justified in the past. Although of course there is still much more to be done, it is wrong to ignore the massive achievements, made particularly over the last fifteen years or so, by these organisations in addressing all of these points, and indeed many others. In particular, it is difficult to sustain Sir Donald's arguments today as generalisations in view of the radical changes implemented by the GMC and the massive programme supported by the medical profession and their corporate bodies. These extend throughout the country and contribute to such things as compulsory clinical audit, clinical governance, policies on transparency and openness, guidelines on treatments and procedures based on evidence-based medicine, formalisation of lifelong training including Continuing Medical Education, revalidation, appraisals, compliance with 'good medical practice', exit examinations to assess competence of specialists in surgery, training of teachers, formal appraisal and training of adjudicators, modernisation of undergraduate medical school programmes with emphasis on communication skills and good doctor/ patient relationships, achieving continuity of care for patients despite EU regulations, meeting new needs of consultants arising from the shortened training programme, and so on.

There is, of course, always room for improvement. If professional bodies are to play a major role in the quality of patient care they must do much more by acting together to demonstrate their professional competence to lead, working alongside their patients, on issues relating to standards throughout the NHS. Helpfully Sir Donald pointed out that the credibility of these professional organisations would be enhanced if self-interest was seen to be explicitly excluded by distancing themselves from those bodies responsible for protecting certain professional interests (eg pay) through their trades union functions. The professional bodies must, however, continue to concern themselves with protecting doctors where there is an impact on patients. The wisdom of this advice is emphasised by the recent contract negotiations where, at a single stroke, GP colleagues have unwittingly undermined their professional standing and commitment to patients by an agreement which now permits them to opt out of weekend and other 'out-of-hours' services. There are many ways that the load can and should be lightened when doctors (or others) are overworked, but we should never forget that sickness can strike at any time and reasonable continuity is a hallmark of 'patient-centred professionalism'.

There has, however, been a worrying trend in recent years of government and managers increasing their direct control over many aspects of patient care (eg what investigations and treatments may be allowed, how long patients wait for surgery, to which hospital service they can be referred, how long they can remain in hospital, when they are to be discharged and whether they must be treated as a day case). These managers, who often do not have medical training, are themselves then torn between meeting targets and government policies on the one hand, and the pressures from the doctors on the clinical priorities on the other. Thus, a double dilemma is created, affecting both managers and doctors.

Very many fundamental questions are raised to which there are no easy answers. How far can, or should, the medical treatment of patients and the medical needs of society be controlled by those *without* medical training and how far does this have implications for the need for professional people in today's medicine? Can their work be done equally well by those working as artisans with a variety of skills to meet whatever standards those in charge of the health service choose to set? Alternatively, should the *quality* of standards of provision of healthcare for society be led by the medical profession? Their experience of working in partnership with patients puts them in a strong position to set out the quality of medical care which can and should be available, taking into account current medical knowledge and the resources available. Such professional leadership does not of course exclude a new order of partnership, as suggested in Chapter 20.

Changing standards for training of doctors

For almost fifty years after the introduction of the NHS, the medical profession has had a major responsibility, through delegated authority, for setting the standards of training for doctors after qualification, for the supervision of postgraduate examinations and for the inspection of training posts and accreditation for specialists, through the Joint Committees for Higher Medical (or Surgical) Training. There are now substantial moves to shift the responsibility for medical training requirements at all levels towards government control; at first by the introduction of the Specialist Training Authority (STA) and most recently by the Postgraduate Medical Education and Training Board (PMETB). On this Board, only a minority of members (6/19) are appointed by the Medical Colleges in spite of the fact that it is the specialist Fellows of the Colleges who continue to be largely responsible for the training programme and the trainees. While it is understandable that government, which takes ultimate responsibility for the NHS, must have a major interest in the quality of the people it employs to run the service, this shift of control could be one of the most insidious ways of undermining professionalism and the quality of medical practice – by simply imposing different standards and orientation to training.

Recent changes led by the Department of Health which have reduced the length, the breadth and the depth of training and experience before doctors are given responsibility as consultant physicians – a responsibility which may involve life and death decisions – are a particular concern. Many members of the profession are accepting this as a *fait accompli*. However, as many young doctors are finding that they are being forced to undertake responsibilities for which they are inadequately trained (and indeed may in some cases have led to their suspension from duty), the Royal Colleges and the GMC may need to stand up and be counted and insist on training programmes which they believe are necessary. The Colleges are having to compensate for deficiencies by setting up new consultant development programmes, recognising that the need for such retrieval exercises should not be necessary. Moreover, these types of 'crash' courses, although adding some valuable components from which we could all have benefited, can never replace adequately areas of medicine which are essentially based on experience. The analogy of fighter pilot training at the time of the Battle of Britain springs to mind. Because of the dire circumstances, their flying hours were cut to the barest minimum before they were sent into action. At that time Britain had its back to the wall and we had no alternative; everyone admired the sheer bravery of these young men but many lost their lives through inexperience. We should not expose either patients or young consultants to parallel risks in medicine today.

A watershed in the profession?

We may now be facing a watershed in the profession, and it is the doctors of the future who will have to make the decision on whether they wish to be employed to undertake a professional task, with all that this entails, or whether they prefer to contract their time and work largely as directed by others. This topic has been discussed in more detail in Professor Tallis' remarkable book, *Hippocratic oaths*.[6] The restrictive specifications in the 2004 consultants' contracts are bringing this central issue to a head.

There is repeated documented evidence from various sources, including the Royal College of Physicians' surveys,[7] that in practice, over the years, the vast majority of consultants worked far beyond their allotted sessions because of their professional commitment, and this has been a critical factor in the maintenance of standards in the NHS. In the past, this was both recognised and appreciated by local management. Indeed, evidence of doctors' dedication to the NHS was that their pay was relatively modest compared to that of doctors in many other countries. This fact underscored their commitment to medicine rather than the financial reward being their priority. So far this voluntary commitment has continued, albeit and sadly with considerably less appreciation than in former times. Warnings were frequently given in the early 1990s 'that when the goodwill runs out it could take more than peanuts to put the NHS together again'. It now looks as if this may be becoming a tragic reality. Quite understandably, in the new contracts, consultants are required to submit very precise timetables of their working week. At the same time, they are often told not to record work exceeding twelve or more sessions because extra work cannot be recognised or paid for. Paying for work and recognising it is being done are of course two quite different things. To expect the written record to reflect one commitment knowing that another is being undertaken in the interests of patients, is an unacceptable form of disguised hypocrisy – but of course hard-pressed local hospitals have little choice. Furthermore, as 'ring fencing' of non-clinical activities becomes more explicit in the new contracts, so time with patients, clinical research and teaching are potentially being seriously compromised. Perhaps even more worrying is that through our acceptance of the EU directives, junior doctors are committed to work to strictly controlled hours. When these doctors become consultants, who will then undertake the extended hours of professional commitment which has been a major bonus for the NHS for so many years?

There is no doubt that there is some truth in the argument that the personal expectations of individuals in today's society have changed. It is alleged that young people today are only prepared to work to satisfy their own life–work balance and that therefore the notion of a dedicated altruistic professional is a thing of the past. Further, with evidence that so many doctors now wish to work only part time, opportunities open for much greater managerial control on the ways in which they work and, unless great care is taken, this risks undermining professional authority where it is most needed – on clinical matters. While I respect those who wish to put their personal lives before their professional commitment, I believe, and indeed I continue to see, that many students enter medicine with the finest and dedicated professional motivation. They have the maturity to understand that the real reward in medicine, and indeed life, is the personal satisfaction derived from what they can give, even when it involves personal compromises – and not in what they take. So often it seems that it is the training system itself which seems to blunt their aspirations and lead to later disillusionment.[8] Of course, there are some who take a different view and I wonder whether they are suited to medicine. The dedicated ones must be recognised and nurtured through their training years by medical leadership if quality medicine as a professional activity is to survive.

Junior doctors (both individually and collectively) will have to bear a major responsibility for deciding whether medicine continues into the future as a profession – in the broadest sense – or whether they choose to abdicate this obligation. While, of course, the much shortened hours and the greater emphasis on training rather than in-service experience has greatly improved the working conditions for juniors, in some respects these changes also raise serious fundamental questions. Is the culture of medicine to be upheld through self-determined professional standards with dedicated commitment to patients, or is it to be developed along the lines of an artisan trade, where others determine the type of training required and dictate what types of patient care is permitted? These questions are addressed further in Chapter 20.

20. A remarkable service –
unfinished business:
A physician's perspective on the NHS

Along with an ever-diminishing group of clinicians, it has been my privilege to have worked within the NHS since it began. This seems to be an opportunity, as a doctor completely committed to the NHS, to recall some of the highlights of its huge successes, as well as some of the things that have, and still are, causing problems. Reforms intended to improve healthcare systems have been part of the business of the NHS over the last fifty years. How have these fared? Why is it that this brilliant social experiment continues to be such a bone of contention, especially in the media and between political parties? The simple fact is that while prescriptive policies may sometimes help, they cannot guarantee good patient care.[3]

The history of the first fifty years of the NHS has been fully recorded,[1,2] particularly emphasising the great improvements in recent years of its operational processes. Less has been written about how these managerial changes have enabled doctors to improve care for patients and maintain the quality of medical practice, although very recently this has attracted more attention. I hope this chapter will help to rebalance the 'bedside end' of a remarkable story of the NHS. Simply for brevity, when I refer to 'the medical profession' or to 'doctors' this is intended to include 'other healthcare workers' wherever it is appropriate.

This chapter takes a broad view of the successes of the NHS over the years and examines how the admittedly continuing difficulties have come about. It dares to suggest some principles to facilitate better progress. While these are essentially my own views based on some fifty years working with patients and management in the NHS, many of the points are substantiated in the recent published literature, as well as by professional colleagues of all ages. However, I do not expect everyone to agree all the time. I also accept that relatively little of the data have been published in peer reviewed journals as would be required for a scientific quality evidence base, but it seemed important to add selected references to emphasise that much of what is written here is not new.

Highlights of success

Very few countries have dared to be as bold as the UK in their national plans for caring for their sick, and the NHS has until very recently been the envy of the world. Not only is healthcare ideologically treated as a human right, the NHS is also seen as a just system where the entire population contributes financially to support those who become sick. The care system it provides is remarkably comprehensive, compared to that of other countries, and its cover is very cost effective in terms of percentage of the national Gross Domestic Product (GDP). Furthermore, it continues to be so in spite of costly technical advances of modern medicine and the ever-rising expectations of the public. It also has many other strengths. It provides the opportunity, as never before, for a comprehensive base for detailed epidemiological information on the prevention of illness. It strives to support medical research of all types to improve medical diagnosis and treatment, in a way that has been envied internationally. Linked with research, it is an invaluable structure upon which to base high-quality training of students and postgraduates, including those from overseas.

Thus for those in charge of the NHS and for those recommending changes, understanding the whole spectrum of this multifaceted public service is vital. It involves many government departments and agencies including the Treasury, Health, Social Services, Education, Research and Development, the Environment, Housing, Benefits, Employment and others – often referred to as OGDs (other government departments). All too often, focussed attempts have been made to improve one part of the service while ignoring or underestimating others. In consequence, what has been potentially a real advance in one area is simply overshadowed by the adverse knock-on effects on others. Nevertheless, in spite of this, the NHS remains a remarkable public service and has enabled Britain to contribute a very great deal to medicine worldwide. One could not ask for a greater accolade. I believe that the vast majority of doctors have been proud to be part of this great national enterprise and by and large they appreciate the efforts made by local managers and government to mastermind this huge endeavour. We now have to face the question – can it be maintained?

The very success of the NHS now threatens its survival, as demand outstrips the purchasing power to provide healthcare. Over the last fifty years, unimaginable advances have been made in all branches of medicine. Many diseases are being prevented, some are now curable and many others are controllable with a good quality of life. In consequence, people are surviving longer and require more medical services, the costs of which have risen steadily. This is distorting the balance between elderly sick people needing care and the relatively diminishing working population needed to support them. The seductive concept proposed by Aneurin Bevan in 1948,[4] that his National Health Service would improve the health of the population to such an extent that costs would actually fall, has proved sadly flawed. Of course, this does not mean that we should abandon our attempts to prevent illness as far as we possibly can.

While it may surprise some, I would suggest that perhaps one of the greatest advances of all in the history of the NHS is that in 2002 the Government made a commitment to increase the percentage of GDP spent on health by 2008, to equal that of most advanced countries in Europe. Provided this funding actually reaches patient services and includes capital developments as well as treatment funding, and is not diverted by costly management and regulatory functions or simply paying off service deficits, the Treasury, in a single stroke, will have made one of the biggest steps forward in the history of the NHS. Along with this, there is a new opportunity to define what the NHS should and should not pay for and in turn to share this with the public so that everyone understands where compromises have to be made.

Many clinical facilities have been transformed over the last fifty years to keep pace with medical advances. A small number of selected illustrations will give a flavour of what has been achieved. Some of these have evolved slowly, supported in turn by many different governments; others have been given particular impetus by various political parties. All deserve to take their share of the credit.

Building programmes

Although new hospital building was slow to begin after the Second World War, particularly because of the severe shortage of funds and lack of building materials, major programmes began in the 1960s and the capital stock of hospital buildings has been totally transformed since 1948. Sadly, momentum in capital investment was lost in the 1990s. In attempts to compensate for this, Private Funding Initiatives (PFIs) were promoted by both Conservative and Labour Governments. These are proving not to be the anticipated panacea. Although they remove capital projects from the balance sheet, the investment (with profits) has to be recouped in the end to make it worthwhile for the investor, and eventually the financial burden in some form must fall on the NHS.

Community services

Coinciding with the Medical Act of 1978, which imposed mandatory training programmes for GPs,[5] fine new general practice centres have been developing since the 1970s. These centres are now to be seen everywhere and this has allowed group practices to flourish with more recent opportunities for the development of General Practitioners with Special Interests (GPSIs), ie appropriately trained doctors in areas such as obstetrics, psychiatry and an increasing number of others. These practices also provide a base for an expanding range of specialist nurses who link with the community. Community practices contribute much to preventive medicine, including immunisation (measles, whooping cough, mumps, Rubella, tetanus), the early detection of hypertension, diabetes, osteoporosis and other long-term controllable conditions and, not least, advice to patients on lifestyle changes, including tobacco smoking, sexual health and obesity. Sadly, such advice has met with much less success because attempts by government to introduce controls are often regarded as an intrusion on individual freedom, even when the consequences of such lifestyle habits cost the NHS vast sums each year. It seems fundamentally wrong that government is forced to raise funds from general taxation to support those who, by their own choice, create a huge and largely avoidable financial burden on the NHS.

The growth and development of infants and toddlers is now routinely checked and the elderly are screened for early detection of their (often) multiple ailments. Greater attention has been paid to disorders relating to stress in the modern environment in all age groups. Much more could be said about the long and proud history of development of community-based medicine in the UK, which has been one of the best services in the world. Currently, however, there is a major concern that general practice, despite recent increased recruitment, is still not attracting anywhere near the numbers of doctors needed and the reasons for this must be addressed (see pages 268–9).

Other community services have also continued to develop over the years and more recently some dramatic innovations have been introduced. For example, the development of NHS Direct in 1998,[6] which handled over six million calls in 2003, has helped to compensate for the shortage of GPs and, through efficient networking, has probably helped protect overloaded accident & emergency services. Likewise, the new freedoms given to pharmacists should help protect both GPs and hospitals from being unnecessarily overloaded with patients with minor problems. These types of service are especially valuable and timely because they recognise the greater empowerment desired by patients. Social services are also providing, amongst other valuable services, care at home for patients who would otherwise have blocked hospital beds. In spite of these efforts, delayed discharge due to lack of alternative accommodation and poor coordination between community and hospital services (often limited by funding and staffing shortages) remain serious problems.

Improvements in treatments and facilities

The quality of hospital facilities and equipment has been vastly improved to keep pace with remarkable advances in scientific and medical technology. Intensive care is unrecognisable compared to twenty or so years ago. In recent years, there has been a major improvement in high-quality, acute medical services, especially in life-saving management of common medical and surgical conditions such as diabetes, heart conditions, infection, stroke, vascular diseases, trauma, etc. Indeed, the advances in the understanding, diagnosis and treatment of medical conditions is little short of staggering. Accident & emergency departments have been strategically redistributed into a smaller number of larger hospitals to allow them all to have sophisticated modern equipment and specialist teams. The more recent development of medical admissions units, with plans to staff these with more specialised teams, have not only kept pace well with modern medical advances, but have again relieved the over-extended accident & emergency departments.

Many other improvements in managing patients include the dramatic reduction in the lengths of stay in hospital – this together with increases in the number of day-stay procedures has enabled hospitals to increase their efficiency and treat a greater number of patients with shortened waiting times (although a distinction has to be made between the improvement of maximum and average waiting times). Amazing advances in surgical techniques, especially keyhole surgery, have transformed the specialty. The emergence of interventional radiology and therapeutic endoscopy has eliminated entirely the need for open surgery for many conditions. It is now asserted that up to 70–80% of elective surgery could be undertaken on a day-stay basis and much of this is due to the dramatic development of 'keyhole' surgery. This is a huge advance. However, whether day-stay surgery is really the most appropriate way to care for *all* these patients needs further consideration before this 'standard' is taken too far as a mandatory target. Many who have actually been day-stay patients would attest to this caution. After surgical interventions, many patients feel quite frail, insecure and lack confidence; they are often in considerable discomfort or indeed pain, they may be fearful and daunted by the prospect of travelling home, often to be left on their own. Frequently, they have to make their own arrangements to travel back again to the hospital over the next few days for stitch removals and other checks, and this often involves considerable time waiting for transport. While day-stay surgery for other than major procedures may be all that the NHS can afford – and it can be a very attractive alternative for some, especially those with strong family support – it is questionable whether under *all* circumstances this expedient approach is acceptable, especially for older patients.

Equality of care

Another notable improvement is the impressive downward trend in mortality from some common lethal diseases, such as some cancers and ischaemic heart disease. However, these are more likely to be due to medical advances and lifestyle changes than anything specifically relating to NHS managerial policies.

Although it has slowed down over the last decade, there was a steady increase in regional specialist services across the country, to augment the quality of care which is beyond the capacity of many district general hospitals. Such services include neurosurgery, some organ transplantation, and complex cardiac and vascular surgery in both adults and children. The designation of regional specialist centres (eg cancer centres and their supporting networks) has also improved and equalised the quality of cancer care throughout the country. These often allow patients to be treated reasonably near to their homes.

Taking a longer-term view, equality of care throughout the country has been considerably improved due to many factors, not least the redistribution of funds (eg through the Resource Allocation Working Party, 1976, and deprivation-weighted capitation-based funding). Equality of care is not, however, a managerial or financial matter alone; professional communication on evidence-based better practice has also helped. For example, with professional leadership, nationally agreed consensus guidelines on many medical conditions have been developed by the Royal Colleges and specialised societies over the past fifteen years or so. These have potentially raised the quality and equality of practice throughout the country. The guidelines are now being expanded by the Department of Health through the National Institute for Health and Clinical Excellence (NICE)[7] (see pages 258, 259) and a wide range of National Service Frameworks for clinical management, involving doctors and managers throughout the country.

While these examples demonstrate some of the national initiatives to improve equality of standards across the country, the balance between 'equity' and 'diversity' (allowing adaptation to the local environment) and the tensions between central control and devolution continue to raise unresolved problems. It seems very improbable that equality of service throughout the country will be improved by the plans to devolve responsibility to the NHS primary healthcare trusts and by the emergence of Foundation hospitals, each with its own financial priorities. The move to

241

ensure that local populations have a greater say in local services is seductively attractive but it may lead to greater differences in service provision in different parts of the country – as different priorities and local opinions prevail.

Organisational improvements and accountability

A number of notable organisational improvements, such as the measures taken to reduce waiting times for treatment, has been achieved and credit for this must be given to the management, working at many different levels in the NHS, as well as to successive governments. Management processes which actually raise the quality of medical practice are also obviously welcome. In particular, professional accountability has improved substantially over the last ten years and should also contribute to equality of service throughout the country. This improved accountability has been achieved by a number of specific initiatives, including medical audit, clinical governance, professional appraisal, continuing education and developments towards revalidation. These are linked with improvements in the transparency on how the profession tackles problems, how hospitals and others deal with complaints, how information and options are provided for patients, and so on. Not least, accountability has been improved through more specific guidance on good medical practice by the GMC.[8] The profession itself, through the Royal Colleges, the specialist societies and the BMA, has done much to collect data and to improve medical standards in a wide variety of ways. These include a large number of seminal publications, not only on medical topics, but on many other things including evidence-based medicine, guidelines on better practice and ethical issues. The Royal College of Physicians has also demonstrated its particular commitment to patients when changes in healthcare with serious knock-on effects have been imposed by law. For example, they published guidance to help preserve continuity of patient care when this was threatened by legal requirements imposed by EU regulations.[9]

Many of the Colleges have also helped management and government on organisational issues. For example, they send independent specialist teams to give specialist advice in a non-threatening way when front line clinical departments have professional problems. In addition, College representatives are often asked to play a major part on many Government technical committees but, as we shall see later, many of the statutory advisory bodies on which the Colleges had their own representatives have now been disbanded.

Constraints of funding have always dominated the medical scene – indeed this was a major factor in stimulating the earliest debates on the need for a nationalised service in the first place. However, financial issues were not regarded as a major concern for doctors in the earlier days of the NHS. There is now a much greater awareness of the need for cost effectiveness and efficiency by those working in the service. However, care must be taken to ensure that cost alone does not override the provision of proven good treatments. The dominating principle of cost containment, augmented by internal market forces introduced in the reforms of 1990, was found to be counter-productive and was partially reversed by a change of government in 1997.

The vast majority of those working closest to patients know full well that the views of patients are vital and that their individual needs vary widely (see Chapter 18). Indeed, doctors have often been criticised for paying too much attention to the individual patient and not enough to population-based information. However, over the years the vast machinery of the NHS has sometimes lost sight of the views of patients. Attempts to ensure that management reorganisation is patient centred are reflected in the titles of several national reviews of the service by various governments (eg *Patients first* (1979),[10] *Working for patients* (1989)[11] and more recently in *Building on the best – choice, responsibility and equity* (2003)[12]). Although their intentions were good, in practice they mainly focussed on organisational and management reforms on the assumption that this would improve patient care – an assumption that does not necessarily follow. The emphasis on 'patient-centred' services is also reflected in the increase in lay membership on a wide variety of committees at all levels of the NHS, the GMC and patient forums. This involvement is welcomed but one needs to remember that the views on priorities held by healthy members of the population can change radically when they themselves become ill. In addition, undue pressure from individual patient groups must not be allowed to distort judgements on the overall provision of services or the distribution of funds.

Litigation

In spite of these major improvements in the NHS, the numbers of complaints and amount of litigation have increased substantially. There are many reasons for this, which do not necessarily indicate a declining service. Amongst these explanations are the greatly increased expectations of the public, the opportunities for large financial awards by the courts, and the new NHS indemnity arrangements which are likely to encourage patients to complain.

Attempts at 'quality' improvement

All are agreed that the central objective in the NHS is to improve quality and the emphasis on this in the 'New NHS' proposals in 1997 was an admirable step forward.[13] 'Quality', however, can be defined in many different ways. Quality of *processes* in the NHS includes quality of management, of regulation, of funding, of information, of training and even assessments of opportunities for clinical developments and research. In these, surrogates to measure achievement are fairly easy and indeed, for some, it is possible to legislate or at least issue quantitative directives (eg implementation of immunisation programmes which will certainly prevent illness and therefore improve life). But others may be irrelevant to quality of patient care. For example, achieving targets to undertake more surgical operations to reduce waiting times does not measure the quality of care received by these patients while undergoing the procedures. Indeed, measurement of the quality of patient care itself, as perceived by both patients and doctors, is far more subtle and such standards cannot be legislated – *pace* Gordon Dunstan! The methodology for measuring these different qualities, which may be quantitative or qualitative, can be surprisingly elusive. Surrogate quantitative measurements (or 'second order' evaluations as described by Baroness O'Neill[14]) can of course be analysed in terms of achieving targets, of transferring patients from hospitals to the community, of length of waiting lists and elective surgery, or of adapting the service to compensate for other deficiencies. One must always remember that these alone do not guarantee quality of care (the 'first order' requirement). This difference is at the heart of the matter.

Some of these endeavours to improve management processes can become double-edged. For example, attempts to monitor improvement in 'second order' quality and processes have resulted in a veritable explosion in the number of regulatory bodies sometimes referred to as the 'NHS alphabet soup'.[15] There is CHAI (now renamed HC), CPPIH, ICAS, NCAA, NICE, PAF, MESB, MANPSA, to mention just a few. Unfortunately, initiatives designed to improve standards so often simply generate new rafts of managers to implement and monitor the well-intended plan. This proliferation can be as frustrating for frontline managers who are trying to run hospitals as for the professionals trying to maintain high standards of patient care. Good management should be about helping healthcare professionals care for patients; not by overburdening managers with the task of imposing directives from a higher authority which, however well intended, have been selected not necessarily for their importance but on the pragmatic grounds of whether they can be measured easily or are politically attractive. There is an important distinction to be made between constructive accountability, such as audit of doctors' professional work, and their compliance with directives.

Sadly, the track record of governments' efforts to assess the effects of their major re-organisational schemes in terms of their effects on the quality of patient care and treatment is in general rather poor. However, credit must be given to two initiatives: the recent Nuffield report (2003), *In quest of quality improvement in the NHS*,[15] and the Healthcare Commission surveys on patients'[16] and staff opinion (2004).[17] The former makes a valiant attempt to assess independently the first five years of progress of the government's plan, *The new NHS: modern, dependable*.[13] It identifies the problems of collecting data on quality and also summarises some very substantial progress. The tabulated list of government publications and announcements over the last five years is impressive. The report sets out the substantial number of managerial and regulatory processes accomplished and the welcomed improvement in funding over the last five years. It also recognises the impressive improvements in the numbers of patients accessing the service for particular conditions based on the achievement of targets – although one has to take some of these with a pinch of salt, recognising the ingenuity of those compelled to comply with such numerical targets. The report also implies that the falling mortality for some cancers and ischaemic heart disease is in some way due to the policy changes and, as welcome as these figures are, this downward trend has been shown for some years and it may not be valid (as implied) to claim that these are due to the introduction of the New NHS plan. For example, the mortality from myocardial infarction had been declining substantially for several years before government targets were introduced.[18]

On the other hand, the document also identifies a number of areas where the New NHS has not yet been shown to be successful. Some are due to lack of data because they are more difficult to measure. However, two other vital areas received scant mention in the report, namely the views of patients and those of doctors. These areas are central to what the NHS is about. The survey evidence so far is not entirely consistent. Some show that a substantial number of patients in the UK (31% in one survey)[19] were dissatisfied with the healthcare system, and doctors (42% generalists and 49% specialists) expressed equally strong views that the quality of care that they could give had deteriorated in the last five years.[19] On the other hand, the recent Healthcare Commission survey on patient opinion gives a more favourable picture where, for example, 91% of patients selected by their criteria found the overall hospital service excellent or at least good.[16] Even this survey, however, demonstrated that patients were not involved enough in their care; they did not receive adequate information; and many had substantial delays in seeing their GP or being admitted to a ward bed following an emergency hospital attendance. Until these issues are addressed seriously with proper input from those directly involved, the gulf between the *improvements* as perceived by managers and statisticians and the *deficiencies* perceived by patients and those actually caring for them, will continue to pass each other as ships in the night.

These data are very much in line with the views expressed so eloquently by Professor Chris Ham (2003).[20] He puts his finger on the fundamental problem:

> *faced with funding pressures on the one hand and service delivery failures on the other, policy makers have entertained radical solutions in the hope that they will lead to improvements in healthcare system performance. In practice, reform has generally fallen short of both the rhetoric and expectations leading to reappraisals of strategies pursued and a search for new policies.*

As he points out, improvements depend on 'making a difference to the experience of patients and service users and this in turn depends on the decisions made by doctors, nurses and other professionals'.

Thus 'there is a gap between policy intent and delivery of care'. In other words, what patients really want and need and what the professional can do to help them, has a very different focus from what policy-makers think will improve management processes. While it might be thought that if management of healthcare and good systems are in place this will automatically equate with what patients really want and what doctors and others can provide, the perverse truth is that the one does not automatically follow from the other. Unless this gap is addressed and closed, the management and policy makers will continue to focus on *quality improvements of management,* often assessed by numerical targets and regulatory processes, and the public and the professions will continue to feel disillusioned and disenfranchised. The fact remains that even when economists and statisticians can show that overall more patients have been put through the system more quickly and more cost-effectively, the quality of medicine is not reflected in numbers alone. In 1985, Rosemary Rue,[21] reviewing the evolution of the NHS, concluded that 'the evolution of the results of management change remains elusive in terms of health and health services', and this seems to remain equally elusive today.

By and large, patients are not interested in quality improvements in regulation or management and they are certainly not interested in measurement methodology or even epidemiological data. In spite of the many major improvements to the NHS over the last fifty years, it still does not always provide a service that meets the perceived needs of the people. Perhaps this is never possible. If this is the case, it must be shared openly with the public.

What has happened in the NHS to allow this gap to develop?

This controversial but fundamental issue must now be tackled. It raises major questions about the relationships between and roles of healthcare professionals on the one hand and policy makers and management on the other; both are necessary to meet the personal needs of members of the public – the 'users' – who, in the end, are paying for the service (albeit through taxation).

Even in the most primitive societies, there has always been a clear distinction between the role and authority of the tribal chief (ie the manager) and that of their 'witch' doctor (ie the professional)! It seems to be an inescapable fact that a clear distinction has to be made between government's relationship with *professionals* (ie people with their independent codes of discipline and conduct, skills, standards, ethics and commitment to the 'user') who are responsible for delivering a service, and their relationship to employees who are *artisans* (albeit sometimes extremely skilled) but who are paid to work to whatever standards and conditions the employers wish to set.

Because of the personal nature of the service – and this applies to other professions including education and law as well as medicine – there is a high degree of interdependence between the professional provider and the user involved. Indeed, the fact is that the skilled and committed professional usually has a closer commitment to the user (patient, pupil or plaintiff) than to the employer. In other words, in medicine the patient/doctor relationship is paramount. This is discussed further in Chapter 18. Anything that weakens or disrupts it will damage patients' confidence in a service in which they often have to trust their lives. At the same time, members of the medical profession working in the NHS are not independent providers (as they would be in private practice) and they must recognise the need for a good working relationship with management and government. To be successful, this partnership must have special qualities – it must be equal, trusting and respectful on both sides.

Government is in the end accountable to Parliament and the people. In its turn, management is responsible to government. The skilled professional in the NHS, however, is accountable for different things, to three distinct 'authorities' – to their patients, to their professional code and ethos, and to managers. This particular triad of accountability adds to the strength of the professionals' overall commitment, rather than diminishing it.

It is worth reiterating what Baroness Onora O'Neill said so eloquently in her Reith Lectures in 2002: 'If we want a culture of public service, professionals and public servants must in the end be free to serve the public rather than their paymasters'.[22]

Thus, on the following pages the case will be made for the absolute necessity for doctors to foster two distinct partnerships – with patients on the one hand and with managers on the other. Lack of understanding or an unwillingness to accept these basic concepts is at the root of many of the continuing difficulties in the NHS. Only by restoring these in a very positive way can the NHS truly begin to meet the needs of the people. Evidence for this contention will be summarised by looking briefly at the history of the NHS under three headings. First, the effects of *organisational* changes on the NHS; second, the changing role of doctors in the professional/management relationship; and third, the factors underlying the dissatisfaction of some patients and the concerns of doctors on quality of healthcare. It will then be possible to draw conclusions about how the situation could be improved.

Management and organisational changes in the NHS

In 1988, Relman suggested that the evolution of health services could be divided into three 'eras'.[23] Although he was referring to the USA, similar trends can be found in the UK.

The first period, from the 1940s to the 1960s, was the **Era of Expansion**. In the UK, there were three areas of expansion: obtaining the cooperation of enough doctors to staff the service; rectifying inequalities in services throughout the country; and renovating the capital stock which had been severely neglected during the Second World War.

At the beginning of the NHS debate in the late 1940s, many clinicians were opposed to the scheme – doctors are an essentially conservative lot – and they were accused by others of simply being motivated by their private practice. While this may have been true for some, one must remember that at this time consultants received no salaries from teaching hospitals and gave all their services to patient care and teaching voluntarily without payment. Their main reason for scepticism was based on their concerns that their independent capacity to treat their patients in the latter's best interest might be compromised and that the cost and scale of such an operation could not possibly be made to work. In this, history has amply demonstrated that they were certainly justified in having reservations on both scores.

However, once the Rubicon had been crossed, the vast majority of doctors joined the service, and became enthusiastic supporters of its ideology. They have been trying to make it work in practice ever since. There is no doubt that the NHS was greatly welcomed by the public, not least because almost everyone has need of it at some time during their lives. Thus no subsequent government so far has dared to abandon its basic principles, although it has certainly become the victim of its own success, and its problems now feature prominently on the agendas of all political parties.

In the early days of the NHS, the gulf between the quality and numbers of staff, and between teaching and non-teaching hospitals, led to inequalities in care of patients. The British trained medical students aspiring to go up the ladder to consultant posts remained at the teaching hospitals, a large number of which (some 30%), for historic reasons, were located in London. Thus in the early days of the NHS, hospitals in the south of England had many more British-trained junior staff than the north which depended on doctors from overseas, coming to this country for postgraduate training. While many of these doctors were outstanding and became leading figures worldwide – and indeed many are close colleagues and Fellows of the various Royal Medical Colleges – many others certainly had a disadvantaged undergraduate training in Asia and had considerable language difficulties which made communication with patients difficult.

The inequalities of junior staff across the country was to some extent counterbalanced by the high quality of ex-service men returning in large numbers from the war. The competition for consultant jobs in the early decades of the NHS was intense and many had to take any post on offer, including those located in what was often regarded as less desirable parts of the country where, as we have seen, the quality of hospital buildings was at that time poor and the junior staff scanty. The contribution to the equality of care in the early days of the NHS by these excellent ex-service men and women, who had already served their country with distinction during the war, should not be underestimated.

It is not surprising that the inequalities, between the staffing and facilities of teaching and non-teaching hospitals, between London and 'the provinces' and between the north and the south, were widely resented by the doctors looking after the patients. It also caused major criticisms about the distribution of funding between London and the rest of the country. For these reasons and as teaching and non-teaching centres throughout the UK improved, the pressures to redistribute funds away from London increased.

In spite of recent criticisms, it should not be forgotten that over the years there has been a sea change in the correction of these inequalities. Some of this is due to the great progress which has been taken towards social equality in general in the UK. More specifically, the hospital building programmes throughout the country, burgeoning from the 1960s onwards, have been one of the great successes of the NHS. The expansion of some of the older medical schools and the successful development of 'newer' ones around the country, including those in Manchester, Liverpool,

Newcastle, Bristol, Birmingham, Sheffield, Nottingham, Southampton, Cardiff, Oxford and Cambridge and others, has substantially shifted the traditional domination of London and Edinburgh. Not least because, along with rebuilding of hospitals and medical schools away from London and the equalisation of standards across the country, medical research of international standing has burgeoned in many centres throughout the UK. The trend towards decentralisation of quality services has been further helped by the lower cost of living outside London, the better quality of life, affordable housing, and the social and educational opportunities in many fine cities. All of these factors have made both clinical and managerial staff appointments outside London increasingly attractive.

The second period described by Relman was the **Era of Cost Containment**, which extended from the 1960s to the 1980s. It focussed on how to contain costs of the ever-increasing demand. Once committed to the ideology of providing free healthcare for all to an equal standard throughout the country, the ensuing problems of how to run the gigantic machine and how to pay for it have been the preoccupation of governments ever since. Governments both to the right and the left have been responsible for what follows. This is not an indictment of any one political party, although it may in places be critical of the intrusion of party politics into a public service which many believe should be more distanced from such immediate (but understandable) political pressures and timescales (see also page 279). There has been no shortage of Reviews, Royal Commissions and Specialist Reports, which scatter like confetti through the history of the NHS. They have in common admirable intentions of trying to maintain the service and contain costs, and considerable rhetoric. In spite of these good intentions, the recommendations in many have been overtaken by others often reversing the decisions of earlier ones, creating what could best be described as the 'Yin Yang' of the NHS. A delicate balance has to be struck between exploring new ideas to solve difficult problems and constant destabilising changes.

A brief and oversimplified summary of some of these attempts by different governments to contain costs while meeting increasing demands gives a flavour of the ever-changing NHS management policies over the last fifty years. It is easy to forget that these repeated and well-intended attempts at reorganisation have resulted in huge costs, both in time and manpower, for those trying to implement them, and who are at the same time trying to maintain the service. When these reorganisations have proved evanescent, confidence in the policy-makers is understandably undermined. It is to the considerable credit to the robustness of all those dedicated to running the service that the NHS has survived and indeed progressed, by endeavouring to build on the best of the successive reorganisations.

The first report to question whether the NHS could meet and fund the demand for healthcare was published in 1956,[24] just eight years after its beginning. Within another ten years, in 1968, it was believed (and the theoretical arguments were strong) that better coordination of Health and Social Security would be achieved if they were merged into a single Department of Health and Social Security (DHSS); this lasted twenty years, until 1988, when it was felt that management would be simplified if they were separated again. Notwithstanding this, the debate has now returned, fifteen years later in 2003, to consider whether they should come together once more to facilitate more 'joined up' inter-department action. There are good arguments to be made for both arrangements, but these may not justify such repeated vacillation when balanced against the massive upheavals they cause.

In 1972,[25] in order to coordinate and manage services within clear geographical boundaries, a whole new tier of management was introduced with the creation of ninety area health authorities (AHAs) which, incidentally, tried to entrain all the undergraduate teaching hospitals to bring their management into line with non-teaching district general hospitals; although their responsibilities were of course very different. In 1979, within a few years of this major reorganisation to introduce AHAs, a Royal Commission[26] was set up to review the organisational problems stemming from them. This was followed by a DHSS report entitled *Patients first*[10] – a title recycled ten years later in the 1989 White Paper as *Working for patients.*[11] This concluded that the multi-tiered system had proved costly, complex and created overstretched lines of communications. In consequence, the AHAs were disbanded in 1982, just eight years after their introduction, and replaced by 192 district health authorities. The re-juggling of the tiers of administration above the district health authorities has continued unabated. In 1992, the sixteen regional health authorities which oversaw the work of the district general hospitals were at first reduced to eight, but in 1996 they were abolished and replaced by regional offices of the NHS Executive and twenty-eight strategic health authorities (SHAs) to oversee management performance, resource allocations, workforce planning and research development. In 2005, there are murmurings that the SHAs may be under review once again. So the pendulum continues to swing.

In 1983, Sir Roy Griffiths[27] rightly recognised that, as the NHS developed, stronger management within hospitals was necessary and that the quality of management had lagged behind that of commerce and industry. Attempts were made to recruit well-paid general managers from industry to provide management leadership, working, as he stressed, alongside clinicians who he hoped would take a larger role in management. He argued that if our problems of inefficiency and waste were corrected by stronger leadership the apparent under-funding of the NHS would be solved.

In 1987 and partly highlighted by the understandably more aggressive attempts by management to control costs, the perceived declining standards of patient care, particularly by covert rationing through waiting lists and the obvious cash shortages, began to attract unfavourable press coverage. As the inadequacies of the service came to public notice, often highlighted by some tragic or unacceptable failure (and the media have not been backward in highlighting these), the three Presidents of the Royal Colleges of Surgeons, Physicians and Obstetrics and Gynaecology endeavoured to persuade the Government to take notice by seeking an audience with a Minister of Health and holding a press conference. While this seemed to be an eminently sensible way to help Government understand some of the grave problems facing the clinical services in the NHS, this did not go down well and the Government of the time undertook a further reform (ten years after the 1979 Royal Commission), which they declared was to be the most radical since the inception of the NHS.

This time the reforms were based particularly on the principles of the commercial world and models provided by economists. The primary consideration was to contain costs and the essential role of the Boards of the new Trust hospitals was to ensure that they remained in positive balance each year. Thus, in 1989 a White Paper[11] was published in which it proposed that the district health authorities (DHAs) would no longer be responsible for running the service. As 'purchasers' they would contract services from 'provider' hospital Trusts working in open market competition. This separation of the 'purchaser' from the 'provider' was considered to be fundamental. Idiosyncratically, however, GPs were encouraged by financial inducements to become 'fund holding' – responsible for 'purchasing' services from hospitals and elsewhere along business lines – as well as ' providing' the service for their patients. Many GPs refused to take up this dual role and the principle of fund holding became a very divisive issue amongst GPs.

Many of the consequences, both for better and for worse, of the 1991 reforms have been discussed elsewhere.[2] Amongst the worse consequences were perceptions of increased inequality in the service and the increased costs of management, with the appointment of 10,000 new managers within three years.[2] One of the most serious, but perhaps inadvertent, effects was that of making cost containment a top priority, over and above care, for Trust Boards. Budgetary considerations took a more dominant role in decision making and this posed a serious threat to some of the core values of the NHS.

The third period, the **Era of Accountability and Assessment**, starting for the UK in the early 1990s, focussed on seeking new strategies to strengthen government regulatory and control systems, with the expectation that these would solve the continuing problems of dissatisfaction with the service. This has been touched on in Chapter 19 and will be discussed in the following section on 'The changing roles of doctors in the professional/management relationship in the NHS' (see pages 254–61) because it relates especially to regulation of the healthcare professions.

After the change of government in 1997, 'purchasing' fund-holding GPs, introduced just seven years before, were disbanded and replaced by 'commissioning' primary care groups which later became primary care trusts (PCGs and PCTs).[13] These bodies are currently responsible for contracting services particularly in the community, as well as with the hospitals. They are charged with the responsibility of improving the quality of the service with more rigorous monitoring of outcomes and performance, and the documentation linked with this is already imposing new pressures on front-line services. They have also taken over many of the 'purchasing' functions of the DHAs. Thus, those GPs involved in PCTs are now also purchasers responsible for deciding on the priorities of service provision against national directives and within a tight budget. Not only does this put them in a position of conflicting interests but it has the potential to undermine the principles of equity of services throughout the country, as different priorities are given at a local level to different services. It also seems to be steering general practice towards a business orientation where all services have an immediate price tag and where costs and contracting once again dominate. In consequence, bureaucracy is becoming burdensome and there is less and less time for patients.

At the end of the 1990s, the 'internal market' principles were largely abandoned because it was perceived that these were fragmenting care. They were replaced by strategic planning. Competition between Trust hospitals, which in any case hardly applied in rural areas, was also shown to be counterproductive, inhibiting collaboration and rationalisation of resources where they were most needed. Therefore Trusts were encouraged to move towards mergers to form larger 'provider' units.

Thus, by about 1998 many of the major principles underlying the 1990 reforms had been abandoned or radically revised. One cannot help feeling that many of these U-turns could have been avoided and money saved if the Government of the time had heeded the constructive analyses and questions submitted by the Academy of Medical Royal Colleges' response to the White Paper of 1989, which expressed the united views of the Royal Colleges and offered a number of positive suggestions (see page 155).

Quite correctly, the New NHS of 1998 tried to place much greater emphasis on the quality of the NHS rather than simply focussing on cost control (see page 244). However, this is not yet the end of the story, because in 2003 Government promoted again the notion of some selected independent 'Foundation' hospitals, which were to have greater financial and other freedoms. These, together with competition created by Treatment Centres, and compulsory tendering from independent hospitals under 'patient choice', recreate the emphasis on market pressures. Thus, as some wit put it, 'the pendulum is again swinging back in a full circle'. Very little information has been given about how the obvious implications for patient care, estimations of staffing requirements, training and medical research will be protected and yet be compatible with the much promoted 'freedoms'. It is a pity that so far there has been no review of the lessons learnt from 1990 or 1997, or how circumstances now differ, to reassure the public that the pitfalls experienced before will be avoided. Indeed, within a few months of their establishment, the Foundation hospitals expressed publicly their concerns that their financial freedoms and profits are to be much more restricted than originally expected. This retraction of freedoms seems very similar to that experienced by Trust hospitals after they were set up in the early 1990s.

Everyone recognises that things cannot stand still and innovative managerial solutions are needed to solve the problems of the NHS, improve efficiency and achieve better controls. These must obviously be supported positively when there is good evidence that change is for the better. However, the wastage in terms of time and money spent in repeated revolutionary radical reorganisation, with scant appraisal of the consequent advantages and disadvantages, and their potential to destabilise other efforts towards greater efficiency, suggest that it is time to take stock and consider what has been learnt in the longer term from all these upheavals. The NHS remains a high priority for public votes. As these can be easily won or lost it puts great pressure on successive governments, with a timescale dictated as much by political agendas as by clinical needs. However, putting major administrative structures in place simply to tear them down a few years later makes no sense and is exceedingly disruptive and expensive, however good the intention at the time. In this age of evidence-based medicine, evidence-based management reforms would be wonderfully persuasive and provide much needed public confidence.

The changing roles of doctors in the professional/management relationship in the NHS

Two principles were recognised from the earliest days of the NHS. The first was the importance to patients of the individual patient/doctor relationship. Although this is now challenged by some, I believe that it remains as important to them today as ever. It would have been useful to include a verification of this principle in the recent Healthcare Commission's patient survey because it is central to issues on quality of patient care. The second was the recognition that the success of the NHS depended on a medical profession committed both to running the clinical service and to helping maintain its standards, working alongside managers.

In general terms, and covering roughly the same time periods as in the organisational evolution, there have been three 'Eras' of change in professional/management relationships. The first (approximately 1948–67) was an **Era of Expansion** of the service where the administration tried to support the demands set out by the doctors. The second (approximately 1967–84) introduced consensus corporate management in an attempt to **control costs** due to rising demand. The third (approximately 1984–2004) was dominated increasingly by government and management in order to **strengthen accountability and regulatory control** of NHS personnel.

Era of expansion: doctors leading

Between 1948 and 1967, the medical service in the hospitals was (for better and for worse) led by doctors; they tried to do their best for their patients within the constraints of medical knowledge and the facilities available at the time, but there was very little – indeed most would agree too little – accountability. They were assisted by a small band of relatively poorly paid administrators. At a local level, the profession as a group worked through the medical committees of their hospitals. Its medical chairman, chosen by them and usually one of the senior clinicians, represented them when working with the administration. Funds were allocated on a historic basis and, however inequitable, which they certainly were, this led to fairly straightforward accounting. Such a system could not possibly last as the impact of growing demand for increasingly costly medical advances became evident.

During this period, the Joint Consultants Committee, set up in 1948, formed the statutory liaison body at a national level, where the profession, represented by the Presidents of the Royal Medical Colleges and the British Medical Association (who represented a major proportion of the GPs) met with the Chief Medical Officer from the Department of Health about four times a year to discuss major *clinical* issues. Trades union matters were discussed separately by the DH and the BMA. Whether this body functioned satisfactorily can be debated. Many certainly felt that its style was too confrontational and its agenda not constructed in a way to promote collaborative work on real problems. However, the principle of a statutory body, as a high-level meeting point between the profession and government is, I believe, sound.

Consensus management

Between 1967 and 1982, advances in medicine made it difficult for administrators alone to handle the expanding NHS and better proactive management was necessary to husband resources. A more formal system of corporate management was gradually introduced. A serious attempt was made in 1967 to strengthen the clinical input into management through the 'cogwheel system',[28] where consultants within their specialty worked together in a small number of divisions (eg medicine, surgery, support services etc), and were encouraged to define their needs to improve the services within the funds available. The medical committee structure continued and the medical committee chairman represented the whole body of consultants when negotiations with management on the priorities between divisions had to be set. This recognised the importance of the clinicians' view on patient care and the value of the professionals, supported by a consensus style, working alongside a small management team. The principle of consensus management and the importance of partnership between the profession and management reflected the spirit of the time. Until 1982, this style of highly participative corporate management continued with doctors involved at every level.[21] Centrally, the Department of Health obtained medical advice from an extended range of statutory advisory and consultative committees on which, *crucially, the medical representatives were appointed from the independent professional bodies,* such as the Medical Royal Colleges and the BMA, and not by government. These included JPAC (Joint Planning Advisory Committee) on manpower and workforce issues, SMAC (Specialist Medical Advisory Committee) on clinical standards, CPME (Council for Postgraduate Medical Training), and SCOPME (Specialist Committee on Postgraduate Medical Education) on medical training issues. Again, the effectiveness of these can be criticised and again, sadly, some of these tended to become confrontational. I suspect that the Department of Health sometimes found them tiresome and the professional representatives often felt that they were a waste of time. Not enough care was taken, on either side, to encourage constructive open debate and positive action. However, the principle of recognising the partnership between government and the medical profession remains crucially important.

Management as leader

Consensus management had survived for about fifteen years but in 1983,[27] following advice from Sir Roy Griffiths, it was then replaced by more conventional business-style management in an attempt to improve leadership, cost control and strategic development, with a general manager, later chief executive, at the helm. As the system developed, the powers of management tended to increase and, with this, the powers of the medical committees were correspondingly diminished. Policies were now developed by the general manager and his small team, and their decisions were taken directly to the Board, sometimes simply for endorsement. Naturally, different hospitals had their own variations on this general theme and they introduced their own new arrangements over different time spans. While many hospitals retained their medical committees, they no longer had any official status in the management structure. The clinical directors, introduced in the late 1980s, then became the main formal link between management and the practising consultants, but they were appointed by management, not the consultant body. Although many of the management principles introduced by Griffiths were good and have survived, all this was not enough to correct the ailments of the NHS, especially its finances and growing public dissatisfaction.

Erosion of the professional/management equal partnership

In the reforms of 1990, the medical profession was largely marginalised. The driving force behind the contractual requirements (eg cost and volume of work) and other targets set by government (eg waiting lists and waiting times etc), were set by managers and purchasers, and these requirements often took priority over meeting the needs of individual patients, as cost dominated the agenda. Thus the principle of a substantial partnership between the profession and management began to be eroded.

Since 1990, various governments have steadily dismantled the various professional/government advisory and consultative committees. JPAC (Joint Planning Advisory Committee) was disbanded and replaced by SWAG (Specialist Workforce Advisory Group) in which the Department of Health took greater control over workforce numbers. In turn, this was disbanded and replaced by the Workforce Review Team with no formal involvement from the professional bodies. Some of the delegated powers (eg accreditation of Completion of Specialist Training) of the Colleges' Joint Committees on Higher Medical (or Surgical) Training were replaced by the Specialist Training Authority (STA), and this in turn was replaced by PMETB (Postgraduate Medical Education and Training Board), with only six of some 19 members allocated for representation from the Royal Colleges. Other aspects of training were developed by the Department of Health under the Calman training scheme. SCOPME, SMAC (Specialist Medical Advisory Committee) and the recently formed CSAG (Clinical Standards Advisory Group), have now lapsed or been more formally disbanded.

Thus there has been a steady shift from the philosophy of partnership, reflected in the joint advisory committees, towards government control of standards, training and workforce numbers.

Building new relationships

On the other hand, different types of interface with the medical profession are now being developed. Some are undoubtedly working successfully on different specific issues. The question is whether these can adequately replace most of the formal joint structures, where the profession as equal partners were responsible for appointing their own representatives and had the right to bring forward their own agenda items requiring attention. It is worth looking at one or two examples.

A government-controlled agency, the National Institute for Clinical Excellence (NICE) was set up as a special health authority in 1999,[7] with members appointed by government but chaired by a senior physician. Amongst its various responsibilities, it provides technical appraisals of new and currently available treatments and sets out mandatory guidance for their availability within the NHS. Clear directives based on good evidence to make new treatments available to patients quickly is obviously helpful to all.

Through seven National Collaborating Centres, organised through the Royal Colleges and supported by the various specialist societies, NICE also supervises the development of some guidelines. By and large the collaborative system seems to work well. Their reports and guidelines are very valuable and the system is a good example of how government and the professional bodies can work together, provided that NICE does not overrule on grounds of costs and exclude well-proven effective treatments without full explanation to the public. However, the guidelines' limitations must also be remembered. Often based on randomised controlled trials, they represent the overall findings for populations, not individuals. Within these, individual responses inevitably vary, so guidelines cannot replace doctors' judgement on their appropriateness for individual patients, although doctors must of course be aware of what the guidelines recommend and be prepared to defend their judgement. This balance is at the heart of good medical practice. The best treatment for individual patients, often being seen at very different stages of disease or with other complicating factors, varies widely and the evidence-based best treatment for them, as individuals, is often not covered adequately in controlled clinical trials. What is right for one patient may be wrong for another and it would be unwise for personalised care to become replaced by protocol-driven medicine (see Chapter 19). Because evidence is always incomplete, the expert panels in charge of the guidelines often have to make recommendations based only on their own judgements. While this may be helpful to practising clinicians and for the time being, it must not assume an unwarranted authority.

If the contributions from NICE summarising the explosion of information in the published literature are applied wisely, this is a very helpful advance. However, great care will be needed to ensure that these guidelines are not used by others as directives or in over-prescriptive ways for regulatory purposes. Moreover, the number of guidelines covered by NICE is in fact quite small. The majority are still provided by specialist societies and other professional bodies. None of these, however, claim for themselves an authoritative monopoly. Let us be clear: the work of NICE itself is not in question; it is the way in which it could be used by others, including regulators, which is the potential danger.[29,30] If guidance from NICE based on incomplete evidence is used by regulators in prescriptive ways, the essential discipline of humility and the awareness of the limitations of medical knowledge could be overruled or disappear and good medical practice could be seriously threatened. There is no monopoly on wisdom.

Another statutory body, the Council for Healthcare and Audit Improvements (CHAI), now renamed the Healthcare Commission, whose membership is largely non-medical, started work in 2004 to promote improvement in quality in the NHS. It has the potential to do most valuable work. If it is to succeed, it will need to work very closely with those responsible for delivering healthcare, understanding the complexity of factors influencing improvements. Problems need solving collaboratively rather than apportioning blame. The quotation 'While the National Institute for Clinical Excellence (NICE) is expected to tell doctors what to do, the new Commission for Health Improvement (CHI) will make sure that they do it'[2] was most unfortunate because it implies that government has turned its back on any concept of a professional/management partnership at a time when it is most needed. Let us hope that this is not the case.

It is important to stress the very many different ways in which the profession continues to find new ways to help government, in spite of the disbanding of so many of the more formal links. Indeed, on specific issues these may be a better way of working. One only has to read the Colleges' regular Commentaries and News Bulletins to see the amount of detailed work being undertaken by different departments in the Medical Royal Colleges to support the government and the NHS. The medical profession also continues to serve on many specific and technical committees (with a membership most commonly appointed by government), and the Colleges and specialist societies in particular spend much voluntary time helping and advising at many different levels. The development of National Service Frameworks to define service standards is another example of joint working between the profession and the DH which has worked quite well. However, it is important to make sure that, when such efforts are made, the conclusions of all these deliberations are actually implemented. Consultation without positive implementation of agreements is not good use of time. Another practical attempt to foster better understanding between physicians and managers, who together are actually trying to run the service, is the national joint meetings organised by the Royal College of Physicians for Trust Board members and physicians from across the country to meet at a national level and share their ideas.

Overall, many feel that the informal liaison between the College Presidents and their representatives and the DH has improved over the last few years compared to the preceding decade, and this is certainly very welcome progress. But this is only the beginning; more formal equal partnership arrangements are also necessary.

Tsars

In addition to the various arrangements for the profession and the DH to work together, individual professional experts (eg Tsars) have been instated by the DH to progress its agendas on specific initiatives. But, however well intended the policies and however well respected these individuals may be, this is no substitute for a real professional/management partnership. This is not to belittle the advice from these experts, especially when they have the confidence of their peers. There is, however, a real danger that the DH has been required to depend too heavily on these individual views, rather than seek directly advice from professional bodies whose constituent members are actually trying to operate the service in many different parts of the country.

The Royal Colleges' need to do more

On the other hand, we must openly recognise that part of the blame for the development of mistrust of professional bodies by government must rest with the profession itself. Individual Royal Colleges may have done much good work separately, but they have not joined together adequately so that the profession can speak with one voice on clinical matters affecting them all. Sir Donald Irvine has set out the evidence for this in several published lectures and highlighted the dire consequences of failure.[31,32] I believe an effective, strong and trusted body, for example developed from the Academy of Medical Royal Colleges, which speaks with a single voice, puts self-interest aside and works independently from the BMA is needed very urgently to speak on clinical matters. This would complement the good work now being done successfully by the Academy of Medical Sciences on medical research. In my view, it should be top of the agenda for all the Royal Colleges and will require working together with strong leadership, which I believe is there. If the Colleges can come together in this way the profession could make a crucial contribution which could not be ignored and which should be welcomed by both the DH and government.

Factors underlying the frustrations of patients and the concerns of doctors

Having outlined very briefly some of the landmark trends in the development of the organisation of the NHS and the changing relationships between the profession and government over the last fifty years, it is now necessary to highlight some of the practical issues which seem to continue to frustrate patients and concern those caring for them. This is not a 'whinge' – that oft-used derogatory term – but an attempt to identify the problems in order to help restore the reputation of a uniquely good social initiative. By tackling these positively, the NHS could maintain its place as one of the most successful models of healthcare in the world.

All the comments made in the following section are of course generalisations, and for a variety of reasons some hospitals and practices seem to have less difficulties than others. I fully appreciate that some of what follows is controversial and that different views will be held. However, I have tried to quote some of the evidence to support their consideration. Further, although the surveys I will quote provide evidence of the serious concerns of many patients and doctors – and some will never be satisfied – they also provide evidence that many patients are pleased with the service and some consultant physicians, albeit a minority, find the quality of their job good or excellent (44% in one survey[33]) (see page 271). While successes should rightly be recognised by everyone, this is not a good reason for ignoring real problems experienced by potentially enthusiastic and committed doctors. Likewise, many local lead managers are making huge efforts to work with doctors not only individually but also through much closer partnerships with clinical directors to identify deficiencies and correct them. Many Trust Boards also appreciate the great efforts being made by their doctors and other healthcare workers to look after patients, often under difficult circumstances, and are as supportive as possible. Such appreciation helps but it does not alone solve real problems. Where healthcare professionals have real concerns, Trusts and PCT Boards have a duty to take these seriously and to find solutions if the NHS is to flourish.

Also, different parts of the country and different types of hospital have different problems. Rural communities have different problems from urban ones, and those working in larger teaching hospitals may experience difficulties not found in smaller district general hospitals; too many overviews of the successes and failures of the NHS ignore these differences. Incidentally, this is where medical organisations which are able to call on a wide range of experience, can often see the wider scope of problems than individual experts.

Without losing perspective on the varying nature and severity of problems in different parts of the country, it is useful to focus on some where there is evidence of widespread concern in order to find some solutions.

Pressure of work and time

Increasing work pressure is undoubtedly one of the biggest problems in the NHS. In one RCP survey increased pressure of work was reported by 89% of consultant physicians, and 64% said that this had reduced the quality of care of their patients.[33] Pressure on time is one of the most serious problems because it impedes patient/doctor communication.[34] This is as true in hospital as it is in general practice.[33-35] The importance of time for patients is central to patients' and doctors' criticisms of the current NHS, as recorded in several independent recent surveys. It prevents patients having time to express their views[35] and doctors explaining adequately the options and risks.[34] Time to discuss problems is crucial if trust with patients is to be built, and so is adequate time to work alongside junior staff to ensure the quality of future generations of doctors.[36,37] Such pressures on time also undermine well intended initiatives such as meeting a wide variety of targets. This exemplifies the inevitable conflict which has arisen between coalface issues and major policy directives.

Workforce shortages

Linked with pressure on time are workforce shortages. The recruitment of doctors from overseas to compensate for manpower shortages, although still quite limited in numbers, is increasing and their supervision requires particular care if patients are not to suffer. Because of their different training backgrounds, difficulties in communication with staff and patients can cause further problems in spite of the statutory language qualification requirements. There is now strong documentary evidence of difficulties with the standards of some locums. In one survey,[33] 91% of consultant physicians reported increasing difficulty in filling locum posts. Thus the problems summarised above are serious.

Demise of small professional teams

Recent changes have largely led to the demise of the close-knit clinical teams of earlier years, where the consultant leadership was clearly defined and where junior doctors in training, the nurses, allied health profession-als (AHPs) and medical students all felt they were playing their own part in a team with the single objective of ensuring quality and continuity of patient care. Patients knew exactly who was in charge and the relationship between the individual patient and doctor in charge was clear. This sys-tem allowed for extremely good communication and when it worked well it was excellent. Of course, it depended greatly on the personalities and attitudes of the clinicians in charge and when it failed, the doctors were in large part to blame.

For many different reasons, hospital clinicians now have to work in larger rotating groups. As in so many things, this has advantages as well as disadvantages. Because of the complexity of modern medicine, many different specialties are often involved in treating an individual patient. New patterns of collaborative work are not only essential but are now the norm. However, one of the disadvantages is that patients often no longer know who is really in change of their particular care. The GMC and the Royal College of Physicians have been trying to tackle the problem of continuity of care[9] in the new NHS, and properly stress that patients must know the name of their 'team'. However, it is not the name of the team that is required, it is the name of the individual person (usually the doctor) who is *ultimately responsible*. This may vary from time to time during the course of an illness, but there should always be an individual in that key role for patients.

Other changes, some of which have been inevitable, have also made care of patients much more difficult. Changes in patterns of nursing have meant that nurses often regard themselves as much less accountable to the consultant and have thereby fragmented the team.[38] Such delegated responsibility can work successfully, but when this blurs the issue of who is ultimately responsible for the patient, then the latter will suffer. In the modern NHS it is not always necessary for the consultant doctor to be the leader carrying ultimate responsibility, but for the sake of the patients, there must always be an identifiable team leader who has the judgement and experience to take responsibility for the final decisions. In the major-ity of cases, patients will expect this to be a doctor. At the end of the day, and after all the data have been collated, a defined treatment plan and policy has to be drawn up with the patient and implemented. The day-to-day care may be teamwork, and several teams may be involved, espe-cially when patients have complex problems, but ultimate responsibility for a coherent treatment plan must be a *personal* partnership between the doctor in charge (at least for the time being) and the individual patient. If this is no longer possible, then it must be openly agreed and the necessary compromises recognised.

Shift systems

The shift system for junior doctors has been introduced out of necessity to meet EU regulations to reduce their working hours, and was originally promoted on the assumption that this would neither compromise continuity of care for patients nor junior doctors' training. Subsequent evidence from the Royal Colleges and elsewhere suggests that neither of these assumptions is correct.[9,33] In an RCP survey, 52% of specialist registrars in training (SpRs) believed that full shifts would severely worsen their training and 66% believed it would severely worsen continuity of patient care.[36]

With the loss of the small clinical team and the limitations on junior doctors' hours, seniors can no longer teach and train their juniors in a real partnership where professional values as well as knowledge and experience can be shared. There is a dislocation between senior and junior staff which makes the latter feel isolated,[38] and wastes teaching opportunities. These together often have knock-on effects on patients. Fixed formal teaching sessions have certain advantages but they do not meet the need to learn from more experienced doctors as they go about their work.

The clock cannot be put back, but this should not be an excuse for accepting unsatisfactory practices. New systems need to be explored to restore some of the successful components of teaching which have been lost and the whole question of the structure and functioning of the new clinical teams in today's medical practice needs urgent reconsideration and resolution.

Patients' expectations

Another much discussed pressure point in the NHS is patients' expectations. They are much better informed about what is possible and justifiably expect it. In addition, changing social attitudes and western affluence are causing a huge increase in patients' expectations. Together with medical advances, the pressures on the NHS have in consequence expanded inexorably. Many new treatments reach the public domain quickly and are of proven and immense value to individual patients, but they can be very expensive; the newer antibiotics, monoclonal antibodies (eg antitumour necrosing factor) in the treatment of rheumatoid arthritis,

Crohn's disease and severe psoriasis, and alpha interferon in the treatment of chronic hepatitis C are just three examples. This raises ethical problems when treatment is denied and financial ones when it is not. Such new treatments may cause tensions and mistrust between patients and doctors when patients feel that the doctors have let them down. It also causes tensions between doctors and management when there is evidence of effectiveness in the medical literature, but availability of treatments depends on individual local authorities (who in turn often await NICE pronouncements), and in the meantime treatment is denied on cost grounds. Since finance is finite, choices have to be made and good communication all round is vital. Nevertheless, patients, doctors and the public will inevitably ask questions when they see money which could be spent on patients diverted into management and bureaucracy.

Politicians themselves have in part been responsible for increasing patients' expectations without recognising the cost of the resources required to meet them. In an attempt to get patient support for the 1989 reforms and to put pressure on those trying to manage the NHS to provide more, not only did government encourage patients to complain if the service did not work for them, but they also published the *Patients' charter*,[39] setting out patients' 'rights' as well as what they were entitled to 'expect'. While this covered many desirable aspects of how doctors should relate to patients, it also raised patients' expectations about their access to treatment, their right to choice and the outcome of their treatment. Some of these expectations were predictably unrealistic.[38] The charter backfired in some ways because while the public wanted equality of standards throughout the country, disliking 'postcode medicine', local residents also wanted local services adapted to local needs. Thus the dilemma between equality and diversity continues, a topic which has been addressed in more detail by Dyson.[40]

Increased management intervention in clinical decisions

As government takes increasing control of decisions on the quality of patient care and of training doctors to look after them, a potential major ethical problem emerges when these standards fall short of what doctors, from their knowledge and experience, believe could and should be available to patients. A well documented example is the introduction of shift systems with the knock-on effect of inadequate 'hands on' experience for trainee surgeons.[37] In other words, however much government wishes to take control of healthcare and training, the fundamental integrity of the medical profession determines their obligatory responsibility for maintaining standards in the interests of the patients, both as individuals and as populations. Tallis discusses this topic in more detail in his recent book, *Hippocratic oaths*.[41]

While the introduction of clinical governance has increased professional accountability in a number of ways and is justified because hospital doctors are NHS employees, this can potentially erode the fundamental basis of patient/doctor partnerships, where doctors need to have reasonable control over their own professional job to which they are committed. *It is not consultant 'autonomy' which is being sought but professional **clinical** authority.* This loss of clinical control is one of the major reasons for doctors' disillusionment with the NHS.[42] As Professor Tallis (p 257) points out,[41] quoting John Bunker,

> *Loss of autonomy does not undermine professionalism where it is a question of subordinating one's practice to established standards: autonomy is given to fellow professionals in a professionally controlled system. Professionalism is, however, undermined when loss of autonomy involves subordination to those trained solely as managers.*

Much more work now needs to be done to clarify a mutually acceptable allocation of responsibility for individual patients between professional and management teams, if patient care is to improve. For example, a surgeon cannot take responsibility when he finds that individual patients on his operating list have been changed without his agreement and without regard for clinical urgency. Neither can physicians be responsible for individual patients when they are discharged from hospital without their knowledge and irrespective of whether the clinician regards them as ready to leave.

Other well documented major problems are the limitations on access by patients to specialist advice when there is a good case and they feel they need it. The efforts to increase patient choice are to be welcomed and are intended to be widened, but currently there is sometimes a practical conflict between meeting the wishes of individual patients and the restrictions placed on GPs by PCTs because of funding limitations. The availability of a second opinion is vital in any healthcare system if professional humility is to be preserved and patients' confidence maintained. However, the option of obtaining a second opinion is not yet included in the current Patient Choice initiative.

Undermined professional responsibility can have another serious consequence. This can be described as the psychology of the 'diminishing double helix'. As clinical responsibility is removed from the profession, doctors become demoralised, they opt out of personal commitment as far as possible and in consequence their standards of performance fall.[43,44] In response, management understandably, but misguidedly, attempts to tighten the reins with more prescriptive regulation. This only leads to a further decline in morale and performance. The downward spiral of the one results in the upward tightening of the spiral by the other, both attributing blame in equal measure. The only way out is for each to regain respect for each others' responsibilities. Work has to be done on both sides.

In spite of their reduced authority, the assessment of the consultants' own performance and accountability has properly become much more rigorous. They are still ostensibly accountable for the successful outcome of their patients' care and for meeting various targets set centrally, in spite of the fact that many of the conditions of that care are no longer under their control. It is not possible to establish effective accountability unless responsibility is linked to authority in the appropriate clinical areas.

Increased bureaucracy

As already mentioned and for a variety of reasons, the overall numbers of managers at various levels have undoubtedly increased very considerably in the last ten years.[2,45] While many managers working at the coalface are overstretched, much of the increase is caused by the monitoring requirements and regulatory controls to meet quality standards, targets and central directives. This has inevitably diverted funds from direct patient care and has sometimes resulted in other wasteful bureaucratic difficulties. Government regulatory bodies – the NHS alphabet soup – have proliferated and are now said to number nearly thirty. This raises fundamental questions about the whole policy, however well intended, of regulation, designed on the assumption that every aspect of a national medical service and its staff can be covered by legislature and central control. This assumption has been challenged on very good grounds by many including two distinguished philosophers – Baroness O'Neill and Gordon Dunstan.[14,3] I understand that very recently a 'bureaucracy buster' has been appointed to advise on their rationalisation and hopefully it will allow an examination in more detail of the fundamental principles of how and when various types of regulation are appropriate. The appraisal should also investigate how such an expensive publicly funded expansion has been allowed to spawn, only to require radical reform within a few years.

This bureaucracy can also contribute to confusion of responsibilities between those who are trying to care for the patients and those managing the system. Amongst the many attempts to monitor clinical performance, targets feature prominently. They should not, of course, be condemned out of hand. Some clinical targets can be both sensible and vital to improve standards, by ensuring the implementation of good clinical practice where there is a clear evidence base. For example, setting a time limit between the onset of symptoms and administration of intravenous fibrinolytic agents for myocardial infarction, or between presentation with some forms of tumour (eg melanoma) and its excision, are both known to save lives. On the other hand, meeting targets and complying with league table criteria or 'star ratings', which interfere with prioritisation according to medical urgency but on which hospitals' funding (and in some cases managers' performance bonuses) may depend, can dominate the system and thus divert, in all sorts of ways, everyone from real patient care. Incidentally, the repeated withdrawal of newly introduced targets because they are later found to be unsuitable does not inspire confidence in this system of performance assessment.[46]

Difficulties for academic medicine and clinical research

The new regulatory systems and specialist training programmes, the new consultant contracts and the new financial flow arrangements (eg tariffs) are conspiring together to make academic medicine and those attempting to support clinical research much more difficult. For example, some professorial posts funded by the NHS when the universities were in financial difficulties in the 1980s are becoming difficult to maintain. The Academy of Medical Sciences set out specific plans in *Strengthening clinical research*[47] which could improve the opportunities for clinical research in the NHS, and this is now being progressed much further by the DH and the MRC through the Health Research Delivery Group chaired by Sir David Cooksey. This is a good example of how professional organisations can and should act in partnership with authority to help strengthen the hand of those in charge of a successful NHS.

Difficulties for GPs

Without criticising how this has come about, all agree that the shortage of GPs is causing grave difficulties in caring for patients, and in some parts of the country this shortage is now at crisis point. Their new contract, which permits opting out of night calls, has inevitably reduced the quality of continuity of service to patients. The weekend service undertaken by GPs who know their patients has been severely curtailed and home visits for those who need it are far less frequent than in the past. Even office hour appointments can be considerably delayed in some places, especially if the patient needs to see the same doctor, because many are now working only part time. Increasing bureaucracy, resulting from general practice becoming progressively orientated towards commercial business principles, is diverting GPs from looking after their patients. In spite of considerable progress in recent years, there can still be unacceptable delays in referrals and diagnosis. As the medical services become increasingly overstretched, treatment plans are often inadequately defined and the principle of integrated care shared between the primary and secondary service – or between secondary and tertiary care – often falls short of what the patient actually needs. To compensate for the latter, various sectors of the profession are being asked to take over areas of medicine for which they are not necessarily adequately trained. There is certainly scope for GPs to acquire added training and experience in various subspecialties of medicine (GPs with special interests – GPSIs) to enable them to take over care of many patients with medical problems previously treated largely by hospital-based physicians. This adds interest for GPs and relieves pressure on the hospital, provided GPSIs are allowed to recognise their limitations. However, some PCTs are being required to monitor the numbers of hospital referrals and, if these data are misinterpreted, this could act as a serious deterrent to necessary hospital referrals. It has also been suggested that GPs might become the general physicians of the future. However, there remains a clear distinction between this type of general medical care and the full training required to practise in the specialty of general internal medicine for adults (or paediatrics), if standards are to be maintained. This again raises the question of breadth and depth of training to cover complex modern medicine as discussed in Chapter 18.

Difficulties for managers

It is important to recognise that many frontline managers feel equally frustrated by the pressures now being imposed upon them as they try to perform a balancing act between supporting the doctors to look after their patients, meeting the various performance targets dictated from above and handling the cascade of directives issued from the centre. They are in an unenviable position.

As a past Chairman of a splendid district general healthcare trust, I have a huge respect for the work that senior managers and their staff are trying to do, and I suspect that many will empathise with what follows. They, together with their Trust Boards, have the responsibility to ensure delivery of services to patients by doctors, nurses and other health professionals whom they employ. They also have to bear the pressures and complaints from the local population, the local press and not least the professionals trying to look after the patients. More importantly, they are 'at the bottom of the pile' and have to carry the burden of the accumulated pressures passed down from a variety of central authorities of the NHS. A few of these are illustrated in Fig 1.

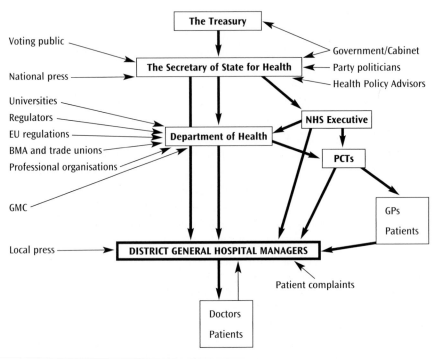

Fig 1. Some of the cumulative pressures borne by the managers of local hospitals. BMA = British Medical Association; GMC = General Medical Council; PCT = Primary care trust.

The growth in centrally directed bureaucracy is an unfortunate inversion of purpose, because much of it has been stimulated by the genuine intention of improving equality of care by more central directives and better regulation. On the other hand, successive governments have been well aware of the damage which can result from too much central control and have made repeated attempts to tackle this. However, the fact remains that both managers and the health professions at the coalface often feel that their attempts to make the best use of available resources are being handicapped by the policies and priorities set centrally, the latter not infrequently inevitably influenced by a political agenda. In addition to all this, there are very few opportunities for chief executives of local non-teaching and teaching hospitals to contribute their views and suggestions in more than a nominal way. Their views are rarely sought and access to senior people in the DH or government has undoubtedly become more difficult. When policy documents are pre-circulated, the consultation time is often so short that it precludes serious consideration by those who could give useful advice.

Further evidence of problems

I believe many of the difficulties outlined above will have resonance with many people and provide some of the explanations for the published results from formal health service surveys. It is worth re-emphasising some of these. In an independent questionnaire undertaken by the Commonwealth Fund,[19] nearly 50% of physicians in the UK felt that their ability to provide good quality care for their patients had worsened over the last five years. This is reflected in the Royal College of Physicians Census 2002,[33] where 64% of consultants felt that the clinical service had deteriorated over the last five years compared to 47% in 1999. This is also reflected by patients' comments in the Commonwealth Fund Survey where 50% of those in the UK felt that they did not have sufficient time with their doctor and 30% were not satisfied with the service. Only 25% were very satisfied. Morale has clearly deteriorated, and in the RCP Census 56% of physicians said that their job satisfaction was poor or only moderate.[33] This view was not age related. The fact is that there is now good evidence that morale amongst doctors in the NHS, which fell significantly in the early 1990s, has not improved over the last ten years. Indeed, three-quarters of doctors in one survey reported that morale had declined over the last five years.[34] On the other hand, this is not universal, and 44% found their job satisfaction good or excellent – so morale is certainly high in some places, especially for those working in more specialised areas.

Nevertheless, in 2002 the Chief Medical Officer was sufficiently concerned about the loss of morale amongst the majority of doctors to ask the Specialist Medical Advisory Committee (SMAC) to look into the matter.[42] The reasons it identified included shortage of resources, EU working directives, the development of strategies without implementation, lack of control over their clinical practice, increasing complaints by patients, poor training and a feeling of being undervalued by managers and government. These concerns have been confirmed by Isobel Allen,[48] in her major work on causes of stress amongst healthcare professionals and the gap which has developed between their core values and management. She also highlights the many practical things that can and must be done to allow healthcare professionals to look after their patients. In spite of the valuable work done by SMAC over the last few years advising the DH and government on such things as medical morale, doctors of the future and ensuring a clinical workforce to deliver national priorities, as well as setting out practical suggestions to improve the situation, few of their concerns seem to have been addressed seriously and indeed the Committee itself now seems to be in abeyance.

Some would like to challenge this evidence[49] and believe that the NHS is working well, which of course in some respects is justified, as noted earlier in this chapter. However, in other respects there are real problems and the fact is that doctors are voting with their feet, and this is a serious sign in any organisation. Many of the best doctors in the land, who have been enthusiastic supporters of the NHS and have devoted their lives to caring for patients within the NHS, are with sadness seeking release. In an RCP study[50] 60% of doctors, and over 75% in the *Hospital doctor*'s study,[34] are leaving or intending to leave prematurely. In the past, many doctors resented compulsory retirement at 65 because they enjoyed the satisfaction of being able to care for their patients with a professional commitment. Today, the majority of consultants seem to be finding that they would prefer to halve their salary and leave before the formal retirement age. The message is clear. This is undercutting workforce numbers and resulting in loss of some with great wisdom and experience – so vital to patients and the training and teaching of future doctors.

In spite of all these difficulties, surveys show that patients by and large still trust their doctors[51] and the patient–doctor relationship continues to be very important to them. Doctors value this partnership as an absolute cornerstone of their professional practice.

In conclusion, all this suggests that in spite of the many improvements in quality of managerial and regulatory processes and the progress made towards achieving selected targets and the huge advances in medical treatments, these alone are simply not enough to solve the more fundamental issue of enabling doctors and other health workers to provide good quality day-to-day care for patients. These are central problems and they will not go away until tackled directly. There are now great opportunities for the profession and management to address them together. Oddly enough they are not insurmountable but, as ever, it is not only policy recommendations that are needed, but also active implementation.

How to get to get the NHS back on course: an exciting opportunity

Having set out boldly the evidence about some of the problems, it is now possible to address with enthusiasm the way towards solutions – many of which do not require extra resources but do need a new culture of trust and working together.

In essence, the NHS should now enter its most mature 'fourth era' as that of '**Partnership and Trust**'. This is not to reject any of the progress achieved during the previous three eras – indeed, they all need to continue. Rather, it is to rebalance and move ahead to a fourth era of cooperation, recognising the duality of the healthcare professions and management as the cornerstone for meeting patients' needs. The local successes already achieved have been due to advanced thinking and practical implementation along these lines. The challenge now is to ensure that these become the norm throughout the NHS. The reasons and justifications underlying the suggestions set out here have been summarised on the previous pages.

1 There is a fundamental and urgent need to create a mutually respecting partnership between those directly responsible for patients and those responsible for the organisation of the NHS. This must be done in practical and transparent ways and at all levels of the NHS. The culture change required involves, as already mentioned, understanding the difference between the medical profession working *with* government as distinct from simply working *for* it and as directed.

2 To achieve this requires clarification and agreement in a number of different fields:
   • the proper *role of the medical profession* in the NHS and the responsibilities and authority that this must carry
   • the proper *role of management* and where its authority must prevail
   • systems of *intelligent accountability* for both the medical profession and management should be agreed
   • the establishment of *intelligent regulation* which can discern between those medical and organisational standards which can be developed and monitored in more prescriptive ways and those where *intelligent trust and judgement* must prevail.

3 The medical profession and its organisations must be able to demonstrate beyond all possible doubt that it deserves the trust and responsibility invested in it. If they fail then the NHS will simply disintegrate, the medical profession will fall into disrepute and the patients will suffer.

4 There is a need to review the numbers and distribution of managers in the NHS where these are contributing to an unhelpful and expensive bureaucracy and regulatory overload.

5 Before major new policies are implemented, much more care needs to be taken to consider their knock-on effects. Too often, solving problems in one crucial area of the NHS has caused serious damage to another.

6 Serious consideration should be given to the fundamental question of the relationship between the NHS and government.

Let us consider how each of these six points might be achieved.

Creation of an improved professional/management partnership

For the sake of patients, how can we recreate a new partnership between the health professions, management and the government in which there is mutual respect for their complementary skills and knowledge? In developing this, a fundamental distinction has to be made between working together to explore ways to improve specific aspects of patient care, and calling upon the profession to find solutions to strategies or policies already decided upon from above. The quality of patient care in the NHS depends not least on very highly trained and rigorously examined members of the medical profession, often with experience gained over more than ten years before they are allowed to take on independent consultant responsibilities for patients, and their ethical commitments to professional codes of practice. This fact has to be recognised when the respective roles of doctors and managers are being defined.

In this quest, the distinction between those organising and those actually delivering the service must not be confused. Such partnerships are essential in all public services but they are no less important in the NHS. Without this proper partnership, it is difficult to see how real progress can be made. This obvious point was made in an Harveian Lecture delivered to the Royal College of Physicians in 1996,[52] but the evidence suggests that, certainly at some levels, this has actually deteriorated rather than improved over the past eight years. To be successful, these partnerships must operate at all levels throughout the service – between doctors and managers at a divisional level, between clinical directors and the non-executive and other executive officers at hospital Board level, and between professional organisations (including the Royal Colleges and other independent professional organisations) and the Department of Health and government at the top. To have credibility with their peers, the doctors in many of these high-level partnerships must be adequately represented, and confidence in them would be enhanced if they were nominated by the profession itself – not by government or the Secretary of State.

Although some may disagree, I suspect that hospital medical committees with their own chairmen can still serve a useful role at a local level as a meeting point for the medical profession to contribute as a group. This could promote a sense of participation, ownership and loyalty so important in any successful enterprise, not as a pressure group but to add cohesion to the whole establishment. The chairman and the clinical director could together then ensure a strong clinical input to management, with a mechanism in place to unite the weight of the profession behind them. This is not an outmoded suggestion. It is simply a practical way of appreciating the contribution of a crucial part of the workforce, a principle recognised as very important in any modern successful organisation, and endorsed, for example, by the nationwide Investors in People initiative.

The achievement of a new professional/management partnership would restore confidence and morale within the healthcare professions. It would ease some of the conflicting pressures on management and would open the way for agreement on necessary compromises which could then be properly explained in a transparent and balanced way to the public and the media, so that false expectations could be avoided and their greater trust generated. The professional leadership is there; it is a matter of a willingness by everyone to work in partnership.

Clinical directors are in a strong position to help redress and establish this new balance at the hospital level, provided that their independent advice is heeded and that they are not constrained by the managerial hierarchy. It will be crucial that they retain the confidence of their colleagues and fearlessly represent the professional view on patient needs as well as ensuring that managerial policies are understood by clinicians when they help to maintain efficient and high-quality working practices. Where policies are imposed which evidently compromise patient care, the clinical director must make sure that management understands, and the reasons are explained to the public. Many excellent doctors have volunteered to be clinical directors; they have done a good job, often under considerable difficulties, and they have taken their management duties very seriously. A number have taken formal managerial training of some kind, including studying for an MBA. Theoretically they hold substantial power to ensure that clinical services are maintained to a high standard in spite of financial constraints and managerial directives. Unfortunately, all too often their job has been perceived as that of trying to persuade their colleagues to meet centrally established targets even if they compromise other parts of the service, or to accommodate funding cuts – so-called 'efficiency savings'. Professionally, clinical directors share clinical codes of practice with their colleagues and this has sometimes been in conflict with their loyalty to management of which they are part. It is not an enviable job. There is also scope for clinical directors – perhaps coordinated through the British Association of Medical Managers (BAMM) – to work much more closely with the Royal Colleges and their corporate professional organisations, for example the Academy of Royal Medical Colleges. The professional medical structures are now in place but they must convince government that they can provide soundly based impartial advice, and government in turn must recognise the importance of this.

At a more local level, trust in the professional teams would be greatly enhanced if non clinically trained managers had greater opportunities to understand much more about the principles of medicine and the clinical nature of the NHS business, which is very different from that of industry or commerce. Lack of recognition of this was partly responsible for some of the failures of the reforms of 1990. Most successful managers of industry, manufacturing or retail recognise the need for their senior staff to have first-hand experience on the 'shop floor'. Although some short courses exist, there is a serious need for greater in-depth understanding. Managers in the NHS should be offered an MSc course or diploma to improve their *understanding* of medicine. The plans and syllabus for such courses have now been developed independently and the options for their university base are being explored actively. This should certainly be welcomed by those responsible for workforce training. Thus, one could envisage the *primo* hospitals of the future having clinical directors with an MBA or the equivalent in management, and managers with an MSc or equivalent in understanding medicine. While this practical innovative idea has been supported in general terms by the Department of Health, the extraordinary lack of nationally recognised and regulated training requirement standards for managers in the NHS and the fragmentation of funding support for further training of middle managers makes the implementation of such ideas extremely difficult. It is a remarkable fact that at a time when nationally stipulated training standards and regulation for professional healthcare workers, especially doctors, are increasingly rigorous, those for most managers are far less well developed and the recently established organisations developed to foster management training and standards through the NHS Leadership Centre, the Modernisation Agency and the NHSU are now to be drastically cut and merged.

Welcome developments include the training of doctors (and other healthcare workers) alongside managers in appropriate areas and the appointment of more managers with a healthcare background. Both of these have been developed by the Modernisation Agency in its leadership programmes. However, so far these are largely limited to managerial programmes and do not address the issue of medical understanding by non-clinical managers. Only when these initiatives are in place will that elusive trusting partnership between the two be facilitated.

Clarification of the responsibilities and authority of doctors and managers

To achieve this new partnership, agreement is needed on some fundamental issues. The need for medical *professionalism* in the NHS has been discussed in Chapter 19. Healthcare for patients cannot be achieved without highly trained and experienced doctors working within and bound by their independent professional code. Their adherence to good medical practice, their personal integrity, their continued competence to practise and their commitment to their patients must be explicit, verifiable and transparent. Once this is established beyond question, their clinical responsibilities and clinical authority should be acknowledged. Directives from management have to be reconciled with doctors' ethical commitment to patients – a commitment which in the end transcends political instructions. Changing organisational systems does not change this fundamental need. Likewise, the proper role of management and its authority has to be understood by everyone. A clear distinction has to be made between the chief executive's responsibility for the quality of the clinical service and the control of clinical decisions involving patient care. If conflict arises this has to be resolved mutually. It cannot be done by prescription. The outcome evidence that these new proposed partnerships are working well could be measured by independent questionnaires designed in partnership, on professional satisfaction with the service they are able to provide, and patients' satisfaction with the service they receive. If successful, patient complaints should fall, the trends towards early retirement by senior doctors should be reversed, the numbers of unfilled consultant posts should fall and recruitment should rise.

Working together, with an equal measure of humility on all sides and with appropriate checks and balances, doctors and managers need to redefine which standards are best 'led' by the profession (including those of clinical practice as well as training and continuing education), which are best 'led' by management (including financial controls, efficiency and many other organisational matters), and which (including national overarching policies and resource allocation) must be led by the government of the day. It is essential to recognise that the word 'led' is used here in a relative sense; each sector must prove their competence and their capacity for joined-up thinking with others.

In trying to run the NHS, a balance has to be struck between regulation, accountability and trust. Baroness O'Neill has analysed with great wisdom the strengths of *intelligent trust* and *intelligent accountability* and the pitfalls of stupid trust and stupid accountability.[14] Her succinct analysis forms a fine basis for a new search for the trust that is so much needed in the NHS. Great practical strides have been made over the past ten years in increasing the *accountability* of the medical profession, including audit, clinical governance, personal appraisals, continuing education and others. As already mentioned, the Royal Colleges and the GMC have taken their responsibilities seriously and contributed much in this area. To quote Baroness O'Neill again, 'accountability comes in many forms, managerial accountability is only one of them'. Professional accountability is certainly another. She also emphasises that trust cannot be eliminated in institutional or social life and that, especially where information is incomplete, which is *always* the case in medicine, judgement is required; knowledgeable and independent judgement is possible when there is reasonable trust.

The profession's need to earn trust

If these aims are to be achieved the profession must demonstrate that they can be trusted – trust is earned, not given. Doctors will shoot themselves in the foot if they fail to demonstrate that their standards of commitment and performance are beyond reproach. If they elect to work within the NHS, they have a responsibility to work, as far as their integrity allows, with managers and government. This requires selfless individual professional integrity as well as leadership and self-regulation from professional organisations, especially for those who are in a position to dissociate themselves from trades union and other self-interested bodies. Doctors must be able to demonstrate that their efforts are for the good of patients and not themselves. If these standards fail they only have themselves to blame (see also Chapter 19).

Review of the number of managers

There is an immediate need to review the numbers and distribution of managers throughout the NHS. While recognising that many at the coalface are as overworked as the doctors and nurses, a large number seem to have been recruited in an endeavour to meet the explosion of regulatory and monitoring procedures. I would emphasise again that where there has been expansion at the local hospital level, this is usually not the managers' fault. So often it has been forced on to them from above in response to overload of regulatory processes. It is alleged that there are now more managers in the NHS than hospital beds. In some places, of course, management is failing because the numbers have been cut and the service is in danger of becoming dysfunctional, while in others the service is failing because there are too many.

Greater consideration of knock-on effects of policy proposals

All new major policy proposals from central and local management or the universities must stand up to scrutiny from many angles *before* attempts at implementation. If this had been done in the past many false starts and U-turns would have been avoided. As we have seen, one of the recurring major difficulties in the NHS is that attempts have been made to solve problems in one priority area without recognising their repercussions on others. Never was this more apparent than in the numerous attempts to reorganise services in London (see Chapter 21). Another example was the concerted efforts made to 'downsize' district general hospitals in the mid-1990s and the transfer of care for patients to the community to reduce hospital costs. Where community services can be improved, for example by the provision of intermediary convalescent care which relieves bed blocking in the acute hospitals, this is clearly very sensible. However, only a few years ago and for other reasons, many cottage hospitals were actually closed by Community Trusts because they were considered – for understandable reasons – to be inefficient, difficult to staff and costly. There were real grounds for both sets of arguments, but they were not considered together. It is reassuring to see that hospital and community services are being considered together in the 1997 strategic plans through the new regional strategic authorities.

The relationship between the NHS and government

Serious consideration should be given to the proposals from various quarters to focus on the fundamental question of the relationship between the NHS and government. Clearly, it is recognised that because of Treasury funding, the Secretary of State must be ultimately responsible to Parliament for fundamental financial and policy issues at a national level. Nevertheless, once these have been established it is timely to consider whether government should be distanced from the day-to-day running of the NHS by setting up some form of Non Departmental Public Agency (NDPB) (see below) for which there are many useful precedents and models.

The advantages – and the disadvantages – of a new operational relationship between government and the NHS have been set out succinctly in the recent King's Fund report, *Government and the NHS: time for a new relationship*.[53] As proposed, this would distance the policy function of government from the immediate running of the health service. Above all, it has the potential to provide some stability to the NHS, and could reduce the constant 'yin yang' and the revolutionary approach which has dogged the NHS for so long. It could pursue a course of planned evolutionary changes when required, with time for full consideration of all the consequences and testing by pilot schemes when necessary. Such an agency would be far better placed to address major issues that are currently being sidelined and liable to disappear by default because of the current focus on other things. It could ensure a more expeditious implementation of good policies which so often seem to fall by the wayside. For example, two outstanding issues needing most urgent consideration are the maintenance of clinical research in the NHS and, linked with this, the maintenance of tertiary/quaternary care (see Chapter 21). The responsibility for overseeing the management of the NHS could be considerably simplified, and it is fully compatible with the overarching authority of Parliament. However, it is unlikely that any political party will willingly forego the opportunity of keeping healthcare issues on the central stage of politics when the NHS has such a high profile in the eyes of the public. So long as this is the case, the political agenda will inevitably sometimes conflict with that of delivering care to patients, and as we have seen, this dichotomy is compromising the success of the NHS.

One cannot blame politicians for working against a foreshortened timetable or giving precedence to issues likely to gain votes, but it may not be good for patients. The penchant of the press for grim stories about the NHS and the extremely rare but disgraceful, criminal or psychopathic behaviour of healthcare staff and professionals (which no amount of legislation or regulation can entirely eliminate) certainly creates further pressures for ministers, and these often distract them from their real responsibilities. It is irrational for the Secretary of State to be held personally responsible for all such events, but this is the present system. It was the recognition of the need to relieve the Secretary of State from such day-to-day responsibilities that resulted in the formation of the NHS Executive in the 1980s. However, it seems it was never given sufficient authority to allow ministers to distance themselves significantly from 'coalface' events. It raises the important question as to whether the creation of a different relationship between government and the NHS would be a better way to try to run a complex and potentially brilliant health service needing long-term stability – a service which should be regarded as a basic social responsibility rather than an expendable political football.

Summary

The aim of discussing selective aspects of the NHS here is to rebalance the 'bedside' part of a remarkable story against the huge managerial changes which have taken place over the years. It acknowledges the need to keep pace with economic changes and scientific advances and applauds the great progress that has been made, but it also recognises the importance of maintaining the right balance between those responsible for organisational issues and those professional people directly responsible for the care of patients.

The chapter dips into history to give some insights on the evidence base of the present situation, and discusses how some of the less successful aspects of the NHS might be tackled. It emphasises the three eras of the NHS – expansion, cost containment and accountability and assessment – and suggests that, without losing the good that each of these has brought, we need to move to a fourth and more mature era of partnership and trust, in order to enable doctors and management to meet the modern requirements of patients.

Good management in the NHS is crucial and great improvements have been made, especially over the last twenty years or so. Many managers work closely with the profession, trying to balance their compliance with central directives on the one hand and the demands from the professionals looking after patients on the other. Their job is not an easy one! The chapter also identifies the gap that has developed between attempts to make improvements through reorganisation of management and regulatory controls and the relatively lesser effect that this is having on the actual quality of care that patients want and that doctors and other healthcare workers are able to give. It applauds the more recent focus on quality in the NHS but recognises that improvements in managerial processes do not necessarily equate with improvements in actual patient care. It is argued that the only way to reduce this gap is for managers and the profession to be allowed to form a much more equal, mutually respecting and trusting partnership at every level of the NHS, where the professional roles and the responsibilities are better defined. The recent shift towards government control in so many areas of clinical care and professional accountability is de-professionalising medicine and has not only widened the gap between government and the profession but has sent a clear message that the NHS is not to be a genuinely shared enterprise. This cannot be in the interests of patients.

The clinical directors and the professional medical organisations, including the Royal Colleges, could play a key role in rebuilding this partnership, but if the professional bodies are to play a greater role alongside government they have much to do. Not only must they demonstrate beyond doubt that they can earn the trust vested in them but they must very urgently come together with strong leadership as a significant entity so that there is a coherent body with whom government may work.

The chapter poses the question of whether a new relationship between the NHS and government would solve many of the problems which have exacerbated dissatisfaction with the NHS for too long. It recognises that changes are vital as circumstances themselves change, but if these are done in a 'revolutionary' way many obvious mistakes are made which have to be reversed a few years later. This is not only very disruptive and a great waste of all-too-scarce resources, including time, but it causes loss of trust in the system, is not good for patients and lowers professional morale. Progress by 'planned evolution' is a far more certain way forward even if it appears to take longer.

As in all public service, intelligent regulation is vital but over-regulation simply creates inefficient and costly bureaucracy. Lightening the heavy hand of external regulation depends on regaining the high ground of trust, and this can only be achieved where all doctors understand that intellectual competence and knowledge must be linked with a demonstration of personal responsibility, integrity, humility and above all co-operation. This is not too much to expect from all those privileged to work in a magnificent organisation dedicated to patients and their health. In spite of the difficulties arising from ever-increasing demands on the service, medicine remains one of the most rewarding and exciting areas of all human endeavour and this must never be forgotten.

21. The clinical/academic partnership: London University and tertiary and quaternary care

To understand what has happened to medicine in London over the last 20 years requires consideration of a series of interdependent factors involving both London University and the NHS. Diagrams can often clarify complex interrelationships better than words (Fig 2).

The following tries to unravel some of the tensions created by the NHS and London University and the effects that these are having on patient care, clinical research, undergraduate teaching and postgraduate training.

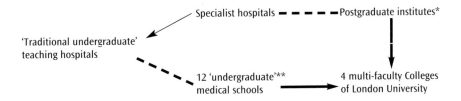

- ▬ ▬ ▬Essential interdependence
- ━━▶Managerial mergers which have taken place over the past 20 years
- ────▶Mergers of some specialist hospitals into 'undergraduate' Trust hospitals
- * Except the Institute of Cancer Research which remained a School of the University.
- ** Except St George's Hospital which retained its own medical school.

Fig 2. The changing interdependency of undergraduate and postgraduate hospitals and their university associations in London.

Over the years, there have been quite properly a number of national reviews which have had a particular impact on London. The conflicts between the theoretical but sometimes imaginative ideas on how things might be done better and the resistance of established and existing patterns of working have often resulted in very slow progress. To highlight just a few of the reports since 1944: there has been Goodenough (1944)[1] – reorganising the future for medical education; Pickering (1962)[2] – establishing postgraduate medical centres throughout the country and reviewing postgraduate centres in London; the Royal Commission under Lord Todd 1968[3] – proposing reorganisation of undergraduate and post-graduate medical education; Merrison (1975)[4] – shifting standards of medical education to the GMC through the Education Committee; and in 1979 another Royal Commission on the organisation of the NHS.[5] Other reports have attempted to tackle the more particular problems in London: Morris (1977)[6] – reviewing the postgraduate specialist hospitals and institutes; Flowers (1982)[7] – merging the London medical schools and integrating them with the four major University of London Colleges; Tomlinson (1992)[8] – addressing the provision of healthcare in London. These were followed by the DH response to Tomlinson (1993), *Making London better,*[9] and a series of specialist subject reviews, as well as setting up the London Implementation Group to ensure action. However, the DH response reversed a number of Tomlinson recommendations and in turn Turnberg (1997),[10] in developing a strategic plan for London post Tomlinson, reversed a number of others. If improvements have not been as rapid or as great as anticipated, it is certainly not for lack of repeated attempts to address the issues.

Attempts to rationalise medical teaching, clinical research and contain costs in London go back a long way. The Royal Commission chaired by Lord Todd in 1968 tried to tackle some of these problems by suggesting streamlining the twelve medical schools in London, reducing them to six and amalgamating them with major multi-faculty Colleges within the University, to improve the basic science research base. The report also suggested aligning the small specialist postgraduate institutes with the undergraduate schools. Many plausible reasons were put forward to justify this: it was a tidier arrangement to bring the relatively small postgraduate activities into the fold; it reduced their purported 'isolation'; it would increase the critical mass in the undergraduate medical schools and the likelihood of augmenting their funding as well as potentially increasing the opportunities for specialty clinical research. The plan was in advance of its time but for various reasons it was shelved.

In the early 1980s Lord Flowers, Rector of Imperial College, was invited by the Vice Chancellor, Lord Annan, to review research in London University in view of the diminishing resources. He attempted to resurrect many of the suggestions made originally by Todd in 1968 to pair the medical schools in London, reducing them from twelve to six and to merge them with one of the four multi-faculty Colleges of the University of London. This met with stiff resistance for many reasons and was initially rejected by two votes by Senate. 'Where Todd proposed, Flowers disposed' was the quip at the time. There followed a frenetic period of reviewing the London academic scene by the Joint Planning Committee and the Joint Medical Advisory Committee of the University, which left postgraduate medicine in a state of great uncertainly. It is probable that in these deliberations there was only a meagre understanding of the special linkage between postgraduate institutes and the specialist hospitals in London, and their inextricable combined role in supra-regional tertiary and quaternary care of patients, postgraduate teaching and research in the NHS.

If provision of medical services throughout the country generally has been in constant flux as the NHS has evolved (see also Chapter 20), then that in London has been even more intense. Indeed, it is remarkable that any continuity of clinical services for patients, teaching and clinical research survived through these frenetic reviews, appraisals, reshuffles, reorganisations, reversals – call them what you will. It is to the enormous credit to people at the coalface that they managed to keep things going and adapt to constantly changing directives.

The problem has been that although there were a number of constructive suggestions for improvement, others proved unworkable or disastrous. For example, the conclusion of the Tomlinson report that money could be saved in London (and transferred to other Regions now able to treat many patients which had previously been sent to London), by cutting the number of beds and transferring patients to the primary sector, was theoretically plausible, but proved flawed. In spite of allocating large sums to improve care in the community, the special factors in London prevented this from having any major effect on relieving pressure on hospital beds. It is true that several smaller hospitals have been closed and this rationalisation should have improved efficiency of the hospital service, but this seems to have done little to provide the hoped-for alternative provision in the community. Likewise, Tomlinson suggested that there should be a cut in student numbers in London which amounted to about 12% at the time, without taking account of the substantial increase in student numbers needed – of which the government was warned at the time – and which has now amounted to a 50% national increase, in which London has naturally wished to play its part.

The postgraduate institutes in London

I have had the privilege to be closely associated with the evolution of the postgraduate institutes in London and their associated specialist hospitals over more than fifty years. Over this time, radical changes have occurred, sometimes by design and sometimes by default. It is important to consider what part, if any, the postgraduate institutes and their associated specialist hospitals should play in the modern NHS, including their contribution to postgraduate training and academic research. Are they outmoded in today's world? Can they be afforded? Can their work be replaced by others? Where do these national assets of the NHS stand in a service which is progressively devolved to 'Regions' and even to 'Districts' throughout the country?

The survival of any academic institution is inevitably profoundly influenced by its funding. The postgraduate institutes have been in a particularly complex situation because they cut across conventional funding sources and have developed as an unorthodox solution to meet a real need. Unorthodoxy never rests comfortably with those trying to rationalise problems, because there is usually a preference for tidy solutions, often lowered to a common denominator. The institutes' emphasis on clinical research is complementary to the basic science strengths of the major UK universities; their postgraduate teaching and training of specialists for the NHS differed considerably from the medical school responsibilities which were primarily for undergraduates; and their specialised clinical services for patients are quite distinct from both District and many Regional services. This specialist postgraduate sector forms a relatively small part of NHS and university budgets and in consequence, when funding is under pressure, it is this sector which becomes particularly vulnerable. However, their track record of international standing in clinical research, and specialist training for home and overseas graduates is formidable and their cost effectiveness in terms of global recognition of the NHS is substantial.

Specialised medicine is not, as many might think, a recent development. Some of the special hospitals were built to meet very different needs a long time ago. The Brompton Hospital, for example, was opened over 150 years ago (1842) to meet the particular needs of patients with tuberculosis; Great Ormond Street Hospital was founded in 1852 for specialised care of ill children; and the National Hospital for Nervous Diseases (Queen's Square) opened in 1860 for paralysed and epileptic patients not adequately accommodated in general hospitals.

The British Postgraduate Medical Federation

Prior to 1996, the Cardiothoracic Institute (renamed the National Heart and Lung Institute in 1989) was part of the British Postgraduate Medical Federation (BPMF). The latter was established in 1946 as a School of London University bringing together many of the postgraduate medical research and teaching institutes in London. These institutes were closely integrated with their specialist hospitals, funded at that time directly from the Department of Health, an arrangement which was often perceived to have left them better off than the London undergraduate teaching hospitals. By the mid-1980s, the constituent members included the Institutes of Cancer Research (linked with the Royal Marsden), Neurology (linked with National Hospital for Nervous Diseases, Queen's Square), Child Health (linked with Great Ormond Street Hospital for Children), Psychiatry (linked with the Maudsley), and Urology (linked with St Peter's, St Phillips and St Paul's Hospitals), the National Heart and Lung (linked with Royal Brompton and now Harefield Hospitals), Ophthalmology (linked with Moorfields Hospital), Laryngology and Otology (linked with the Royal National Throat, Nose and Ear Hospital, Gray's Inn Road), Eastman Dental and the Hunterian Institutes. The BPMF also included the Postgraduate Deans of the Thames Regions who supervised the postgraduate training programmes for junior doctors in the whole Thames Region (with a population of around 10 million). This postgraduate school thus had a major responsibility for medical research and the training programmes for doctors needed for the NHS in which the specialist hospitals played an important part. It certainly operated on a very substantial scale. The Postgraduate Medical School at the Hammersmith Hospital left the BPMF to become an independent school of the University in the late 1970s.

Funding pressures

University funding for the institutes had always been extremely difficult to obtain and they received a much smaller proportion of their funding from London University than the undergraduate medical schools. The funding of the Institute of Diseases of the Chest (named thus prior to its merger with the Institute of Cardiology and renamed the Cardiothoracic Institute in 1972) was no exception and was humorously described by Jack Pepys in his famous Christmas lecture as the 'Destitute Chestitute Institute'!

In the early 1980s, higher education funding started to become even more difficult to obtain and London University became critically short of funds. This coincided with the collapse of the long-standing agreement between the MRC and the University, where if a research programme grant from the MRC had proved successful over five years, the University was obliged to take it over. Lecturers and other university posts were massively cut throughout the country and this threatened, not for the first time, to undermine the supply of trained academics to staff future senior posts. The MRC funding for medical research had also been reduced from the earlier Rothschild (1971)[11] agreement, when about a quarter of its medical funds had been transferred to the Department of Health and Social Security (DHSS) with the intention of encouraging more clinically applied research. Like so many government-led good intentions in medicine, the report failed to recognise that the DHSS had no effective infrastructure in place to handle and distribute this type of research funding. In due course Sir Henry Yellowlees, Chief Medical Officer at the DHSS at the time, wisely handed it back to the MRC, with a Concordat agreement to earmark funds for more clinically orientated research, provided it met rigorous quality standards. Even this was not very successful and the projects supported were often viewed as somewhat second rate because inevitably they lacked the pristine rigour of 'pure' research. Admittedly, it must be recorded that it was often the clinical members rather than the scientists on the MRC research boards who were hypercritical. It is of interest that in 2004 a new initiative was agreed between government and the new Director of the MRC, Colin Blakemore, to promote clinical research once again, and the Health Research Group has now been established under the Chairmanship of Sir David Cooksey.

In about 1984, the plight of the lectureships and the serious consequences for academic medicine was at last appreciated and a national competition for, inelegantly termed, 'New Blood lectureships' was set up, funded by Government but managed by the MRC. We were unreasonably pleased that our own application from the Cardiothoracic Institute was successful and graded fourth in the whole country.

Funding for respiratory research

At that time, each Unit within the Department of Medicine at the Cardiothoracic Institute was largely responsible for its own external funding. My own small research group had mainly depended on a series of competitive three-year project grants from the MRC, which at the time suited us better than programme grants, because they fitted in with our particular research strategy where we were exploring new techniques in a number of different fields. We also had generous support from charities such as Action Research, the Mercers Company and from the pharmaceutical industry. The latter were often extremely generous and on some occasions pharmaceutical companies including Fisons, Glaxo and Boerhringer Ingleheim would support a lecturer for 2-3 years without any limiting conditions, because of the trust and goodwill we had established with them while undertaking, without prejudice to the results, independently conducted long-term clinical trails of their products. In later years, this generosity was much less easy for them, in no small part due to pressure from their shareholders who demanded a greater proportion of the company's profits. Funding then became much more specifically related to studies on their own products and this gave us far less freedom to study the clinical research questions we believed to be important. This valuable flexible unallocated funding from non-government sources became much more difficult.

Funding for respiratory disease research has always been particularly difficult to obtain because, sadly, the image of chest disease was regarded as related to the so-called 'working classes'. Tuberculosis had been brought under control with the new anti-tuberculous medication and chronic bronchitis (largely due to smoking and therefore regarded as the patient's fault) did not have the same charisma amongst academics as some other developing fields. In part, of course, our lack of success was our own fault for failing to capitalise on the new laboratory technologies which were being explored in other specialist fields – hence our intensive efforts in the Institute to correct this state of affairs, outlined in earlier chapters.

It is also true, of course, that very common diseases such as chronic bronchitis, asthma and lung cancer have less public and academic appeal than more erudite rarities or more 'fashionable' conditions including heart disease, childhood diseases and other cancers. When I was asked to serve on the Systems Board of the MRC in 1983, we undertook a review of the apportionment of its funds to different clinical areas and we found that only 4% of these supported respiratory projects of various types. This was grossly disproportionate to the burden of chest complaints, in terms of both morbidity and mortality, in the UK population.

This funding 'black hole' was one of the main reasons why Professor Malcolm Green masterminded the creation of the British Lung Foundation (BLF) in 1985 which now provides £1.5 million per annum for research and patient support. This was a very remarkable vision and achievement from a single dedicated person who had outstanding organisational and business skills and the charisma to attract large numbers of others to a cause to which he was totally committed. Others have now joined him to carry on the good work in the BLF and we all know there is still a long way to go. However, the core organisation is now firmly established. Most importantly, it shows what can still be done when one man has a really compelling idea with the belief, energy and enthusiasm to match it.

Development of the BPMF, 1980–96

Some of the small specialist institutes (including Urology and Dermatology) had quite small research programmes and their main strength from the academic viewpoint was their home and overseas postgraduate training programmes. However, because of their small size and their very inadequate accommodation they transferred out of the BPMF to undergraduate medical schools in the mid-1980s. At this time, it was agreed to leave the six large institutes under the BPMF as a school of the University.[12] Their role in clinical research was endorsed when the NHS decided to fund the postgraduate hospitals directly as Special Health Authorities (SHAs) (1981). These two decisions together consolidated the commitment to tertiary and quaternary care medicine in the NHS and recognised that this could not and should not be separated from high-class clinical research and postgraduate teaching and training.

In spite of the difficulties of university funding, the growth in the BPMF research grants progressed well and had risen from £5 million in 1980/81 to over £16 million in 1986/7.[13]

At this time, Professor Michael Peckham became the Director of the BPMF and immediately set to work to overhaul its entire strategy. Not only was each institute subjected to a detailed independent review, but the BPMF developed an overall coordinated strategic direction for its research, encouraging both collaboration and focus. Clearly, such a radical change took some time to yield results, but in the second Research Assessment Exercise (RAE), only three years later (1989), progress was already demonstrable, if somewhat patchy. Several institutes were performing better than any of the undergraduate medical schools and none were worse.[14] In addition, the BPMF had achieved more MRC grants than any other medical school in London University and obtained more MRC units. However, there was still much more to be done.

By the 1992 RAE, there had been a transformation. Total external research funding over a four-year period (1988–92) for those institutes receiving some funds from the university had risen to around £75 million, with four institutes graded 5 (ie research of international standing in one or more categories of assessment).[15]

Thus, based on external and national evaluation, the track record of research undertaken by the institutes was developing rapidly to an international standard. This success was helped in a major way by the clinical facilities available in their associated specialist hospitals. Indeed, in 1988 the management executive of the NHS had endorsed the position of SHAs in relation to their University counterparts and they were regarded as 'centres of outstanding performance in teaching, research and service'.[16] But as we shall see, all was to change.

There were many problems with the delivery of healthcare in London and inequitable funding between the metropolis and other parts of the country was being challenged. Few if any would disagree that equity throughout the UK is imperative, but some of the special pressures on the metropolis are not always understood. For example, the large numbers of asylum seekers and the huge numbers of visitors create a disproportionate disease burden in London, but this is not covered by conventional census figures and is therefore poorly measured by the planners. In 1992 the government commissioned Professor Tomlinson to review NHS services in London and the implications for undergraduate and postgraduate activities.[8] In spite of the demonstrable burgeoning of the BPMF Institutes and their ever-closer liaison with their specialist hospitals in clinical research, all the old arguments about their potential inadequacies and the advantages of merging the specialist hospitals with undergraduate hospitals, and the institutes with multi-faculty Colleges, were resurrected once again. This was all rather like those who declared that the bumblebee cannot fly because of the theoretical aerodynamics of its wings, but because the bumblebee does not know these things, it goes off and flies anyway. The remarkable progress and contribution being made by the BPMF seemed to be largely ignored.

In 1989 the government White Paper on the NHS reforms had appeared and by the mid-1990s it was decided that the SHAs should cease to have direct funding: the hospitals should become Trusts and compete in the internal market for funding on a level playing field with all other hospitals. Professor Peckham, who had left the University and BPMF to become the Director of the new Research and Development Unit in the Department of Health (1991), was given the responsibility of reshaping the funding base for the SHAs in all sorts of complex ways in an attempt to preserve their clinical research programmes. In additional, 'Culyer' funding went some way to compensate for the added costs of research and development. But Professor Peckham did much more than this. He redeveloped the entire strategy of research and development in the NHS. He recognised the importance of technological advances in healthcare and set up mechanisms to speed the introduction of scientific advances into clinical practices. He ensured that treatments were as far as possible founded on evidence-based assessments, and that there were opportunities to identify clinical problems and instigate clinical research programmes to solve them. He set up regional programmes with many high quality regional directors so that practical health services research permeated every region. In short he was largely responsible for developing the innovative idea that the modern NHS should incorporate high-quality health services research.[17]

Thus it was that an NHS initiative on hospital provision and a government policy imposing an internal market mode of operation – a policy abandoned some six years later because it proved to be divisive – on all hospitals (albeit some fulfilling very different functions) had a very profound effect on the university research and teaching components, so crucial to tertiary and quaternary care within the NHS. In this way, it was the NHS initiatives which began to threaten the existence of the BPMF. Following the Tomlinson report, pressures on the postgraduate institutes continued to increase. In 1994, the Institute of Psychiatry decided to link with King's College and in 1997 it joined formally. In 1995 the National Heart and Lung Institute (NHLI) started negotiations to join Imperial College – also finally achieved in 1997. Once some of the constituent members of the BPMF had for understandable reasons left, the existence of the BPMF inevitably became more vulnerable, especially because there were many people in the University who had a long-standing determination to incorporate the institutes into the four large London Colleges anyway.

In consequence, the BPMF was disbanded in 1996 and gradually all the institutes were amalgamated in various ways with multi-faculty Colleges of the University. It is a bizarre fact that in the RAE of the same year all the postgraduate institutes in the BPMF were now graded 5, recognising their international status, and two were awarded the elite grade 5*. The old and wise adage – 'if it ain't broke don't fix it' – springs to mind. The multi-faculty Colleges will now be under pressure to prove that they can sustain the productivity of these institutes as well as the previous arrangement.

Merger of postgraduate institutes with multi-faculty Colleges

The conditions of the mergers of the institutes into the Colleges varied and it will be interesting and indeed important to observe which arrangement proves to provide the optimal environment for the institutes in the future. Unfortunately, it will be difficult (and probably impossible) to track the trends of performance through the Research Assessment Exercises because the Higher Education Funding Council for England (HEFCE) has substantially changed the criteria for evaluation and it will no longer be possible to compare like with like. The Institutes of Neurology, Child Health, Ophthalmology, Laryngology and Otology and the Eastman Dental were affiliated with UCL in 1995-6; they remained on their existing sites alongside their specialist hospitals. Importantly, the Institutes of Neurology and Child Health at first retained independent funding and each remained as an independent cost centre for research assessment. After full merger in 1997 this arrangement was initially maintained but I understand that the independent cost centre status and ring-fenced funding may be less secure in the future. A somewhat similar situation also pertains with the Institute of Psychiatry, though it retains a good deal of independence because of the special funding provided in consequence of achieving 5* on two successive years. The National Heart and Lung Institute (NHLI) pursued a different route. It merged fully with Imperial College in 1996 and became in effect a Department in the Imperial College Faculty of Medicine. The main advantage to the Institute has been a closer collaboration with some of the basic science departments and this has been facilitated by their close geographical proximity. In passing, it should be noted that if the new plans mature to relocate the NHLI along with the Royal Brompton and Harefield Trust on a new site in Paddington (plans which in 2005 have become yet again *sub judice*) (see also Chapter 17), this close geographic co-location, regarded by the University policy-makers in the 1980s as a vital reason for aligning medical schools with basic science multi-faculty Colleges in the first place, will actually be lost. Interestingly, the Institute of Cancer Research (which, it must be recognised, has no University funding) has chosen to resist merging and has now become an independent College of the University. Since this was achieved it has almost doubled its independent research funding and seems to be finding this arrangement very satisfactory.

On the positive side, there is no doubt that many individuals and units have forged new links and benefited from the new opportunities for collaboration brought about by these mergers, and there have certainly been some inspired leaders in the host organisations trying to develop major new research strategies. There have also been substantial financial advantages to the host organisations because a proportion of the HEFCE awards are redirected towards them. Of course, such transfer of funds may be for the overall benefit of all and fully justified, but at the same time care has to be taken that it is not to the detriment of important established clinical research programmes or the development of new ones in the institutes. There are instances where senior academic vacancies in the institutes are not being advertised to bring in new people, but the funding is being used to reconfigure other departments. Moreover, as the institutes become progressively aligned with strategic policies of the large multi-faculty academic Colleges, the previously very close and productive application of their work to clinical research in collaboration with their specialist hospitals may become more difficult to maintain. This will need watching very carefully because it is this special clinical association which has been the key to much of their international recognition.

Most would agree that, following mergers, the managerial bureaucracy has usually increased costs, not decreased them through efficiency savings, as so confidently predicted.

The human dimension of mergers

The problem with so many of the strategic decisions imposed on medicine over the last two decades is that while there may be a compelling case to solve one particular problem, especially in the short term, no such solution will survive the longer term test of time unless all the major facets of the problem have been satisfied. Organisations have to meet the criteria to maintain the *quality of the academic and clinical service*, the *economic viability of the plan*, and the *'human dimension' of the people doing the work*, on whom the whole thing depends.

That the scientists and doctors have had the resilience to adapt to their new environments and continue with their work is a great credit to their adaptability. It is now up to both the host Colleges and the institutes to ensure that they take full advantage of the enlarged critical mass of their new environments to enable them to achieve even greater things.

This will be helped if more attention is now paid to some of the principles of how to create an environment of optimal working conditions. As is well known, there is a fine line between developing large enough organisations to be financially efficient with a critical mass to undertake research of international quality (a rationale endorsed by College Accreditation Committees) on the one hand, and on the other ensuring that smaller more personal groupings can flourish where the 'human dimension' is fostered. It is vital to recognise these human aspects in addition, of course, to the very important strategic issues. There must be a constructive compromise where individuals can feel proud of being part of a larger organisation but still retain their local loyalties within a friendly environment, where they can be respected and recognised as individual contributors. In takeovers it is often apparently trivia which can be so damaging. For instance, where organisations have to merge, the enforced expunging of local logos (which have often been used for a very long time) on the naïve assumption that this will somehow force individuals to identify with the new order, is irksome and simply causes resentment and is counter-productive. There are many ways that the best of the old can be incorporated with sensitivity and subtlety into the best of the new. The model used by Salvador Moncada in the UCL Wolfson Institute, now located in the old UCH building, and that adopted at the Institute of Hepatology under the direction of Professor Roger Williams, are just two interesting examples where I believe consideration of the human dimension has been given much thought. These two Institutes, while ultimately part of University College London with all its advantages for collaborative research and managerial support, also have a large measure of independence. Within the overall umbrella of each Institute, the lead researchers work in quite small teams with no more that 12–20 people and are given very considerable autonomy. Professor Sir Paul Nurse, the previous director of the Imperial Cancer Research Foundation, subscribed to a similar formula. No doubt there are many different models of good practice but sadly there are innumerable other examples where large impersonal bureaucratic organisations have caused individuals to feel submerged and undervalued and this is simply not conducive to good work.

Opportunities for research collaboration without mergers

In all these managerial reshuffles, one of the factors which has been almost totally ignored is the unique opportunity afforded in London to form collaborative research partnerships with complementary laboratories in other institutions *without the need for managerial driven mergers*. This was probably much easier in the past. In 1985 at the Cardiothoracic Institute we reviewed the number of research partnerships outside our own Institute but within London University and the teaching hospitals to counter criticisms of isolation. On a specified test date there were 225 different active joint projects between our Institute Departments and others within London alone. This is a very cost-effective way of sharing resources and interests with complementary groups and improving communication with others around the capital. Sadly, this flexibility of working has in some instances been made more difficult because the larger Colleges have now been forced into competition with each other for funds, and the Research Assessment Exercise has certainly led to restrictive practices on some occasions, with Colleges fearing that their 5* grade will be compromised if credits have to be shared. I recognise that this is not inevitable but it is frequently reported to occur in practice. Also, with the increasing imposition of business methods and the imperative to generate income, rigorous cross-charging within joint projects is becoming the norm. This practice may be unavoidable but it is certainly inhibiting collaboration, especially when exploring new innovative ideas in the early stages.

The hierarchy of services in the NHS

One of the major factors contributing to the quality and cost-effectiveness of the NHS is the hierarchy of services it provides. This is needed for several reasons. Different types of services and facilities are required depending on the varying complexity of the clinical problem, and there is also a need to provide quality undergraduate training for new doctors. Provision for postgraduate training is essential to ensure quality expertise for future specialists, and a commitment to clinical research with appropriate academic facilities is crucial to explore the cutting edge of medicine. The latter requires both specialist clinicians and scientists. This hierarchy, with some degree of overlap, has developed in the NHS at four complementary levels, allowing a cost-efficient quality service.

Primary care has greatly extended the care that can be provided in the community by general practice and this has been transformed in quality and extent over the last fifty years. It now cares for many patients previously treated largely as hospital outpatients.

Secondary care in district general hospitals has been extended so that many quite advanced procedures can now be undertaken close to patients' homes. Sometimes they also participate in undergraduate teaching, taking students from core teaching hospitals. They also play an important role in training junior newly qualified doctors.

Tertiary care at 'Regional' centres augments the work of DGHs where more complex procedures and facilities and doctors with subspecialty skills are required. They are often, but not always, associated with a core 'teaching' hospital linked with its undergraduate medical school and university. Many patients can now receive special care at these regional centres who would previously been transferred to one of London's specialist hospitals.

Quaternary care is provided at no more than two or three supra-regional centres in the UK where there is a critical mass of specialists to allow full subspecialisation within single disciplines. These hospitals work at the 'cutting edge' of medicine; they are expected to care for the most complex cases and to explore new practical and theoretical ideas in common and less common diseases. Their research is usually of international standing, as validated by HEFCE Research Assessment Exercises, and they contribute importantly to specialist and supra-specialists' postgraduate training for both home and overseas doctors. They are often able to represent the UK as ambassadors on the international scene. There is a subtle difference between the supra-regional centres which provide specific facilities for special treatments (eg transplantation, and some cancer therapies), and the quaternary centres holding a broader brief for advancing individual fields in medicine, although of course there is often overlap. In addition, the tertiary/quaternary sector provides a very cost-effective safety net, resolving the dilemma of equality versus diversity of local services discussed in Chapter 20. For example, where a particular patient or groups of patients cannot receive appropriate specialist care locally, there is still provision for this in the NHS at the national tertiary/quaternary centres, *provided that this is accessible without local restrictions.* This four-tiered structure makes a major contribution to the cost-ffectivness and success of the NHS.

The contribution of tertiary and quaternary care

Since I have been associated with tertiary and quaternary care for the major part of my working life, it is appropriate to expand on this aspect of the NHS and give a brief summary of what this sector has contributed to the NHS as well as to academic medicine, where some of the perceived advantages and disadvantages lie, what has happened in recent years and, most particularly, the very real dangers facing tertiary and quaternary care more generally in the NHS at the present time.

The postgraduate specialist hospitals in London, together with the Hammersmith Hospital, are not only examples of the overlap between tertiary and quaternary sector as defined above, but go a step further because of their very special relationship with their own academic institutes, as well as basic science and other departments within the University of London. While a major part of their work meets the needs for tertiary care in the Thames Regions, they also contribute as quaternary centres for patients with special problems from all parts of the UK. This is due to their critical mass of subspecialists and their research strengths. By convention, 'tertiary care' is the term often used to incorporate quaternary care, and for convenience in this chapter I will sometimes use the word 'tertiary' in a broader way to cover both categories.

For historic reasons, the tertiary and quaternary referral specialist hospitals have mostly (but not always) been located in London. They presented a particular problem because, on the one hand, there were theoretical reasons (notably their size and in many cases their buildings) which made some of them unviable, but on the other hand many, in spite of this, had a remarkable international reputation for their care of special groups of patients, in postgraduate teaching and/or clinical research. This made it very difficult to absorb them into undergraduate hospitals or to disband them, in spite of the numerous attempts at rationalisation discussed earlier in this chapter.

It is an incontrovertible fact that the international postgraduate training programmes for both UK and overseas doctors held at the specialist postgraduate hospitals (including the Hammersmith, Great Ormond Street for Children, the National Hospital Queen's Square, the Royal Brompton Hospital for heart and lung disease, the Maudsley for psychiatric disease, Moorfields Eye Hospital, St Peter's, Paul's and Phillip's Hospitals for urology, St John Hospital for skin, and others, have been recognised throughout the world over many decades. One of the reasons for this was that these hospitals allowed for the development of a range of subspecialties that could not be found in any single undergraduate hospital. They were freely accessible for special referral of NHS patients and as their institutes expanded, clinical research flourished in many of the larger ones. Because of the experience gained by treating, in sufficient numbers, groups of patients under the NHS, the UK was able to build a reputation for clinical research on the international stage, which was often more difficult in other countries, including particularly North America.

In the past, any local consultant, general practitioner or indeed a patient who wished for a second opinion and was willing to travel, simply asked for an appointment. Thus, there was real choice for patients. Because of these hospitals' accessibility from a wide catchment area, they were able to build up a wide experience not only of uncommon disorders but also of patients with common diseases presenting with difficult problems. Further, there was no bar to follow-up of patients so long as they were willing to return. Thus, it was possible to study not only the longer-term results of treatment but also the natural history of persisting diseases – areas of research notoriously difficult to undertake elsewhere.

Until the reorganisation of London services and the rest of the country since 1990, we were most fortunate to have had a window of opportunity which combined the development of new clinical and laboratory techniques with great flexibility and support from the NHS. These together allowed our collaborative approach to clinical care and relevant laboratory research to develop as the forerunner of what is now called translational research. We took advantage of linking easily with anyone in London who shared our special interests and could give added value to the patient through joint care. Thus it was, for example, that my own patients with eye problems associated with pulmonary sarcoidosis were seen jointly with Mr Crick at King's College Hospital and after his retirement with Dr Peter Wright at Moorfields, both of whom had a particular expertise in this field. Likewise, those with lung disease associated with rheumatoid arthritis were seen jointly with Professor Sir Ravinder Maini of the Kennedy Institute and Charing Cross and those with associated systemic sclerosis were seen jointly with Professor Carol Black at the Royal Free Hospital. Those with some rare forms of pulmonary haemorrhage due to Wegener's granuloma, systemic lupus erythematosus and Churg Strauss syndrome requiring special treatment were managed jointly with Professor Sir Keith Peters and the late Dr Martin Lockwood at the Hammersmith. The opportunity to work jointly with selected international experts, located at different hospitals, but all within a ten-mile radius, was a huge advantage to the patient and one which would have been much more difficult if the Brompton Hospital had been restricted to a single undergraduate teaching hospital where, however good in general terms, the full range of other *subspecialty* experts in *every* discipline could obviously never exist. The freedom of linking with a wide range of outstanding people with very special experience was to the great advantage of patients with these very difficult problems and was greatly appreciated by them.

Sadly, the changes in funding, including cross-charging and other managerial restrictions, have made systematic individualised joint programmes of this sort much more difficult and this needs to be addressed. The Turnberg report of 1997[10] repeatedly emphasised the importance of clarifying proper support for tertiary care in London but no firm plans have yet been put in place to demonstrate commitment to this policy to ensure that patients can continue to access these services, and that the financial and research arrangements are appropriate. Until this is done – and the matter is very urgent – one of the most important quality facets of the NHS is at risk of being lost, simply by default.

The London Specialist Commission Group is trying to tackle the problems being faced by tertiary and quaternary care but they have a huge task. The additional costs of patient care and research must be backed up by proper arrangements for access to the service for the special minority group of patients who need tertiary care and who are crucial to clinical research, development and advanced postgraduate teaching. Part of these additional costs were initially covered by 'Culyer' funding. However, this has now been modified and redistributed through the 'Support for Science' and 'priority needs and funding' schemes which may prove to be more restricted in the types of projects which can be supported. Generally speaking, research and development funding is not keeping pace with clinical investment and, since the R&D funds are increasingly and properly being spread around the country, this may impact disproportionately on the tertiary and quaternary services in the metropolis.

It should not be forgotten that the tertiary referral service by the specialist hospitals has provided a relatively inexpensive and efficient way of contributing to quality and training of specialist consultants in the NHS. However, as organisational and management arrangements in London medicine have come under increasing scrutiny, the unorthodox and perceived privileged position of these specialist hospitals came under increasing criticism, in spite of the fact that most of them had devised ways of overcoming their potential limitations and, when reviewed rigorously, they have been shown not only to be performing well but also contributing substantially to the Regional and supra-Regional service of the NHS.

Rather than being recognised for their particular contribution to tertiary and quaternary care in the NHS, they came under attack from many quarters, sometimes through lack of understanding and sometimes, sadly, I suspect through vested interest. I believe that none of the accusations actually stand up to fair scrutiny; the contribution of these specialist institutions to healthcare and research was complementary and different from other parts of the service. They were alleged to be 'isolated' hospitals (although they all had close links, often including joint staff appointments, with more general hospitals close by); they did not cover general emergencies (although many provided a special emergency service within their own specialty and many general hospitals have now lost their A&E departments); their small size could not cover a critical mass of expertise (although in fact they had a much greater critical mass within their specialty than the specialist departments of most other teaching hospitals); they were isolated from basic sciences (although as described earlier in this chapter their track record of working extensively with others in the University of London and elsewhere was well documented); the clustering of specialist hospitals in London was resented by those in other parts of the country (although a number of other excellent tertiary referral services have been built up in other cites); they did not pull their weight in the training of junior doctors or undergraduate students (but of course they contributed much more than many others in postgraduate specialist training at junior and more senior levels); they 'siphoned off' the most interesting patients at the expense of non-teaching hospitals (but of course the patients required special care that others could often not provide); and patients did not wish to travel (although many patients chose to do this when their special needs were met more appropriately). Importantly, they were perceived to receive preferential funding as Special Health Authorities, which was understandably resented by others who had been forced to become Trusts and compete in the internal market. (The obvious solution here should have been to recognise and fund tertiary and quaternary centres properly as Special Health Authorities in other parts of the country as well as London.)

All these arguments were raised in the various London reviews and were rehearsed yet again in the Tomlinson review of 1992.

Perhaps those in charge of running these special services in London and the rest of the UK should now join together and, with the support of the Academy of Medical Sciences, take the initiative to define in detail the needs for tertiary and quaternary care, research and advanced teaching, and in this way prevent a wedge being driven between the metropolis and the rest of the country, to the detriment of them both.

What then has become of these hospitals and their institutes over the 35 years since Todd first suggested that they should be merged with undergraduate hospitals in London? The smaller hospitals, such as the St Peter's, Paul's and Phillips, and St Johns, had to be incorporated into teaching hospitals, due to their inadequate buildings. Their beds have been substantially reduced and their institute teaching and research programmes continue but often on a limited scale. Their clinical contribution is little more than that of a department in any other large undergraduate hospital. However, the extraordinary fact is that all the larger specialist hospitals have *so far* in fact continued on their existing sites and some have retained their independent Trust status, in spite of the continued perorations based on theoretical arguments that their continued existence should be disallowed. Others have fairly recently lost their independent Trust status and with it their independent financial control. Once this occurs the strategic management control of the special tertiary and quaternary services inevitably goes with it – especially if the 'host' Trust hospital is in financial deficit. Whether the international standing of a specialist hospital can survive under these circumstances is unknown but it certainly seems a very high-risk policy. It is heartening to hear that in West London the vital importance of retaining independent management and financial control is acknowledged at a senior academic level. Whether these views will be endorsed at ministerial level in the present climate is unknown. Some argue that specialist hospitals clustered in London should not survive in the modern NHS, whatever their Trust status. Central government has to decide whether tertiary and quaternary services are essential components of its National Health Service; if they are, then active steps should be taken to ensure that they are not destroyed, wherever they are located.

Over the years, larger specialist departments have been built up around the country and many have developed excellent research programmes. Indeed, a few have been able to develop subspecialties with supporting research on a scale as large as those of the larger specialist hospitals in London. These should be acknowledged as quaternary referral centres and funded appropriately, but there is no good reason to destroy those which already exist when they are demonstrably making a special contribution to the NHS. The Turnberg Strategic Review emphasised that appropriate mechanisms needed to be in place to maintain tertiary (and quaternary) care, and active practical steps now need to be taken to ensure this. These centres are also threatened by at least four other changes. The new consultants' contract are compromising time for clinical research; the new financial arrangements for money to follow patients do not allow for the complexity of these patients; the reallocation of Culyer funds already mentioned may cause difficulties for some centres; and while patient choice of hospital for secondary care is being encouraged there are no arrangements yet for choice for patients requiring second opinions or tertiary care. Currently, in practice patient referral outside their local area is often refused, although there are indications that this may change as the scope of patient choice extends. Government must intervene urgently before it is too late.

Devolution and decentralisation of the management of the NHS are also having an impact on the four-tiered structure of the NHS. Devolution certainly has many advantages for primary and secondary care, and some tertiary services are certainly required in every Region. However, other tertiary and all quaternary services need to be considered separately. As we have seen, these special services are internationally recognised as playing a vital part in the quality of the NHS and provide a crucial service for patients with real problems and, particularly but not exclusively, those with less common and complex diseases. To allow these to disappear by default because of managerial preferences in London and political devolutionary policies would be a tragedy. The consequent dumbing down of the NHS, settling for the standard of a lower common denominator under the guise of equality of service throughout the country would soon be rumbled by the intelligent public, but perhaps only after it is too late.

There is a fundamental strategic issue to be addressed by government as to whether the NHS wishes to maintain the current standards of care for the British people, which includes tertiary and quaternary referral for those with special problems who require it, or whether this sector of healthcare is to be abandoned. The choice is clear.

'Undergraduate' teaching hospitals in London

Others are better placed to assess in detail the changes in London 'undergraduate' teaching hospitals. The following brief summary is included simply to illustrate some of the trends towards specialisation that have taken place and their effects on patients and students.

For those criticising the concentration of hospitals and the allocation of funds to London, it must not of course be forgotten that London and the South East of England had and have a very large population requiring care – around 20% of the UK. The traditional teaching and specialist hospitals in London contribute substantially to the so-called Thames Regional services, working alongside the more local 'district' service provided by the large number of other hospitals – often now having University status – and increasingly involved in the undergraduate teaching programmes. In addition, the historic concentration of teaching hospitals and the tertiary care specialist hospitals, which had been established in London, together with their academic undergraduate and postgraduate medical schools, gave rise to some unique opportunities for collaboration, not only between each other but with other outlying centres.

The mergers of the undergraduate medical schools in London obviously had repercussions for their associated teaching hospitals. All of these hospitals were, of course, required for the NHS care of the London population and could not be moved or closed simply to fit in with the University's rationalisation plans. Thus, in fact most of the hospitals remained on their existing sites and the medical schools had to adapt around them. Some ingenious schemes were developed, such as the fibre-optic links between Charing Cross and Westminster, to facilitate joint teaching sessions.

One of the remarkable facts about the radically changing scene of the NHS and academic medicine in London is that so few attempts have been made to assess the long-term outcomes of all these well intended reorganisations. Such appraisals are needed to better inform management, the profession and the politicians. A detailed independent analysis is necessary so that any advantages can be endorsed and any disadvantages corrected and avoided in the future. While ardently committed to the importance of appraising the work of others, neither the NHS nor the universities have shown much enthusiasm for examining the outcomes of their own far-reaching decisions. Where this has been attempted, as for example the Turnberg report (1997)[10] reappraising the assumptions and recommendations of Tomlinson 1992,[8] many of the original assumptions proved flawed. Improvements in primary care proved very difficult for entirely predictable reasons. Thus, there were no savings on the hospital service and better data showed that London did not have an excess of beds over other parts of the country and the recommendation for bed cuts of 15–20% should not have been implemented. The demand for treatment in London had not fallen, as predicted by Tomlinson, because of the reforms planned to improved Regional services outside London. This was probably due, as mentioned earlier, to the disproportionate disease burden in the metropolis but this was not included in the conventional census.

It is important, therefore, to consider in very general terms what seems to have happened in London over the last ten years following this reorganisational flurry.

Merger of the management of NHS teaching hospitals

As the strategy of the internal competitive market proved flawed, so hospital Trusts in London were encouraged to merge on the assumption that this would reduce costs – an outcome for which, by and large, there is as yet little evidence. Nevertheless, and for other reasons, there may be potential advantages.

Although two teaching hospitals (UCH and Westminster) were closed entirely, the latter has been redeveloped as the Westminster and Chelsea, first merging with Charing Cross Hospital but later, along with Charing

Cross, realigning with Hammersmith Hospital. A new UCH is opening in 2005 on the Euston Road site and, together with the Royal Free Hospital, should facilitate better provision of specialist services than the smaller departments in the pre-existing hospitals. The Middlesex will probably close. Since the new UCH has only a relatively small local catchment population, it will also be interesting to see what effect this new hospital has on the neighbouring teaching hospitals, especially St Mary's. The merged St Bartholomew's and the London have reorganised their services but continue to function on both sites. It appears that the overall capacity cannot meet the local demand and more provision in East London is urgently needed. Guy's, St Thomas's and King's merged as a single Trust but continue on their three original sites. This has again allowed a rationalisation of specialist services.

Thus, the biggest change would seem to be a trend towards a reorganisation of specialist services so that individual hospitals, which previously included most of the medical and surgical disciplines, have become more restricted in their range of service provision. Students, therefore, have to move between hospitals for different types of training, and patients have to move around to receive different types of care. Merged hospitals and Trusts do not seem to have achieved financial savings and the suggestion that these mergers would allow a reduction in London funding appears flawed. Overall, the facilities in London seem to continue to be overstretched at a time when patient demand and student numbers have been substantially increased.

Where specialist postgraduate hospitals have been incorporated or affiliated with teaching hospitals, they have often taken over a major part of the service component of that specialty within the conglomerate, thereby shifting away from their tertiary and quaternary care role. The old-fashioned oft-repeated argument that the specialist hospitals were 'isolated' from multidisciplinary general medicine in many ways now seems to wear thin. As we have seen, it is the erstwhile 'general' hospitals which, through mergers, have tended as individual hospitals to become more specialised, covering a smaller number of different disciplines and with fewer retaining their own A&E departments – the existence of which was one of the major arguments used to disband specialist hospitals in the 1980s. As patients need a variety of care so they now have to move around from site to site in exactly the same way as patients moved from a specialist hospital to a neighbouring one, if they required other expertise. Curiously, the movement of patients between hospitals within the same Trust but located on different sites, often a mile or two apart, does not seem to raise the same criticisms of isolation as were used against the specialist hospitals. I hear of no evidence that costs have been reduced with these new managerial structures. Rather, management tends to increase as the conglomerate increases in size, especially as they increase the number of managers.

Overall, the restructured clinical services provided by these merged hospital Trusts demonstrate how London has responded to the requirements of modern medicine, but socioeconomic factors linked with this huge conurbation will mean that its problems will always be different from most (but perhaps not all) parts of Britain.

Some effects on undergraduate teaching

Once all the undergraduate medical schools except St George's had been merged with the four large Colleges of London University (St Mary's, Charing Cross and Westminster incorporated with Imperial College; University College Hospital, the Middlesex and later the Royal Free incorporated with University College; St Bartholomew's and the London incorporated with Queen Mary's and Westfield; and St Thomas's, Guy's and King's College Hospitals incorporated with King's College), this arrangement allowed Senate to decentralise management from Senate House to the four large Colleges and this was welcomed by some of the University's critics who believed that London University was much too big.

While others have a far greater understanding of undergraduate matters, to someone with an outside view it is evident that some curiously inconsistent policies have evolved in the organisation of undergraduate medical education in London. The University, for perfectly good reasons, has spent the last twenty years making the case and following the policy to align medical schools with multi-faculty academic institutions to improve the opportunities for clinical and basic collaborative research. With the exception of St George's, it has discarded the previous structure of medical schools embedded within teaching hospitals. At the same time, the GMC has, for equally good reasons, introduced an integrated clinical and basic sciences programme, requiring for its success the closest possible co-location of medical school and hospital. Only UCL is close enough to some of its clinical facilities to conveniently adapt to this integrated approach. Thus, just at a time when co-location of clinical and basic science facilities are most needed, they have in some cases actually been severed. A further paradox arises in that two new medical schools in different parts of England have been created and funded as teaching institutions *only* where the importance of linkage with basic research from a multi-faculty university has apparently been regarded as unnecessary. It is remarkable how basic principles can be overruled in the name of diversity. These schools are now at a great disadvantage in trying to retrieve the situation and establish a good quality research base.

When these restructuring problems are added to the trend towards more outpatient and day-stay management of patients, it is difficult to see how adequate and properly supervised direct student/patient contact time can be provided in small enough groups to provide essential experience. Clinical experience will presumably need to be shared around a number of hospitals – which is little different from the past – but with more structured learning based at the centre, teaching at scattered sites raises obvious difficulties. Clearly, there will be a greater reliance on hands-off substitutes, including IT telemedicine, robots and the like, but how far these will prove appropriate or to the students' satisfaction, time alone will tell. As has been emphasised repeatedly, the acquisition of all the skills required in medicine needs far more that 'virtual' teaching. Students have to learn that patients are highly individual and that the complex interactions of the disease and their reactions to it, require time and personal contact to understand. There are components of apprenticeship training in medicine which should not be eliminated. The strong and renewed emphasis on personal professional standards being stressed by the GMC urgently need focussed attention and these cannot be left as 'classroom' subjects. This, together with the pressures of increased numbers of students and the difficulties of London transport, will certainly test the ingenuity of deans. However, these are resourceful people and no doubt they will overcome these problems.

Are esprit de corps *and local loyalties still important?*

Other things have happened which some will consider less important. The ethos of loyalty to and pride in the traditional teaching hospital, developed over many years, created a particular cohesive rapport between consultants, patients, students and other professional staff, especially senior nurses. This generated an *esprit de corps* which fostered a common trust and created an atmosphere where the value of role models was recognised and in consequence learning flourished. Some will say that in modern medicine these more subtle aspects of attitudes in professional training no longer matter and that, in any case, some consultants were far from ideal role models! Others would argue that the ethos of the traditional student/teacher partnership made a very important contribution to instilling many of the subtle professional attitudes, including professional commitment, ethical behaviour and a professional compassion, which cannot easily be replaced by lectures, seminars, computerised programmes or other forms of distance learning. Unless a strong rapport is fostered between the consultant leaders and students, it will be impossible to provide an environment where these subtle skills of professionalism in medicine can be handed on. This cannot be regarded as an outmoded concept of yesteryear because today's medical educationalists are now so convinced of its importance that medical students are to be formally examined on their attitudes to and communication with their patients. The fact is that there are some things which do not change.

Conclusion

It is evident that the face of clinical medicine, of undergraduate and post-graduate teaching and the organisation of clinical research in London has probably undergone a greater transformation than anywhere in the country over the last 15 years. It will be fascinating to revisit the scene in a decade or two to assess how it has flourished and to see whether it has succeeded in maintaining its international contribution to medicine.

EPILOGUE

22. The life part of the life–work balance

So, at the end we need to come back to the beginning and look at how very good fortune has allowed me the huge privilege of having my cake and eating it - to see and experience so much in medicine and also to have such a wonderful life at home. I have deliberately left this part of the story to the last because in so many ways it is a sort of coda - although you might think it should come at the beginning. The reason for including this chapter is to show young women at the beginning of their careers and young men contemplating a long-term partnership with a woman doctor, that however arduous the work part, it is still possible to have a full family life with children as lifelong friends where neither parent has had to miss out on professional opportunities. Many of our medical contemporaries will testify to this; some of them have had larger families and greater challenges but have found equal fulfilment. We believe the secret is always to try to give more than one receives but with the right family this is very hard to achieve because they have been so generous.

Bits of this story have already been covered in other chapters but some are picked up here, partly for the family record and more particularly because they are central to the philosophy of Richard's and my life together over the last 62 years.

There are other forms of 'equal opportunities' than the conventional one. There has been the equal opportunity for Richard and me to pursue our individual professional lives and at the same time to value our shared interdependence. Another is the opportunity to strive for an equally full life at home as well as at work. This can only be done if both really enjoy home making as much as work, even if at times the home bit is more chaotic than organised. What follows tries to give a flavour of the life side of our work–life balance.

The great advantage of being busy is that one can justify being selective. We both had a good excuse for avoiding those things that we regarded as a low priority, such as tidying up or going to dances. We hardly ever dine out on our own because we prefer to eat at home even if the cooking is less adventurous. The fact is time at home becomes very precious.

311

Richard and I met in 1943 and became engaged at Oxford in 1945, but because we both had so much work to do we decided not to get married until we were qualified. Thus Richard lived at home with his parents in Highgate and I with mine in Hampstead. Both our families were exceedingly supportive. Sadly, Richard's father, who was Senior Surgeon at the Middlesex Hospital, died in 1949, just six months before our wedding. One of the most touching things was that so many of his consultant colleagues wanted, out of affection and respect for him, to come to the wedding. This took place on 21 January 1950 at St Dunstan's Church in Fleet Street which was being used as the interim Temple Church (where my parents were married exactly 30 years before) after the latter had been bombed during the war. Thalban Ball played the organ for us and the men's Temple Church choir sang. The reception was held at the Apothecaries Hall. Roger Gilliatt, our contemporary at Oxford and later Professor of Neurology at Queen's Square, was best man and was also 'volunteered' to stand in as locum house surgeon for Richard while we went on honeymoon for a week at the Swan Hotel on the shores of Lake Grasmere.

Richard's family had lived in Highgate with a sizeable garden since 1932. His father, with great foresight, had obtained planning permission for two building plots within the garden and had given one each to Richard and his sister. Thus, in 1952 we decided, with family support, to build our own small house. After the war there were severe restrictions on both size (maximum of 1500 square feet including upstairs and down) and the cost – an arrangement that suited us well as housemen each earning just £150 per annum. Because of these restrictions, conventional designs were very difficult. Eventually, we sketched out our grand piano on to a blank sheet of paper and planned the house around it. This I suppose was a practical but somewhat unconventional solution which in many ways reflected the principle on which we have solved most other problems. In 1953 we moved in and the first delivery of coal disappeared into the mud because there was nowhere to put it.

We gradually developed the garden with much help from Richard's mother who was a great expert. This garden proved our salvation over the next 40 years because Richard was in effect on call almost continuously (when he was not overseas) to back up his team and look after his personal patients. We were able to be active outdoors and at the same time be available at short notice for emergencies.

Thus a very happy and supportive extended family enclave flourished in Highgate. Richard's mother was also extremely busy as a doctor working in antenatal and children's clinics in the East End. However, her stalwart companion, 'Woodgie', would come to the rescue when there was a transportation crisis. It was also fun for the girls to grow up with their cousins next door. Before they went off to Bedales school, Noodle was the mainstay at home, but we tried to share activities with them as often as possible. They spent time with Richard in his workshop and both have developed a mechanical and practical bent. We painted together and shared music; the Robert Meyer Children's Concerts at the Festival Hall were a regular event. We shared dressmaking together and later they both made many of their own clothes. Richard had an arrangement with them that he would pay for a new dress length of material provided that they showed him the completed previous 'number'. Gillian became a very keen gardener and this led her to read Botany at Exeter University, and it has remained a great interest ever since. Gradually, as the girls got bigger and needed more space, we added bits to the house and this developed into a series of five-year rolling building programmes. After 40 years we handed it over to Lynne when we retired to Exeter, but we kept the woodshed and turned it into a granny flat accessed through the greenhouse - unconventional but practical. Thus at least part of the family property which had been the base support of so much of our life–work balance lives on within the family, after 70 years. What a debt of gratitude we owe to Richard's parents. As the girls grew older, the redoubtable Noodle retired to live with Richard's mother and was replaced by a series of wonderful Swiss *au pairs*, several of whom have come back to visit us since.

We had not intended to send the girls away to school. However, Gillian had recurrent chest infections and was missing a lot of time from school; we thought she might be better in the country and have more opportunities for creative arts which were already becoming very important to her. Following the family tradition, she chose Bedales and spent most of her free time in the 'Barn' pursuing many crafts and in the workshop learning all manner of carpentry. Her health was much improved but she was devastatingly homesick. Although it was not in our original plan, the only sensible solution was to sent Lynne to join her and keep her company. This for her was equally successful and she was able to spend much of her time in the music school playing with many extremely musical friends. This experience laid the foundations for her to obtain her ARCM (Associate of the Royal College of Music) in her gap year. Both obtained their university entrance places from Bedales and Lynne met her future husband there. Gillian became the only member of the family to obtain both a science and an arts Honours degree – one in botany and one in ceramics. Thus, the school served both of them well in very many ways. The drawback was that Richard and I missed them greatly and in those days there were only very few visiting weekends for parents. The best unorthodox but practical solution to this problem was to accept the post of Chairman of the Board of Governors when this was suggested, after Richard retired from the

Board. In this way we got to see the girls more frequently. However, we felt that the real advance would be to get them home more often at weekends. The Headmaster's sister-in-law, Dr Joan Slack, who was a contemporary of ours at Oxford (who also had a son at the school) shared our wish for more frequent home exeats for all the children. She and I decided this was a high priority in the interests of modernising boarding education. Fortunately, the Headmaster, Tim Slack, was very supportive, and much more flexibility in weekend leave was duly arranged. I also learned many transferable skills while Chairman, including much about the professional art of teaching and education, the essentials of chairmanship, building that crucial working partnership between the chairman and headmaster (alias chief executive), fund-raising and controlling building programmes on a very tight budget. All of these came in very useful later and I shall always be grateful to Tim for my initiation.

At about this time, by great good fortune we 'acquired' Mr Bill, who could turn his hand to anything and did. He improved the garden, he met the girls at the station and brought them home, he chauffeured us to and from the airport almost every week, or so it seemed, and to the Palace on two celebrated occasions when Richard received his CBE and I a DBE; he did the shopping, the cooking and took the dogs to the vet. He relished particularly finding someone who could repair or provide almost anything for us, however improbable. He was not an ex Desert Rat for nothing. He was with us for over 20 years and died two years ago; we miss him greatly.

School holidays presented a problem because they were considerably longer than our hospital leave. Our extended family provided huge support. The priority for holidays was to have a home life together – hotel holidays were artificial and inappropriate. At first we borrowed Richard's parents' holiday home in Studland in Dorset and everyone loved the freedom and peace. Later, we acquired our own house at a nominal rent from the Bankes Estate. It was and is unique. It is surrounded by farmland and its garden runs directly down to a protected sandy beach. Without getting out of bed we could check whether the sea was suitable for a before-breakfast water ski – if it was not we simply went back to sleep.

Richard, being devoted to everything to do with water, indulged in a range of craft for various water sport pursuits – sailing, water skiing and wind surfing. Maintenance of the equipment was, I think, as rewarding as the activity itself. The whole point of the holiday was to create a home from home. We were together and did not have to go anywhere or do anything in particular unless we wanted to. At the same time, everyone could do their own thing. There was music making, painting, walking the dogs, riding on Ballard Down, in the forestry or along the South Beach in the winter. Today, Cliff End is still in the family on a long-term lease and its setting is now protected by the National Trust. It remains a focal point for the three generations of the family at Christmas and in the summer; when we meet together it provides exactly the same home-from-home base as it always did, giving respite from the distracted life everyone with energy and enthusiasm always seems to lead. There is perhaps even more music making and water sport. From the age of about seven, the girls were better at most things than we were – but I follow the advice of GK Chesterton, that if a thing is worth doing it is worth doing badly, but I would add, so long as one is having fun.

We ventured abroad occasionally for special things. As elderly beginners, we introduced the girls to skiing, although Lynne and Richard enjoyed it more than Gillian and I. When the girls were about six and eight years respectively we had some special holidays in Sestre Levante in Italy with the families of some other Oxford friends. Because Richard and I wanted to see some of the art in Florence and Siena but the girls were really too young to concentrate for long, we devised a scheme to pay them 100 lire for every 100 devils they could find in the pictures. Their focussed attention greatly impressed the other visitors who did not know of the financial arrangements! Interestingly, when Lynne returned some twenty years later with her husband she still recalled much of the detail. All of which shows that bribery pays.

I cannot end this part of the tale without including an outline sketch of what Richard has been up to throughout our 54 years of marriage because it is a crucial part of our venture together. His academic and rowing achievements at Oxford have been recorded in Chapter 4. His quite remarkable surgical career deserves another book of its own to record adequately. I can do no more than select just a few highlights to give a flavour of this. He designed for himself an almost unique training programme that will probably never again be possible: covering surgery in almost every specialty as well as obtaining his Membership of the Royal College of Physicians the hard way, by examination; he is, I believe, one of the only two survivors who have the Triple Fellowship of the three Royal Colleges of Physicians, of Surgery, and of Obstetrics and Gynaecology. He was appointed to the consultant staff of the Middlesex Hospital and the specialist postgraduate hospital, St Paul's, and the Institute of Urology. He set up the Urodynamic Unit at the Middlesex, and was one of the 'founding fathers' of the new subspecialty of reconstructive urology, establishing one of the very few specialist reconstructive urological units in the UK. He developed many reconstructive operative procedures which continue to be in current use. He designed and made prototypes in his workshop of many of his own instruments and published a large number of highly original papers. He supervised many doctorate students as well as training a large number of surgeons who have become distinguished consultants in this country and overseas. In the 1960s he created the Urological Service in Bermuda, and since his appointment to the consultant staff of the Royal Prince Alfred Hospital in 1973 he operated in Australia for two weeks every year. His international reputation as a specialist in reconstructive urology has led to so many overseas visiting professorships that I have lost count, and to many overseas Honours. Just occasionally, special joint meetings were created for us both in America and these were known as 'puff and pee' or 'wee and wheeze' meetings. One of our greatest honours was to each be awarded and receive at the same time an Honorary DSc from New York University. He was honoured with a CBE for services to surgery and in retirement has written a surgical *magnus opus* on functional uro-gynaecological reconstruction with 1,400 original illustrations in colour. His entry in *Who's Who* is deservedly much longer than mine.

Thus, together we seem to have been quite busy. Richard not only tolerated my heavy schedule but he positively encouraged me to take on anything that seemed to be worthwhile or exciting. This unstinting support made all the difference.

Although brief, I hope that these vignettes on family life help to counterbalance any misconception that ours have been wholly professional careers. Indeed, in spite of all the 'you have been warned' experiences over the years, medicine as a profession is continuing into the fourth generation in our family. Lynne is now a Consultant Physician and Professor of Rehabilitation Medicine and so far two of our grandchildren are medical students, well on their way to qualifying. I hope this will give encouragement to aspiring doctors who also value their family life as much as their work and show that it is possible to have the best of both worlds. Of course, I recognise that we have been extremely fortunate in so many ways with wonderful families to provide encouragement when we were young and support when we were older. In turn, however, we were able to look after Richard's mother, Noodle and my sister in our home when they became terminally ill so that each of them could be at home with the family at the end.

Many compromises have to be made, there are always disappointments and the going can often be tough, but the rewards and interest far outweigh the difficulties.

My greatest of all debt of gratitude is to Richard, Gillian and Lynne for their love, and for giving so much in so many ways.

References

Chapter 18

1 Commonwealth Fund. International Health Policy Survey (2002). www.cmwf.org.uk
2 Healthcare Commission (2004). *What patients think about the NHS.* www.healthcarecommission.org.uk
3 Specialist Medical Advisory Committee (2001). *Doctors for the future.* www.advisorybodies.doh.gov.uk
4 O'Neill O (2004). Accountability, trust and informed consent in medical practice and research. Samuel Gee Lecture. *Clin Med* 2004;4:269–76.
5 General Medical Council (2001). *Good medical practice.* GMC, London.
6 Mori Social Research Institute (2004). A Survey of Trust and Public Opinion of Doctors. BMA, London.
7 Dunstan G (1973). *The artifice of ethics.* The Moorhouse Lecture. King's College London.
8 Department of Health (2003). *Building on the best. Choice, responsiveness and equity in the NHS.* The Stationery Office, London.
9 Royal College of Physicians of London. *Report of the Committee on the Supervision of the Ethics of Clinical Investigations and Institutions* (1971). RCP, London.
10 Kirklin D, Richardson R (2001). *Medical humanities.* RCP, London.
11 King's Fund. *Westminster/Chelsea research report on humanities in hospitals.* King's Fund, London, in preparation.

Chapter 19

1 O'Neill O (2002). *Called to account.* Reith Lectures. BBC, London.
2 O'Neill O (2004). Intelligent trust, intelligent accountability and professionalism. Lloyd Roberts Lecture. *RSM News;* Spring Issue, 37:10.
3 Dunstan G (1973). *The artifice of ethics.* The Moorhouse Lecture. King's College London.
4 Samanta A, Samanta J (2004). Regulation of the medical profession; Fantasy, reality and legality. *JRSM* 97:211–218.
5 Irvine D (2004). Patient-centred professionalism. Gordon Arthur Ransome Oration. *Ann Acad Med (Singapore)* 33:680–5.
6 Tallis R (2004). *Hippocratic oaths: medicine and its discontents.* Atlantic Books, London.
7 Federation of the Royal Colleges of the United Kingdom (2003). *Census of consultant physicians in the UK, 2002: Data and commentary.* Royal College of Physicians, London.
8 Allen I (1997). *Committed but critical.* Health Policy Research Unit, BMA, London.

Chapter 20

1 Rivett G (1997). *From cradle to grave. Fifty years of the NHS.* King's Fund, London.
2 Greengross P, Grant K, Collini E (1999). *The UK National Health Service 1948–1999.* DFID Health Systems Resource Centre, London.

3 Dunstan G (1973). *The artifice of ethics.* The Moorhouse Lecture. King's College London.
4 The Medical Act 1946. HMSO, London.
5 The Medical Act 1978. HMSO, London.
6 NHS Direct (1998). www.nhsdirect.nhs.uk
7 National Institute for Clinical Excellence (2003). *A guide to NICE.* NICE, London.
8 General Medical Council (2001). *Good medical practice,* 3rd edition. GMC, London.
9 Royal College of Physicians (2004). *Continuity of care for medical inpatients: standards of good practice.* Prepared by Metz D, Chard D, Rhodes J, Pounder R. RCP, London.
10 Department of Health, Social Security and Welsh Office (1979). *Patients first.* HMSO, London.
11 Department of Health (1989). *Working for patients.* HMSO, London.
12 Department of Health (2003). *Building on the best – choice, responsiveness and equity.* The Stationery Office, London.
13 Department of Health (1997). *The new NHS: modern, dependable.* The Stationery Office, London.
14 O'Neill O (2004). Intelligent trust, intelligent accountability and professionalism. Lloyd Roberts Lecture. *RSM News,* Spring Issue **37**:10.
15 Leatherman S, Sutherland K (2003). *The quest for quality in the NHS.* The Stationery Office, London.
16 Healthcare Commission (2004). Patient Survey Report: *Adult inpatients.* Picker Institute Europe. www.healthcare commission.org
17 Healthcare Commission (2004). 2003 NHS Staff Survey. NHS Staff Survey Advice Centre, Aston Business School. www.healthcarecommission.org.uk
18 Peterson S, Peto V, Rayner M (2004). *Coronary artery disease statistics.* British Heart Foundation, London. www.heartstats.org.uk
19 Commonwealth Fund. International Health Policy Survey (2002). www.cmwf.org
20 Ham C (2003). Improving the performance of health services: the role of clinical leadership. *Lancet* **361**:1978.
21 Rue R (1985). In Walton J, Beeson PB, Bodley Scott R (eds), *Oxford companion to medicine,* vol 2, p 818. Oxford University Press, Oxford.
22 O'Neill O (2002). *Called to account.* Reith Lectures. BBC, London.
23 Relman AS (1988). Assessment and accountability. *New Engl Med J* **319**(18):1220.
24 Ministry of Health (1956). *Report of the Committee of Enquiry into the cost of the National Health Service* (Guillebaud Report). HMSO, London.
25 Department of Health and Social Security (1972). *Management arrangements for the reorganised National Health Service.* HMSO, London.
26 Royal Commission on the National Health Service (1979). HMSO, London.
27 NHS Management Inquiry (1983). *The Griffiths report.* Letter to the Secretary of State. DHSS, London.
28 Ministry of Health (1967). *First report of the Joint Working Party on the Organisation of Medical Work in Hospitals* (Cogwheel Report). HMSO, London.
29 Samanta A, Samanta J, Gunn M (2003). Legal considerations of clinical guidelines; will NICE make a difference? *JRSM* **96**:133–8.
30 Samanta A, Samanta J (2004). Regulation of the medical profession; fantasy, reality and legality. *JRSM* **97**:211–18.
31 Irvine D (2004). Time for hard decisions and patient-centred professionalism. Duncan Memorial Lecture. *MJA* **181**(5):271–4.
32 Irvine D (2004). Patient-centred professionalism. Gordon Arthur Ransome Oration. *Am Acad Med (Singapore)* **33**:680–5.

33 Mather HM, Connor H (2002). Coping with pressure and acute medicine. The third RCP Consultant Questionnaire Survey. www.rcplondon.ac.uk/professional/survey

34 Doctors disillusioned with the NHS (2003). *Hospital Doctor,* August 2003. www.hospital-doctor.net/hd_achive

35 Healthcare Commission (2004). *What patients think about the NHS.* www.healthcarecommission.org.uk

36 Mather HM (2003). The implementation of the European Working Time Directive for specialist registrars in acute medicine by August 2004. Findings of RCP surveys of clinical directors, College tutors and SpRs. *College Commentary* (Suppl 1).

37 Howell DM., Scott NA (2004). Surgical training derailed: the view from the tracks. *Ann R Coll Surgeons England* (Suppl) **86**:264–5.

38 Allen I (1997). *Committed but critical.* Health Policy and Economic Research Unit, BMA, London.

39 Department of Health (1991). *The patients' charter.* HMSO, London.

40 Dyson R (2003). *Why the new NHS will fail and what should replace it.* Matthew James Publishing, London.

41 Tallis R (2004). *Hippocratic oaths: medicine and its discontents* Atlantic Books, London.

42 DH Standing Medical Advisory Committee Advice (2002). *Medical morale.* www.advisorybodies.doh.gov.uk/smacmoraleadvice.htm

43 DH Standing Medical Advisory Committee Advice (2001). *Doctors for the future.* www.advisory bodies.doh.gov.uk/smac/smacdoctorsfuture.htm

44 Griffiths J (2003). *Hospital Doctor's* Health of the Profession Survey. *Hospital Doctor* 7 August, News: 2.

45 NHS hospital and community health services non-medical staff in England 1992–2002. *Statistical Bulletin.* www.publications.doh.gov/uk/public/sb0302

46 New targets and standards to improve the quality of care. Secretary of State announcement 21 July 2004. Department of Health press release 2004/0269.

47 Academy of Medical Sciences (2003). *Strengthening clinical research.* Report of an Academy working group. AMS, London. www.acmedsci.ac.uk

48 Allen I (2003). Stress amongst healthcare professionals: working together to prevent stress in our hospitals. Royal Society of Medicine, 10 April (personal communication).

49 Stevens S (2005). The NHS works. *Prospect* Feb 2005:32.

50 Federation of the Royal Colleges of the United Kingdom (2003). *Census of consultant physicians in the UK, 2002.* Royal College of Physicians, London.

51 Mori Social Research Institute (2004). *A survey of trust – public opinion of doctors.* BMA, London.

52 Turner-Warwick M (1996). *The marvel of the lung and human responsibility.* Harveian Oration. Royal College of Physicians, London.

53 Dewer S (2003). *Government and the NHS – time for a new relationship.* King's Fund, London.

Chapter 21

1 Ministry of Health and Department of Health for Scotland (1944). *Report of the Interdepartmental Committee on Medical Schools.* The Goodenough Report. London, HMSO.

2 Ministry of Health (1962). *Postgraduate medical education and the specialties* (Chairman: Sir George Pickering). *Reports; public health and medical subjects No 106.* London, HMSO.

3 Parliament (1968). *The Royal Commission on Medical Education.* The Todd Report. London, HMSO.

4　The Committee of Enquiry into the Regulation of the Medical Profession (1975). The Merrison Report. London, HMSO.

5　Parliament (1979). *The Royal Commission on the National Health Service* (Chairman: Sir Alec Merrison). HMSO, London.

6　Morris NF (1978). *Commission of Enquiry into the Postgraduate Institutes of London.* The Morris Report. University of London, London.

7　*London medical education – a new framework* (1980). The Flowers Report. University of London, London.

8　Department of Health (1992). *The Report of the Enquiry into London Health Services, Medical Education and Research.* The Tomlinson Report. HMSO, London.

9　Department of Health (1993). *Making London better.* HMSO, London.

10　Turnberg L (1997). *Health services in London. A strategic review.* The Stationery Office, London.

11　*A framework for Government research and development* (1971). The Rothschild Report. HMSO, London.

12　Grahn MF, Morrow SE (2002). *Adapt or perish: from bench to bedside: an appreciation of the British Postgraduate Medical Federation 1945–1996.* Commissioned by University of London (unpublished).

13　*Ibid,* Chapter 7, p 119.

14　*Ibid,* Chapter 8, p 128.

15　*Ibid,* Chapter 8, p 131.

16　National Health Service Management Executive (1988). *The role of Postgraduate Special Health Authorities: National Health Service.* NHSME, London.

17　Peckham M (2000). *A model for health. Innovation and the future of health services.* The Rock Carling Fellowship. The Nuffield Trust, London.

Index

Page numbers in italics indicate photographs or figures. MTW means Dame Margaret Turner-Warwick. Sub-headings under Turner-Warwick, Dame Margaret and Richard, are in chronological order; all other subheadings are in alphabetical order.